QUIZ LINX

THE QUIZZERS' QUIZ BOOK

First published in Great Britain in 2019 by

i2i Publishing, Manchester

A catalogue record for this book is available from the British Library.

ISBN 978-1-9162285-5-9

Contents

PART 4 – Jumbo Themed Quizzes

30 questions per quiz:

QUIZ 71: **Mr President**

QUIZ 72: **Tutti Frutti**

QUIZ 73: **What Car?**

QUIZ 74: **Something Fishy**

QUIZ 75: **The Building Society**

QUIZ 76: **Meet the Trotters**

QUIZ 77: **In a State**

40 questions per quiz:

QUIZ 78: **Flower Power**

QUIZ 79: **The Body Beautiful**

QUIZ 80: **Game for a Laugh**

50 questions per quiz:

QUIZ 81: **City to City**

QUIZ 82: **Gizza Job**

QUIZ 83: **Going Underground**

60 questions per quiz:

QUIZ 84: **Birds of a Feather**

QUIZ 85: **Pop the Question**

PART 5 – All Kinds of Everything

60 questions (30 pairs):

QUIZ 86: **Coronation Street Pairs**

40 questions (20 pairs):

QUIZ 87: **Pop Music Pairs**

20 questions:

QUIZ 88: **Olympics Host Cities**

50 questions:

QUIZ 89: **Entertainment Peters**

30 questions per quiz:

QUIZ 90: **Just Williams**

QUIZ 91: **Doctor Who**

QUIZ 92: **Simply Red**

QUIZ 93: **It's All Great**

QUIZ 94: **Alliterative Names – BB's**

QUIZ 95: **From A to B**

QUIZ 96: **Alternate A's**

QUIZ 97: **-oo Endings**

QUIZ 98: **The First and the Last**

QUIZ 99: **So Good They Named It Twice**

QUIZ 100: **Rhyming Pairs**

Acknowledgements

I would like to thank Lionel Ross at i2i Publishing for his help and support throughout the course of writing this book. He was very helpful in terms of guiding me through the various stages of writing the book, for which I am very grateful.

I would also like to thank Jenny Ryan, better known to many as 'The Vixen' on ITV's *The Chase*, for kindly agreeing to write the Foreword. I know her free time is very limited, especially so in recent times with appearances on *Celebrity MasterChef* and *The X Factor: Celebrity*, so I really appreciate her help.

My family, of course, deserve my most heartfelt thanks, given the boundless contributions they have made to my life over many years. My mother and father were always the perfect role models and sacrificed so much during my formative years to provide a loving family home, a good upbringing and the best of educations, for which I shall be forever grateful.

Finally, but by no means least, I would like to thank my wife of the best part of 30 years, Margaret, whose patience through the months of me burying myself away in my study to first research and then write this book also deserves my eternal thanks. She was also my sounding board during every stage of the process and is my rock at all times. Thank you.

Foreword

by Jenny Ryan

(from ITV's *The Chase*)

Quizzing is a hobby which brings people together. Whether you are an armchair quiz show addict, a pub quiz regular or a stalwart of your local quiz league, chances are you are testing your grey matter alongside other people.

My interest in quizzing was sparked by my family, and in particular my grandad Kevin, a huge quiz fan. He would always have a quiz book to hand, so if there was a quiet moment after tea it was likely an impromptu quiz match would break out!

Quizzes, like the ones in this book, are meant to be shared and enjoyed with other people. There is something for everyone in these pages, whether you're a quiz novice or an ardent quizzer, and in fact you'll probably need to pool your knowledge to answer everything, especially in the link quizzes! However, if you're anything like my grandad you will also enjoy simply opening up this book and testing your knowledge during some quiet time on your own.

There are many quiz books out there with varied rounds and different grades of questions but the fact that every quiz in this book has a different theme running through it adds another dimension. An added bonus is the fact that every answer has additional material related to the answer, giving further ammunition to test everyone with!

So whether you use this book for family teatime entertainment, to warm up your quiz teammates or simply to do some quiz 'studying' on your own – or even to practise for a TV quiz show audition – I wish you luck, I hope you have fun, and most of all I hope it brings you together.

Keep quizzing!

Jenny Ryan

October 2019

Introduction

What makes a good quiz book?

I asked myself that question many times before embarking on writing this book as I wanted to try to produce just that, if I could, but ideally one that was also distinctly different to most of the others available.

There are many quiz books on the market and many of them follow a similar pattern. They may be separated into questions that are graded by difficulty, but often easy questions are far too easy and hard ones can be next to impossible, which renders quite a number of the questions of no real use.

The quizzes may also be separated into different subjects, but someone who is an aficionado of pop music and sport, for example, may be distinctly less interested in quizzes about history or politics, let's say, or indeed vice versa, again leaving only part of the book of interest.

The other overriding factor is that each quiz is broadly the same, with 20 or 30 questions and 20 or 30 answers, which can become very predictable after a while.

Each quiz in this book therefore includes:
- (a) Questions with different levels of difficulty – easy, medium and hard
- (b) Questions on a variety of subjects – e.g. Music, History, Sport, Places, TV etc.

(c) A different theme running through every quiz – some links to be guessed and some given
(d) Quizzes of varied lengths – from 10 questions per quiz up to 60 questions per quiz!

The links to be guessed are not too difficult but you may need to answer a few questions before finding the link. When the link is given, that should help you to answer some of the more difficult questions.

There are 100 quizzes in total with over 2,000 questions, but in addition, for every answer there is some additional information given which means another 2,000 or so facts to potentially use as extra questions.

Although this book can certainly be enjoyed by an individual to improve their quiz knowledge and to challenge themselves to solve the links, it will probably work even better in a small group, especially with a nominated quizmaster.

However, whether you just enjoy leafing through the book and testing yourself in some leisure time, or whether you prefer to wait until a group of you are together at a party or at Christmastime, for example, to test that grey matter and get those competitive juices flowing, I hope you enjoy the book and I thank you very much for buying it.

Ian Greensill

October 2019

Playing and Scoring

Each quiz's questions are not only graded (easy: 1 point; medium: 2 points; hard: 3 points) but include different subjects to choose from in each graded category. Assuming there are two teams with a quizmaster, you could, for example, score each quiz on points scored. (For information a quiz with 10 questions has a total of 20 points available, 20 questions has 40 points and so on.)

- The first thing to decide is whether players are going to be able to select the difficulty of question to answer or whether, for example, all the easy questions are asked first
- The quizmaster may allow teams to choose a subject they want to answer questions on
- They may simply ask the questions in turn to each team, bringing in an element of pot luck
- Players may opt to answer a 3-point hard question if there is a subject they are particularly strong in, or if they are a few points behind
- The questions can be handed over to the other team to score bonus points if the first team give an incorrect answer
- The link of course in some quizzes needs to be guessed and you may, for example, give a 5 points bonus to any team getting that right
- The quizzes which require the link to be guessed will probably work best if the players / teams write down

the answers in order to give them a better chance to work out what links them all

- All answers also have bonus facts which could also be used as bonus points

These are just a few ways that the scoring and playing of the game could be organised, but there are no hard and fast rules, so maybe just make up your own rules!

1. **TV:** What is the name of Rigsby's cat in *Rising Damp*?
2. **Food & Drink:** What is the dish made with chicken breasts stuffed with garlic, herbs and butter?
3. **Science & Medicine:** What is the condition that causes hostages to have sympathy towards their captors?

4. **Sport & Games:** Which British boxer lost world heavyweight fights against Floyd Patterson in 1959 and Muhammad Ali in 1966?
5. **History:** What was the name of the Duke of Wellington's horse?
6. **Music:** Which songwriter wrote 'White Christmas' and 'There's No Business Like Show Business'?
7. **TV:** Which former Manchester United striker joined *Homes Under the Hammer* as a presenter in 2015?

8. **Mythology:** Which son of King Priam and Queen Hecuba abducted Helen of Troy?
9. **Films:** Which 2014 film starred Ranulph Fiennes as a hotel concierge?
10. **Music:** Which 1989 song was the only UK No. 1 hit for Simple Minds?

WHAT IS THE LINK BETWEEN ALL OF THE ANSWERS?

1

EASY (1 Point)

1. **Vienna:** Vienna is home to the famous Schönbrunn Palace.
2. **Chicken Kiev:** Kiev is the capital of Ukraine and lies on the River Dnieper.
3. **Stockholm Syndrome:** Stockholm encompasses 14 islands in a Baltic Sea archipelago.

MEDIUM (2 Points)

4. **Brian London:** No. 1 London is the address of Apsley House, home of the Dukes of Wellington.
5. **Copenhagen:** Copenhagen is linked to Malmo in Sweden by the Öresund Bridge.
6. **Irving Berlin:** Berlin became Germany's capital again after unification in 1990. Bonn had been the capital of West Germany from 1949 until 1990.
7. **Dion Dublin:** Dublin is in the province of Leinster and stands at the mouth of the River Liffey.

HARD (3 Points)

8. **Paris:** Paris is known as 'The City of Light' and was called Lutetia by the Romans.
9. ***The Grand Budapest Hotel***: Budapest is made up of 2 districts – Buda and Pest – separated by the River Danube.
10. **'Belfast Child':** The ill-fated RMS *Titanic* was built by Harland and Wolff in Belfast.

2

1. **Music:** Which soul group's biggest hit was 'Feel the Need in Me' in 1973?
2. **Food & Drink:** What was the previous name of the confectionery sweets called 'Starburst'?
3. **History:** What is the name of the Hawaiian base of the US Pacific Fleet attacked by Japan in 1941?

MEDIUM (2 Points)

4. **TV:** Which sci-fi series ran from 1979 to 1982 and starred Joanna Lumley and David McCallum?
5. **Sport & Games:** Which jumps jockey was most associated with the horses Kauto Star, Big Buck's and Hurricane Fly?
6. **Films:** Which 1971 James Bond film was the last to star Sean Connery?
7. **Music:** Which comedian had a 1975 hit with 'Funky Moped'?

HARD (3 Points)

8. **Geography:** What are the ribbons of strong winds called that move weather systems around the globe?
9. **Sport & Games:** Which bookmakers have sponsored the Eclipse race run at Sandown every July since 1976?
10. **TV:** Which actress played Grandma Mole in *The Secret Diary of Adrian Mole Aged 13¾*?

WHAT IS THE LINK BETWEEN ALL OF THE ANSWERS?

ANSWERS QUIZ No. 2: LINK – GEMS

EASY (1 Point)

1. **Detroit Emeralds:** The song reached No. 4 in 1973 and then No. 12 when rereleased in 1977.
2. **Opal Fruits:** The slogan 'Made to Make Your Mouth Water' was created by Murray Walker, the motor racing commentator.
3. **Pearl Harbor:** The 2001 film about the attack starred Ben Affleck, Kate Beckinsale and Josh Hartnett.

MEDIUM (2 Points)

4. *Sapphire & Steel*: David McCallum also starred as Illya Kuryakin in *Man From Uncle*.
5. **Ruby Walsh:** His sister Katie was also a jockey and his brother is married to former jockey Nina Carberry.
6. *Diamonds Are Forever*: Sean Connery was back after George Lazenby did just one film, but Sean Connery was replaced after this film too; Roger Moore took over in *Live and Let Die*.
7. **Jasper Carrott:** His daughter is Lucy Davis who played Dawn Tinsley in *The Office*.

HARD (3 Points)

8. **Jet Stream:** The jet stream was first identified in the 1920s over Mount Fuji in Japan.
9. **Coral:** Gala Coral merged with Ladbrokes in 2016 to form Ladbrokes Coral plc.
10. **Beryl Reid:** She appeared in the 1973 film *No Sex Please, We're British* with Ronnie Corbett.

QUIZ No. 3: GUESS THE LINK

EASY (1 Point)

1. **Music:** What was Donny Osmond's first UK hit in 1972?
2. **Films:** Which 1984 martial arts film starred Ralph Macchio in the title role?
3. **TV:** Peter Howitt played which character in the TV series *Bread*?

MEDIUM (2 Points)

4. **Music:** Which girl group had a No. 1 hit in 2002 with a cover of Blondie's 'The Tide is High'?
5. **Sport & Games:** Chicago has two MLB baseball teams – Chicago White Sox is one, what is the other?
6. **Music:** Charlotte Church had a No. 2 hit in 2005 with which song?
7. **TV:** Which actor played Archie Mitchell in *EastEnders* and Mick Shipman in *Gavin & Stacey*?

HARD (3 Points)

8. **Places:** What is the tiny island called off the south-west coast of the Isle of Man?
9. **Films:** Which actor plays Sebastian Wilder in the 2016 film musical *La La Land*?
10. **Music:** Which group had a No. 3 hit in 1971 with 'Johnny Reggae'?

WHAT IS THE LINK BETWEEN ALL OF THE ANSWERS?

ANSWERS QUIZ No. 3: **LINK – ANIMAL YOUNG**

1. **'Puppy Love':** He also had No. 1 hits in 1973 with 'The Twelfth of Never' and 'Young Love'.
2. **The Karate Kid:** Ralph Macchio also starred in the films *Crossroads* and *My Cousin Vinny*.
3. **Joey Boswell:** Peter Howitt wrote and directed the 1998 film *Sliding Doors*, starring Gwyneth Paltrow and John Hannah.

MEDIUM (2 Points)

4. **Atomic Kitten:** The group was founded by OMD frontman Andy McCluskey. Jenny Frost replaced Kerry Katona in 2001, but when they reformed in 2012, Katona replaced Frost.
5. **Chicago Cubs:** The Cubs won the World Series in 2016, their first title for 108 years.
6. **'Crazy Chick':** Charlotte Church started as a classical singer and released her first album, *Voice of an Angel*, in 1998.
7. **Larry Lamb:** Archie Mitchell was murdered by Stacey Slater on Christmas Day 2009.

HARD (3 Points)

8. **Calf of Man:** It is separated from the Isle of Man by Calf Sound and covers an area of less than 1 square mile.
9. **Ryan Gosling:** He starred opposite Rachel McAdams in the 2004 film *The Notebook*.
10. **The Piglets:** This was their only hit record, but it was one of the many pseudonyms used by Jonathan King.

QUIZ No. 4: GUESS THE LINK

EASY (1 Point)

1. **Places:** What is the name of the huge stone structures built as tombs for pharaohs in ancient Egypt?
2. **Sport & Games:** Which cricket ground is the home ground of Surrey County Cricket Club?
3. **Transport & Travel:** A V6 engine is an internal combustion engine with six what?

MEDIUM (2 Points)

4. **TV:** Which TV gameshow hosted by Phillip Schofield, first shown in 2009, involves contestants carrying out challenges in a transparent box?
5. **Pot Luck:** What is the name of the HQ of the US Department of Defense?
6. **Sport & Games:** What is the playing area within the bases called in baseball?
7. **Places:** Which is the most northerly circle of latitude?

HARD (3 Points)

8. **Animals & Nature:** Which endangered bird of prey with a forked tail has the Latin name *milvus milvus*?
9. **TV:** What was the name of the BBC soap that ran from 1981 to 1983 based on a North Sea ferry?
10. **Places:** Which New York area used to be called Longacre Square?

WHAT IS THE LINK BETWEEN ALL OF THE ANSWERS?

ANSWERS QUIZ No. 4: **LINK – SHAPES**

1. **Pyramids:** The Great Pyramid of Giza is the oldest of the Seven Wonders of the World and the only one largely intact.
2. **The Oval:** It hosted England's first football match v Scotland in 1870 and also the first FA Cup final in 1872.
3. **Cylinders:** It is called a V-engine as the cylinders are arranged in two banks in a V-shape.

4. *The Cube*: The first person to win the £250,000 for 'Beating the Cube' was Mo Farah in a celebrity version in 2012 after the London Olympics.
5. **The Pentagon:** It is based in Arlington, Virginia, close to the site of the US Military Cemetery.
6. **Diamond:** It is called a diamond purely because of the shape of the playing area.
7. **Arctic Circle:** Kaffeklubben Island in Greenland is the northernmost point in the world.

8. **Red Kite:** Despite near-extinction in the UK, it has now been successfully reintroduced.
9. *Triangle*: The show featured Kate O'Mara and a young Larry Lamb appeared in each episode.
10. **Times Square:** It also the hub of the Broadway Theatre District and the site of the famous 'ball drop' every New Year's Eve.

EASY (1 Point)

1. **Pot Luck:** What is the name of the comic strip written by Charles Schulz featuring Charlie Brown?
2. **Sport & Games:** Which country won their fifth World Cup when they beat Germany 2-0 in the final in 2002?
3. **Pot Luck:** Which nursery rhyme has the second line 'The mouse ran up the clock'?

MEDIUM (2 Points)

4. **Music:** What was the name of Laurel & Hardy's UK No. 2 hit in 1975?
5. **Sport & Games:** What was the name of Leicester City's home ground until they moved in 2002?
6. **Music:** Which singer had a No. 1 hit in 1989 with Gene Pitney with a cover of 'Something's Gotten Hold of My Heart'?
7. **Animals & Nature:** Which tree, also known as a conker tree, has the Latin name *Aesculus hippocastanum*?

HARD (3 Points)

8. **TV:** What was the name of the small town in *Little House on the Prairie*?
9. **Music:** Which singer had top 10 hits in the early 80s with 'Eighth Day' and 'Will You'?
10. **TV:** Actor Billy Murray played which corrupt detective in *The Bill* from 1995 to 2000, returning periodically in later episodes?

WHAT IS THE LINK BETWEEN ALL OF THE ANSWERS?

EASY (1 Point)

1. **Peanuts:** It was launched in 1950 and also features Snoopy, Charlie Brown's pet beagle, and a bird called Woodstock. NB The peanut is eaten like a nut but is strictly a legume!
2. **Brazil:** Both goals were scored by Ronaldo who also won the Golden Boot with eight goals.
3. **Hickory Dickory Dock:** The rhyme is reputed to be about Exeter Cathedral astronomical clock.

MEDIUM (2 Points)

4. **'The Trail of the Lonesome Pine':** The song featured in their 1937 film *Way Out West* sung by the Avalon Boys. The 1975 hit was heavily promoted by DJ John Peel.
5. **Filbert Street:** The new stadium changed its name from the Walkers Stadium to the King Power Stadium in 2012.
6. **Marc Almond:** He was one half of successful 80s group Soft Cell with David Ball.
7. **Horse Chestnut:** Unlike sweet chestnuts, horse chestnuts are inedible and toxic to animals.

HARD (3 Points)

8. **Walnut Grove:** It is a town in Minnesota, the home of Laura Ingalls Wilder, the author of the books, and main character and narrator in the TV series played by Melissa Gilbert.
9. **Hazel O'Connor:** Both songs were from the 1980 film *Breaking Glass* in which she starred.
10. **Don Beech:** Billy Murray went on to play another villain, Johnny Allen, in *EastEnders* from 2005 to 2006.

QUIZ No. 6: **GUESS THE LINK**

EASY (1 Point)

1. **TV:** Which HBO fantasy TV show is set on the continents of Westeros and Essos?
2. **Pot Luck:** Which pre-decimal coin was worth five shillings?
3. **Food & Drink:** Two spices are obtained from the nutmeg tree – nutmeg is one, what is the other?

MEDIUM (2 Points)

4. **History:** Colonel Blood is best known for trying to steal what from the Tower of London in 1671?
5. **Music:** The tune to 'Land of Hope and Glory' was taken from which series of six marches by Sir Edward Elgar?
6. **TV:** What was the name of the 1997 documentary about Elton John: *Tantrums and...*?
7. **Animals & Nature:** What is the name mainly used for a stoat in its white winter coat?

HARD (3 Points)

8. **Films:** Which 1953 Biblical film epic, starring Richard Burton, Jean Simmons and Victor Mature, is about a Roman tribune in charge of the unit that crucifies Jesus?
9. **Sport & Games:** Which famous horse is the only horse to win four out of the five British Classics in 1902 – 1,000 Guineas, 2,000 Guineas, Oaks and St Leger?
10. **History:** The five beaches used for the D-Day landings were Utah, Omaha, Gold, Juno and...?

WHAT IS THE LINK BETWEEN ALL OF THE ANSWERS?

1. *Game of Thrones*: It was adapted from the first fantasy novel of *A Song of Ice and Fire* by George R R Martin.
2. **Crown**: It was worth 60 old pence and the last crown coin was minted in 1965.
3. **Mace**: The nutmeg tree *Myristica fragrans* is indigenous to the Moluccas (the Spice Islands).

MEDIUM (2 Points)

4. **Crown Jewels**: St Edward's Crown is used to crown monarchs (named after Edward the Confessor). The current version was made for Charles II in 1661.
5. **'Pomp & Circumstance'**: The words were put to music on the suggestion of King Edward VII.
6. *Tiaras*: It was made during his 'Made in England' tour and directed by his husband David Furnish.
7. **Ermine**: The ermine is also known as the short-tailed weasel.

HARD (3 Points)

8. *The Robe*: It was the first film to use the widescreen technology CinemaScope.
9. **Sceptre**: She was also unlucky not to win the Derby where she finished fourth, after having had a foot injury and then being left at the start.
10. **Sword**: Sword was the most easterly of the five beaches and the assault was led by British troops along with those from France, Poland and Norway.

QUIZ No. 7: **GUESS THE LINK**

EASY (1 Point)

1. **Science & Medicine:** Which chemical element has the symbol Cl and the atomic number 17?
2. **Sport & Games:** With what do you get presented when you play for an international football team?
3. **Food & Drink:** What is the term used for a night out drinking in multiple pubs or bars?

MEDIUM (2 Points)

4. **Animals & Nature:** Red Admiral and Cabbage White are types of what?
5. **TV:** What does Popeye have tattooed on his forearm?
6. **Music:** Who duetted with Jennifer Warnes on the 1987 hit '(I've Had) The Time of My Life' which featured in the film *Dirty Dancing*?
7. **Science & Medicine:** What is the common medical term for when poor blood flow to the brain results in cell death and possible damage to the brain?

HARD (3 Points)

8. **Sport & Games:** Greg Louganis from the USA won Olympic gold in 1984 and 1988 in which sport?
9. **TV:** Which Liverpool-born writer wrote the sitcoms *The Liver Birds*, *Butterflies* and *Bread*?
10. **Sport & Games:** The Mosconi Cup is played between teams from Europe and the USA in which sport?

WHAT IS THE LINK BETWEEN ALL OF THE ANSWERS?

EASY (1 Point)

1. **Chlorine:** The most common compound of chlorine is sodium chloride (common salt).
2. **Cap:** The term is now used generically for many sports e.g. rugby union, cricket etc.
3. **Pub Crawl:** The origin of the term is unclear. Whether it is because the pubs used to be close together or whether people ended up on all fours after a few drinks nobody is sure!

MEDIUM (2 Points)

4. **Butterfly:** This is also a culinary term to cut a thicker piece of meat into two thinner parts.
5. **Anchor:** This is the name used for the person who runs or swims the last leg of a relay.
6. **Bill Medley:** He was one half of the Righteous Brothers along with Bobby Hatfield.
7. **Stroke:** Stroke is also a position in rowing, closest to the stern and next to the cox, who essentially sets the pace for everyone else.

HARD (3 Points)

8. **Diving:** He won the gold in 1988 despite banging his head on the diving board in the preliminary rounds.
9. **Carla Lane:** She was also one of the main writers of *Bless This House*, starring Sid James and Diana Coupland.
10. **Pool:** The trophy is named after Willie Mosconi, an American pool player who was called 'Mr Pocket Billiards' which is an old name for the game of pool in North America.

QUIZ No. 8: **GUESS THE LINK**

1. **Music:** Which song reached No. 1 for Kajagoogoo in 1983?
2. **Theatre:** What is the name for the area of seats on the ground floor of a theatre?
3. **TV:** Which character was played by Una Stubbs in the TV show *Worzel Gummidge*?

MEDIUM (2 Points)

4. **Music:** According to Ronan Keating's 2000 No. 1, 'Life is a...?
5. **Theatre:** The song 'You'll Never Walk Alone' comes from which Rodgers and Hammerstein musical?
6. **Science & Medicine:** What is the US name used for The Plough, an asterism in the constellation Ursa Major?
7. **Sport & Games:** Ivan Mauger and Ole Olsen were 1970s world champions in which sport?

HARD (3 Points)

8. **Music:** Which 1987 Bruce Springsteen album has the same title as a Dire Straits song from their *Making Movies* album, released in 1980?
9. **Pot Luck:** Which outdoor accessories were originally called Hanways?
10. **Music:** Which 1969 Roy Orbison song contains the line 'Step up and play, each machine seemed to say, as I walked round and round the......'?

WHAT IS THE LINK BETWEEN ALL OF THE ANSWERS?

EASY (1 Point)

1. **'Too Shy':** The name of lead singer Limahl is an anagram of his surname, real name Chris Hamill.
2. **Stalls:** Where there are multiple elevated seats, the lowest and best area is called the dress circle.
3. **Aunt Sally:** Worzel Gummidge was a scarecrow played by Jon Pertwee.

MEDIUM (2 Points)

4. **Rollercoaster:** This was the second consecutive No. 1 for the former Boyzone lead singer after his first hit 'When You Say Nothing At All' also reached No. 1 in 1999.
5. *Carousel*: This was the second Rodgers and Hammerstein musical, released in 1945 after the success of their first musical *Oklahoma!* in 1943.
6. **The Big Dipper:** Ursa Major is the Latin name for the Great Bear constellation.
7. **Speedway:** Ivan Mauger won six World titles and Ole Olsen won three.

HARD (3 Points)

8. *Tunnel of Love*: Despite being a familiar and popular track, the Dire Straits single only reached No. 54 in the UK charts.
9. **Umbrellas:** The name stems from Jonas Hanway, the first man in London to dare to be seen using one, around 1750.
10. **Penny Arcade:** The song only reached No. 27 in 1969 and it was his last solo UK hit before he died in 1988, although he did have a number of posthumous hits.

EASY (1 Point)

1. **Sport & Games:** Who was the manager of the Celtic team when they won the 1967 European Cup?
2. **Pot Luck:** What is the name of the mortar used to fill in the gaps between wall and floor tiles?
3. **Music:** Which group's first UK No. 1 hit was 'Coz I Luv You' in 1971?

MEDIUM (2 Points)

4. **Places:** The largest island in Scotland, in the Outer Hebrides, is Lewis and......?
5. **Food & Drink:** What is 'white wine' in Spanish?
6. **Films:** Which actress played a missionary in China in *The Inn of the Sixth Happiness*?
7. **Words:** What do you call a maker of arrows?

HARD (3 Points)

8. **Art & Literature:** In John Steinbeck's *Of Mice and Men*, the two main characters are called George and......?
9. **Sport & Games:** Which former Tottenham Hotspur and Derby County hard man was manager of Derby County when they won the First Division in 1975?
10. **Places:** Apart from London, there are Tate Galleries in Liverpool and which Cornish town?

WHAT IS THE LINK BETWEEN ALL OF THE ANSWERS?

EASY (1 Point)

1. **Jock Stein:** Tony Osaba played Jim 'Jock' McClaren, becoming the first black Scottish actor on primetime TV.
2. **Grout:** Peter Vaughan played the fearsome 'Genial' Harry Grout or Grouty. He also appeared in *Citizen Smith* and played Maester Aemon in *Game of Thrones*.
3. **Slade:** The prison was supposed to be in Cumbria, but it shows the gates of a disused prison in St Albans.

MEDIUM (2 Points)

4. **Harris:** Ronald Lacey played Harris, the much-disliked, ginger-haired Teddy Boy.
5. **Vino Blanco:** A young David Jason played Blanco Webb, made up to look like a very old man.
6. **Ingrid Bergman:** Patricia Brake played Fletcher's daughter Ingrid, who actually married Lennie Godber in the sequel *Going Straight*.
7. **Fletcher:** Ronnie Barker starred as Norman Stanley Fletcher – 'a habitual criminal who accepts arrest as an occupational hazard'.

HARD (3 Points)

8. **Lennie:** Richard Beckinsale played Godber – he lived with his girlfriend Denise in Smethwick.
9. **Dave Mackay:** Fulton Mackay played Mr Mackay, but his first name is never mentioned.
10. **St Ives:** Ken Jones played snitch 'Horrible' Ives, noted for always saying 'Ere listen...'

1. **Music:** Which 1975 song was the first UK No. 1 hit for the Bay City Rollers?
2. **TV:** Which TV series starred Tim Healy as Dennis, Kevin Whately as Neville and Jimmy Nail as Oz?
3. **Music:** Which 1956 song by Bill Haley & His Comets contains the line 'After a while crocodile'?

MEDIUM (2 Points)

4. **Art & Literature:** Which novel by Ernest Hemingway tells the story of an Italian soldier in the ambulance corps in WW1?
5. **Music:** Which 2001 hit for the Stereophonics starts with the line 'San Francisco Bay, past pier thirty-nine'?
6. **TV:** Which TV series stars Nicholas Lyndhurst as Gary Sparrow, an accidental time-traveller with a double life?
7. **Food & Drink:** Which hoop-shaped whole grain breakfast cereal by Nestle comes in a variety of flavours including multigrain, honey and chocolate?

HARD (3 Points)

8. **Pot Luck:** Which Indian steelmaking company took over the British company Corus Steel in 2007?
9. **History:** What is the name of the archaeological complex that was the traditional seat of the High King of Ireland?
10. **Art & Literature:** The fourth book in the *Hitchhikers' Guide to the Galaxy* series was called '.......and Thanks for All the Fish'?

WHAT IS THE LINK BETWEEN ALL OF THE ANSWERS?

EASY (1 Point)

1. **'Bye Bye Baby'**: Their other No. 1 was 'Give a Little Love'.
2. **Auf Wiedersehen, Pet**: The four series were set in Germany, Spain, USA and Cuba.
3. **'See You Later Alligator'**: The group's only UK No. 1 hit was 'Rock Around the Clock' in 1955.

MEDIUM (2 Points)

4. **A Farewell to Arms:** The book was published in 1929 and became his first bestseller.
5. **'Have a Nice Day'**: The group's only UK No. 1 hit was 'Dakota' in 2005.
6. **Goodnight Sweetheart**: There were 6 series in total that ran from 1993 to 1999.
7. **Cheerios:** In North America, Usher gave away free downloads of his new song 'Clueless' in some special boxes of Honey Nut Cheerios.

HARD (3 Points)

8. **Tata Steel:** The company was renamed Tata Steel Europe in 2010.
9. **Hill of Tara:** The site is located near the River Boyne, the site of a famous 1690 battle.
10. **So Long**: The books were written by Douglas Adams who was just 49 when he died in 2001.

EASY (1 Point)

1. **Sport & Games:** Which golfer, with the real first name Eldrick, won his first Major at 21 when he won the 1997 US Masters?
2. **Music:** Which single by Tight Fit got to No. 1 in 1982?
3. **Pot Luck:** In imperial weights and measures what is one sixteenth of a pound?

MEDIUM (2 Points)

4. **TV:** What was the name of the chimpanzee in the Tarzan films and TV series?
5. **People:** What was the nickname of the armed robber and murderer Donald Neilson?
6. **Transport & Travel:** The XE, XF and XJ are models produced by which car manufacturer?
7. **Shopping & Fashion:** Africa, Inca, Alaska and Java have been fragrances of which brand of deodorant?

HARD (3 Points)

8. **Animals & Nature:** What is the name of the seal that is the second largest species of seal in the Antarctic, named because of its throat that is white with black spots?
9. **Shopping & Fashion:** In 1948 the Dassler brothers split their sport and casual footwear and clothing business into 2 companies: adidas and which other?
10. **TV:** Which US sitcom that ran from 2009 to 2015 starred Courteney Cox as divorcee Jules Cobb?

WHAT IS THE LINK BETWEEN ALL OF THE ANSWERS?

1. **Tiger Woods:** He became the youngest player at 24 to have won all 4 Majors when he won the 2000 Open at St Andrews, beating Jack Nicklaus by two years.
2. **'The Lion Sleeps Tonight':** The song was originally a hit for the Tokens in 1961 but it was later released as 'Wimoweh' by Scottish singer Karl Denver.
3. **Ounce:** There are also 14 pounds in a stone, 112 pounds in a cwt and 2,240 pounds in a ton.

4. **Cheeta:** The original *Tarzan* books were written by Edgar Rice Burroughs.
5. **The Black Panther:** He was found guilty of four murders in 1976 and received a life sentence.
6. **Jaguar:** Jaguar Land Rover became a subsidiary of Tata Motors in 2008.
7. **Lynx:** Lynx is owned by Unilever and is known as Axe in some other countries.

8. **Leopard Seal:** They do not have any obvious ears but can still hear very well.
9. **Puma:** The head offices of both companies are in Herzogenaurach, Germany.
10. *Cougar Town:* Jennifer Aniston, Lisa Kudrow and Matthew Perry all made guest appearances.

EASY (1 Point)

1. **Music:** Which group's first 2 releases, '5 Colours in Her Hair' and 'Obviously' went to No. 1 in 2004?
2. **Fashion:** What is the name of ASDA's clothing brand?
3. **Transport & Travel:** The DMC-12 is the only model of car made by which Northern Irish car manufacturer?

MEDIUM (2 Points)

4. **Art & Literature:** What is the surname of the family who adopt Paddington Bear?
5. **Music:** What is the forename of the father of singer Kim Wilde, also once a singer?
6. **Films:** In which year did actor James Dean die?
7. **Music:** Which Chuck Berry song starts with the line 'Deep down in Louisiana close to New Orleans'?

HARD (3 Points)

8. **Entertainment:** Which comic strip character was on the front page of the *Beano* from 1948 to 1974 when Dennis the Menace took over?
9. **Sport & Games:** Which American female tennis player won the Australian Open in 2001 and 2002, also winning the French Open in 2001?
10. **Films:** Which 1972 comedy film starring Ryan O'Neal, Barbra Streisand and Madeline Kahn was loosely based on the 1938 film *Bringing Up Baby* and also paid homage to Bugs Bunny?

WHAT IS THE LINK BETWEEN ALL OF THE ANSWERS?

1. **McFly:** The 4 band members are Tom Fletcher, Danny Jones, Harry Judd and Dougie Poynter. This was Marty's surname in the film.
2. **George:** The label is named after its original designer George Davies, who also set up fashion chain Next in the 1980s. George was Marty's father's name.
3. **DeLorean:** This was the make of car used for the time machine in the film.

MEDIUM (2 Points)

4. **Brown:** Christopher Lloyd played Doctor Emmett Brown.
5. **Marty:** Michael J Fox played Marty McFly.
6. **1955:** This is the year that they went back to in the time machine in the original film.
7. **'Johnny B Goode':** This is the song that Marty McFly plays on stage back in 1955.

HARD (3 Points)

8. **Biffo (The Bear):** Biff Tannen is the nemesis of the McFly family, played by Thomas F Wilson.
9. **Jennifer Capriati:** Jennifer was Marty's girlfriend.
10. ***What's Up, Doc?*:** Christopher Lloyd's character was mainly referred to as 'Doc'.

QUIZ No. 13: **GUESS THE LINK**

EASY (1 Point)

1. **Music:** Whose first UK hit was 'Release Me' which got to No. 1 in 1967?
2. **Sport & Games:** Who took over as England cricket captain after Kevin Pietersen resigned in 2009?
3. **TV:** Which TV family, who lived in the Blue Ridge Mountains in Virginia in the 1930s, starred in a show that ran from 1972 to 1981?

MEDIUM (2 Points)

4. **Food & Drink:** Which beef dish comprises fillet steak topped with pâté foie gras, served with a Madeira and truffle sauce?
5. **TV:** Which character did Wendy Richard play in *Are You Being Served?*?
6. **Films:** Which 1992 film about a family's pet St Bernard was the first in a series of eight films in the franchise?
7. **TV:** Who starred as Jonathan Hart in the TV series *Hart to Hart* which ran from 1979 to 1984?

HARD (3 Points)

8. **People:** Which actress married Ringo Starr in 1981?
9. **Sport & Games:** Which horse trained by Aidan O'Brien was European Champion Sprinter in 2001 after winning the July Cup and the Nunthorpe Stakes?
10. **Music:** According to Donna Summer's 1987 song, whom did she want to have dinner with?

WHAT IS THE LINK BETWEEN ALL OF THE ANSWERS?

ANSWERS QUIZ No. 13: **LINK – COMPOSERS**

EASY (1 Point)

1. **Engelbert Humperdinck:** He also had another No. 1 hit in 1967 with 'The Last Waltz'.
2. **Andrew Strauss:** Strauss played for Middlesex for his entire career.
3. *The Waltons*: The show was narrated by eldest son John-Boy, played by Richard Thomas.

MEDIUM (2 Points)

4. **Tournedos (Beef) Rossini:** The dish is named in honour of the composer, famous for the 'Barber of Seville' and 'William Tell'.
5. **Miss (Shirley) Brahms:** Wendy Richard also played Pauline Fowler in *EastEnders* from 1985 to 2006.
6. *Beethoven*: The first four sequels had musical names, being *Beethoven's 2nd, 3rd, 4th and 5th*.
7. **Robert Wagner:** Wagner was married to Natalie Wood until her accidental death from drowning in 1981 when out sailing with Wagner and Christopher Walken.

HARD (3 Points)

8. **Barbara Bach:** She played the Bond girl Anya Amasova in *The Spy Who Loved Me*.
9. **Mozart:** The horse retired after his three-year-old season but died the following year from colitis.
10. **Gershwin:** George Gershwin died of a brain tumour at just 38, having collaborated with his brother Ira, who wrote the lyrics, on many famous musical works, especially 'Porgy and Bess'.

1. **TV:** Which cartoon character's brother is called George and has friends called Rebecca Rabbit and Suzy Sheep?
2. **Transport & Travel:** What is the nickname of the pass in the Peak District that starts east of Glossop and carries the A57 road from Manchester to Sheffield?
3. **TV:** Which knitted character starred with Johnny Vegas in advertising campaigns for ITV Digital and PG Tips?

MEDIUM (2 Points)

4. **Films:** Which Ang Lee film released in 2000, about a Chinese warrior stealing a sword, is the highest grossing foreign language film?
5. **Science & Medicine:** What is the common name for the star Sirius, found in the constellation Canis Major?
6. **TV:** Which TV puppet first appeared on ITV's TV-am in 1983 and was largely hailed as its saviour at the time?
7. **Music:** Which Rolling Stones song, their second UK No. 1 hit, was about a bird that was 'too lazy to crow'?

HARD (3 Points)

8. **Places:** Which island sits below Niagara Falls?
9. **Films:** Which 1998 film starring Robert Redford and Kristin Scott Thomas featured Redford as a trainer with a remarkable understanding of horses?
10. **Music:** The Who's bass player John Entwistle had which animal nickname because of his strong constitution?

WHAT IS THE LINK BETWEEN ALL OF THE ANSWERS?

1. **Peppa Pig:** The series was created by Neville Astley and Mark Baker and first aired on Channel 5 in 2003.
2. **Snake Pass:** The road was engineered by Thomas Telford and opened in 1821.
3. **Monkey:** ONdigital started in 1998 but was rebranded as ITV Digital in 2001 before going into administration in 2002, largely due to an unaffordable deal with the Football League.

4. ***Crouching Tiger, Hidden Dragon:*** Ang Lee also directed, amongst others, *Hulk* (2003), *Brokeback Mountain* (2005) and *The Life of Pi* (2012).
5. **Dog Star:** Sirius is the brightest star in the night sky.
6. **Roland Rat:** one of his colleagues was Kevin the Gerbil, the 'number one ratfan'.
7. **'Little Red Rooster':** The 1964 record was their second UK
    No. 1 after 'It's All Over Now' had been their first No. 1 earlier that year.

8. **Goat Island:** The island lies between the American and Canadian Falls and used to be called Iris Island.
9. ***The Horse Whisperer:*** Redford helps the injured horse of a teenage Scarlett Johansson in one of her earliest roles.
10. **The Ox:** Entwistle was also nicknamed 'Thunderfingers' due to the speed of his playing.

1. **Music:** Which group, whose members included Ben E King, had a UK No. 2 hit in 1960 with 'Save the Last Dance for Me'?
2. **Science & Medicine:** Which planet is 'The Red Planet'?
3. **Places:** What is the name of the purpose-built town near Birmingham associated with the Cadbury family?

4. **TV:** In the late-1960s children's animated TV series *The Herbs*, what kind of animal was Parsley?
5. **Sport & Games:** In, for example American football and baseball, what is the name of the halt in play where the clock stops and coaches can talk with the players?
6. **History:** On which ship did Fletcher Christian lead a mutiny against Captain Bligh in 1789?
7. **Science & Medicine:** What is the name of the galaxy that contains our Solar System?

8. **Music:** The Rah Band had a UK No. 6 hit in 1977 with which instrumental song?
9. **TV:** The early-1970s children's TV series revolving around seven children whose den was an old London bus in a scrapyard was called *Here Come the...*?
10. **History:** Which battle, one of the earliest recorded, took place in 490 BC when a Persian army invaded Athens?

WHAT IS THE LINK BETWEEN ALL OF THE ANSWERS?

29

EASY (1 Point)

1. **The Drifters:** The group were originally formed to be a backing group for Clyde McPhatter.
2. **Mars:** Mars is the second-smallest planet in the Solar System after Mercury.
3. **Bournville:** As George Cadbury was a Quaker, no public houses were ever built in Bournville.

MEDIUM (2 Points)

4. **Lion:** Other characters included Dill the Dog, Sir Basil, Lady Rosemary and Bayleaf the Gardener.
5. **Timeout:** In American football, each team is allowed three timeouts per half.
6. **HMS *Bounty*:** In the 1962 film *Mutiny on the Bounty*, Marlon Brando played Fletcher Christian and Trevor Howard played William Bligh.
7. **The Milky Way:** Andromeda is the nearest galaxy to our own, about 2.5 million light years away.

HARD (3 Points)

8. **'The Crunch':** The Rah Band had another UK No. 6 hit in 1985 with 'Clouds Across the Moon'.
9. ***Double Deckers*:** The series featured Melvyn Hayes, who was in the film *Summer Holiday*, also set on a London bus, and a young Peter Firth who starred as Harry Pearce in *Spooks*.
10. **Marathon:** Although the Persians tried to conquer the Greeks many times, it was the Greeks who eventually conquered the Persian Empire under Alexander the Great in the 330s BC.

1. **Sport & Games:** What is the small plastic peg on which a golf ball is placed for driving?
2. **Music:** Who is the lead singer of Jamiroquai?
3. **Science & Medicine:** The aqueous humour and vitreous humour can be found in which part of the human body?

MEDIUM (2 Points)

4. **Places:** The city of Chester stands on which river?
5. **TV:** *The Laughter Show*, which ran from 1984 to 1986, featured Les Dennis and his comedy partner up until his untimely death – he was known as Dustin...?
6. **Music:** Donny Osmond, Carly Simon, Bronski Beat and Annie Lennox all had hits with different songs called what?
7. **Animals & Nature:** An apiary is the home of which insect?

HARD (3 Points)

8. **Words:** Which is the only word that sounds the same if you remove the last four letters?
9. **History:** Longbows were traditionally mainly made from which wood?
10. **Places:** The city of Exeter stands on which river?

WHAT IS THE LINK BETWEEN ALL OF THE ANSWERS?

ANSWERS QUIZ No. 16: LINK – LETTERS OF THE ALPHABET

EASY (1 Point)

1. **Tee:** Before tees were invented, golfers used to carry buckets of sand and use small mounds to tee off from.
2. **Jay Kay:** His real name is Jason Luís Cheetham.
3. **Eye:** The aqueous humour is between the cornea and the lens and the vitreous humour is between the lens and the retina.

MEDIUM (2 Points)

4. **Dee:** The River Dee forms part of the border between England and Wales.
5. **Gee:** Dustin Gee, real name Gerald Harrison, died of a heart attack in 1986 aged just 43 whilst in panto in Southport.
6. **'Why':** The records were released in 1972, 1982, 1984 and 1992 respectively and they all got into the top 10.
7. **Bee:** Bees make honeycombs in hexagonal cells as that is the most efficient shape for them to store the honey.

HARD (3 Points)

8. **Queue:** Q and Z are the only two Scrabble letters worth ten points.
9. **Yew:** All yew trees are from the genus Taxus.
10. **Exe:** The headquarters of the Met Office has been in Exeter since 2003.

QUIZ No. 17: **GUESS THE LINK**

EASY (1 Point)

1. **Pot Luck:** What is the name of the comic verse of 5 lines where lines 1, 2 and 5 rhyme and so do lines 3 and 4?
2. **Music:** In the music hall song, where was it a long way to?
3. **TV:** George Baker starred as which detective on TV, based on a series of books by Ruth Rendell?

MEDIUM (2 Points)

4. **People:** Frank Pakenham was better known as which 'Lord' who controversially campaigned on behalf of Myra Hindley?
5. **Sport & Games:** Which Cambridge United striker joined Manchester United in 1992 but broke his leg and was sold to Coventry City after 12 games?
6. **TV:** Richard Chamberlain starred as which TV doctor?
7. **Music:** Who was the lead singer with Altered Images?

HARD (3 Points)

8. **Politics:** Who served as the US Secretary of State from 2013 to 2017, having also been the Democrat candidate who lost to George W Bush in the 2004 election?
9. **Sport & Games:** Which former England all-rounder played for Derbyshire from 1990 until 2003 before spells with Lancashire and Hampshire?
10. **Entertainment:** Which DJ took over presenting the Radio 2 Drivetime Show in 2010 when Chris Evans moved to the Breakfast Show?

WHAT IS THE LINK BETWEEN ALL OF THE ANSWERS?

ANSWERS QUIZ No. 17: **LINK – COUNTIES OF ROI**

1. **Limerick:** Actors Richard Harris and Todd Carty were born in Co Limerick.
2. **Tipperary:** Tipperary is home to the racecourses at Clonmel and Thurles.
3. **(Inspector Reg) Wexford:** Horseracing trainers Aidan O'Brien and Jim Bolger were both born in Co Wexford.

4. **Lord Longford:** The author Oliver Goldsmith, who wrote *The Vicar of Wakefield*, was born in Co Longford.
5. **Dion Dublin:** Singers Bono, Bob Geldof, Ronan Keating and Chris de Burgh are all from Dublin.
6. *Dr Kildare*: Arthur Guinness was born in Celbridge in Co Kildare.
7. **Clare Grogan:** Ennis is the county town of Co Clare, which is in the province of Munster.

8. **John Kerry:** Tralee is the county town of Co Kerry, which is in the province of Munster.
9. **Dominic Cork:** Entertainer Danny La Rue and footballer Roy Keane were born in Cork.
10. **Simon Mayo:** The first female PM Mary Robinson and X Factor judge Louis Walsh were born in Co Mayo.

1. **Geography:** The Great Barrier Reef in Queensland consists of which type of marine life?
2. **Films:** Which actor starred in *When Harry Met Sally* and *City Slickers*?
3. **Art & Literature:** What is the name of the one-legged pirate in *Treasure Island*?

MEDIUM (2 Points)

4. **Music:** Which song was Elkie Brooks's first UK chart hit?
5. **TV:** Which TV sci-fi series that ran from 1979 to 1982 starred Joanna Lumley and David McCallum in the title roles?
6. **Science & Medicine:** Which metal has the chemical symbol Pt?
7. **Music:** Which group had a UK No. 4 hit in 1973 with 'Feel the Need in Me'?

HARD (3 Points)

8. **Animals & Nature:** The giant panda is from which country?
9. **TV:** The 1980s TV series *Girls on Top* starred comediennes Dawn French, Jennifer Saunders, Tracey Ullman and who else?
10. **Places:** What was the name of Ghana before 1957?

WHAT IS THE LINK BETWEEN ALL OF THE ANSWERS?

ANSWERS QUIZ No. 18: LINK – WEDDING ANNIVERSARIES

1. **Coral:** 35 years of marriage.

2. **Billy Crystal:** 15 years of marriage.

3. **Long John Silver:** 25 years of marriage.

4. **'Pearl's a Singer':** 30 years of marriage.

5. *Sapphire & Steel*: 45 years of marriage.

6. **Platinum:** 60 years of marriage.

7. **Detroit Emeralds:** 55 years of marriage.

8. **China:** 20 years of marriage.

9. **Ruby Wax:** 40 years of marriage.

10. **The Gold Coast:** 50 years of marriage.

1. **Food & Drink:** Pesto is an Italian sauce made with pine nuts, Parmesan, garlic and which herb?
2. **Entertainment:** Which late Radio 2 DJ presented the BBC coverage of the Eurovision Song Contest from 1980 to 2008?
3. **Politics:** Who was the British prime minister from 1990 to 1997?

4. **Sport & Games:** Which football club play at Plainmoor?
5. **Films:** Which film, based on an F Scott Fitzgerald book, starred Robert Redford and Leonardo DiCaprio in the title roles in 1974 and 2013 respectively?
6. **Food & Drink:** Which salad dish consists of walnuts, celery, apples and grapes in mayonnaise?
7. **Sport & Games:** Which Chilean-born manager was in charge at Manchester City from 2013 to 2016?

8. **TV:** Which actress starred in *The Liver Birds* as Beryl, alongside Nerys Hughes who played Sandra?
9. **Music:** The 1993 cover of the Harold Melvin song 'The Love I Lost', which reached No. 3 in the UK charts, was by West End featuring whom?
10. **Films:** What was the name of the sequel starring Sidney Poitier to the film *In the Heat of the Night*?

WHAT IS THE LINK BETWEEN ALL OF THE ANSWERS?

EASY (1 Point)

1. **Basil:** Basil Fawlty was played by John Cleese and the name came from Basil Street where Cleese used to live.
2. **Terry Wogan:** Brian Hall played the chef Terry Hugh, who used to work in Dorchester but not at the Dorchester!
3. **John Major:** Major Gowen was played by Ballard Berkeley.

MEDIUM (2 Points)

4. **Torquay United:** The series was set in Torquay and was based on a hotel in Torquay where the Monty Python team once stayed.
5. ***The Great Gatsby*:** Miss (Ursula) Gatsby played by Renee Roberts was one of the permanent residents.
6. **Waldorf Salad:** This is the title of the ninth episode of only 12 ever made, which features an American couple who ask for the dish.
7. **Manuel Pellegrini:** Manuel was the Spanish waiter from Barcelona played by Andrew Sachs.

HARD (3 Points)

8. **Polly James:** Polly was the maid-cum-waitress played by Connie Booth. At the time she was the real-life wife of John Cleese until they divorced in 1978.
9. **Sybil:** Basil's wife Sybil was played by Prunella Scales who is married to actor Timothy West.
10. ***They Call Me Mister Tibbs!*:** Miss (Abitha) Tibbs was another permanent resident played by Gilly Flower.

QUIZ No. 20: GUESS THE LINK

EASY (1 Point)

1. **Sport & Games:** Which Chicago Bulls basketball player starred in the 1996 film *Space Jam*?
2. **TV:** What was the name of Lady Penelope's chauffeur in the TV series *Thunderbirds*?
3. **Pot Luck:** Which newspaper ran the headline 'Gotcha' after the *General Belgrano* was sunk during the Falklands War?

MEDIUM (2 Points)

4. **Music:** Which 1986 Paul Simon album features the song 'You Can Call Me Al'?
5. **Films:** What was the name of the 1994 comedy drama film about two drag queens driving across Australia in a tour bus – *The Adventures of ...... Queen of the Desert*?
6. **Music:** What is the name of Marc Cohn's highest UK chart hit which reached No. 22 in the charts in 1991 – 'Walking in ......'?
7. **Films:** Which 1997 film starred Demi Moore as the first woman to train in the US Navy Special Forces?

HARD (3 Points)

8. **Religion:** Who was the elder brother of Moses?
9. **Sport & Games:** The first Open Championship was held at which Scottish golf course in 1860?
10. **Music:** The song 'Keep on Jumpin'' was a 1996 hit for Todd Terry, but which group called the ...... Experience had a simultaneous Top 10 hit with the same song?

WHAT IS THE LINK BETWEEN ALL OF THE ANSWERS?

39

ANSWERS QUIZ No. 20: LINK – ELVIS PRESLEY

EASY (1 Point)

1. **Michael Jordan:** Elvis's backing group were called the Jordanaires.
2. **Parker:** Colonel Tom Parker was his manager.
3. *The Sun*: Sun Records discovered Presley and recorded his first songs, but his contract was sold in 1955 to RCA Victor.

MEDIUM (2 Points)

4. *Graceland*: Graceland is the name of his mansion in Memphis, Tennessee.
5. **Priscilla:** Priscilla Wagner married Elvis in 1967.
6. **Memphis:** Elvis died in his Memphis home in 1977.
7. *G I Jane*: *G I Blues* was a 1960 film, released just after his own time in the army, which featured the songs 'Wooden Heart' and 'Didja' Ever'.

HARD (3 Points)

8. **Aaron:** Aaron was Elvis's middle name.
9. **Prestwick:** Prestwick Airport in 1960 is the only time that Elvis set foot in the UK. His military plane stopped there for refuelling on his way back to the USA.
10. **Lisa Marie:** Lisa Marie is the name of his daughter born in 1968, who went on to marry Michael Jackson in 1994 but they were divorced in 1996.

QUIZ No. 21: GUESS THE LINK

EASY (1 Point)

1. **Pot Luck:** Whom did Prince Andrew marry in 1986?
2. **Sport & Games:** With which football club did Tom Finney play for his entire career?
3. **Music:** Which group had a No. 1 hit in 1976 with 'You To Me Are Everything'?

MEDIUM (2 Points)

4. **Art & Literature:** Which Shakespeare play features the Montagues and the Capulets?
5. **Films:** Who had a three-year relationship with Tom Cruise after they appeared together in the film *Vanilla Sky*?
6. **History:** Which English monarch reigned from 1837 to 1901?
7. **Food & Drink:** Which confectionery company make the Ripple chocolate bar?

HARD (3 Points)

8. **Politics:** Who was the prime minister of Canada from 2006 until 2015?
9. **Places:** Which is the most populous of New York's five boroughs?
10. **Maths & Numbers:** In darts, what is the lowest number that cannot be achieved with one dart?

WHAT IS THE LINK BETWEEN ALL OF THE ANSWERS?

ANSWERS QUIZ No. 21: LINK – DAVID BECKHAM

EASY (1 Point)

1. **Sarah Ferguson:** Beckham played under manager Alex Ferguson for all of his Manchester United career.
2. **Preston North End:** He went out on loan to Preston North End during the 1994–95 season, scoring two goals in five appearances, including directly from a corner.
3. **The Real Thing:** He played for Real Madrid between 2003 and 2007.

MEDIUM (2 Points)

4. *Romeo and Juliet:* His second son is Romeo James born 1 September 2002.
5. **Penelope Cruz:** His third son is Cruz David born 20 February 2005.
6. **Queen Victoria:** His wife Victoria's maiden name was Adams and they married on 4 July 1999.
7. **Galaxy:** He played for LA Galaxy between 2007 and 2012.

HARD (3 Points)

8. **Stephen Harper:** His daughter is Harper Seven born 10 July 2011.
9. **Brooklyn:** His eldest son is Brooklyn Joseph born 4 March 1999.
10. **23:** He chose the No. 23 shirt at Real Madrid and LA Galaxy because it is the same number that Michael Jordan used to wear for the Chicago Bulls.

1. **Music:** Which US group had 1983 UK hits with 'Africa' and 'Rosanna'?
2. **TV:** Who was the inventor and scientist in the TV puppet show *Thunderbirds*?
3. **Films:** Which 1994 animated film tells the story of Simba trying to follow in his father Mufasa's footsteps?

MEDIUM (2 Points)

4. **Music:** Which 1973 Elton John song starts with the line 'When are you gonna come down, when are you going to land'?
5. **Science & Medicine:** Which element has the chemical symbol Sn?
6. **TV:** Worzel Gummidge, played by Jon Pertwee in the TV series shown from 1979 to 1981, was what type of character?
7. **Music:** Which US group had their biggest UK hit in 1987 with 'Alone' which reached No. 3?

HARD (3 Points)

8. **Art & Literature:** Which author created the amateur sleuth Lord Peter Wimsey?
9. **Food & Drink:** Which brewery brew the cask ale 'Directors'?
10. **Music:** According to Elvis Costello, 'The Angels Wanna Wear My......'?

WHAT IS THE LINK BETWEEN ALL OF THE ANSWERS?

ANSWERS QUIZ No. 22: LINK – *THE WIZARD OF OZ*

EASY (1 Point)

1. **Toto:** Toto is Dorothy's dog, a male in the film but was actually a female Cairn Terrier called Terry.
2. **Brains:** The Scarecrow wants a brain.
3. *The Lion King*: Bert Lahr stars as the Cowardly Lion.

MEDIUM (2 Points)

4. **'Goodbye Yellow Brick Road':** Dorothy has to follow the yellow brick road to the Emerald City to see the Wizard of Oz.
5. **Tin:** Jack Haley stars as the Tin Man.
6. **Scarecrow:** Ray Bolger stars as the Scarecrow.
7. **Heart:** The Tin Man wants a heart.

HARD (3 Points)

8. **Dorothy L Sayers:** Judy Garland stars as Dorothy Gale.
9. **Courage:** The Cowardly Lion needs some courage.
10. **Red Shoes:** Dorothy wears some magic ruby slippers. These were silver in the original book but were changed to red to take advantage of the new Technicolor film process.

1. **Music:** Which female duo had a 1988 UK No. 2 hit with 'Push It' and also got to No. 4 with 'Twist and Shout'?
2. **Sport & Games:** In the game of Cluedo, what is the name of the man represented by the yellow piece?
3. **Food & Drink:** What is the main ingredient of the Eastern European soup borscht?

4. **Places:** Bromsgrove, Kidderminster and Redditch are in which English county?
5. **Music:** Which Spanish group had a 2002 UK No. 1 hit with 'The Ketchup Song'?
6. **Sport & Games:** What was the name of the dog who found the Jules Rimet Trophy after it had been stolen four months before the 1966 World Cup?
7. **Pot Luck:** Llantrisant is home to which organisation that supplies all the coinage to the UK?

8. **Music:** Which group, made up of Noel Edmonds, Keith Chegwin and Maggie Philbin, had a UK No. 15 hit in 1981 with 'I Wanna Be a Winner'?
9. **Places:** Castlebar is the county town of which Irish county?
10. **Music:** Which early-70s group featured both Elkie Brooks and Robert Palmer, although they didn't have any UK hit singles?

WHAT IS THE LINK BETWEEN ALL OF THE ANSWERS?

EASY (1 Point)

1. **Salt-n-Pepa:** Cheryl James was 'Salt' and Sandra Denton was 'Pepa'.
2. **Colonel Mustard:** The other original suspects were Miss Scarlett, Mrs Peacock, Rev Green, Prof Plum and Mrs White.
3. **Beetroot:** You can use beetroot juice to measure acidity – in acid solution it turns pink and in alkali solution it turns yellow.

MEDIUM (2 Points)

4. **Worcestershire:** Worcestershire County Cricket Club play their home games at New Road.
5. **Las Ketchup:** Ketchup has alternatively been named catsup in some countries and is still called that in the southern US states and Mexico.
6. **Pickles:** Pickles was a black and white collie dog but sadly died the following year when he was strangled by his collar whilst chasing a cat!
7. **Royal Mint:** The Royal Mint was founded in 886 and was originally in the Tower of London.

HARD (3 Points)

8. **Brown Sauce:** All three group members were TV presenters on BBC's *Multi-Coloured Swap Shop*.
9. **County Mayo:** Mayonnaise is made using oil, egg yolk and either vinegar or lemon juice.
10. **Vinegar Joe:** Robert Palmer also formed part of The Power Station with members of both Duran Duran and Chic.

QUIZ No. 24: **GUESS THE LINK**

1. **Music:** Which Elton John song starts 'I remember when rock was young, me and Suzie had so much fun'?
2. **Food & Drink:** Which dish consists of sausages in Yorkshire pudding batter?
3. **Words:** Which word can mean an observer, a school pupil with special duties or another word for a computer screen?

MEDIUM (2 Points)

4. **Music:** Culture Club's first UK No. 1 was 'Do You Really Want to Hurt Me' but what was their second?
5. **Films:** What was the name of Michael Douglas's character in the 1987 film *Wall Street*?
6. **Food & Drink:** What is the name of the drink that is half lager and half cider?
7. **Music:** Which group had hits in 1967 with 'Happy Together' and 'She'd Rather Be With Me'?

HARD (3 Points)

8. **Places:** What is the most southerly point of Great Britain?
9. **Pot Luck:** What is the name of the indentation in a brick?
10. **Food & Drink:** The avocado is also known as the ....pear?

WHAT IS THE LINK BETWEEN ALL OF THE ANSWERS?

EASY (1 Point)

1. **'Crocodile Rock':** The song was a US No. 1 but only reached No. 5 in the UK in 1972.
2. **Toad in the Hole:** The 1929 play *Toad of Toad Hall* was based on Kenneth Grahame's 1908 book *The Wind in the Willows*.
3. **Monitor:** Monitor is a type of lizard, the largest of which is the Komodo dragon which is the largest living species of lizard.

MEDIUM (2 Points)

4. **'Karma Chameleon':** Some chameleons can change to any colour but most turn from brown to green and back. Their eyes can also work independently.
5. **Gordon Gekko:** *Money Never Sleeps* was the sequel subtitle after one of Gekko's quotes from the original film.
6. **Snakebite:** In the UK some landlords stopped serving it, believing that people got more drunk off it, but there is no scientific evidence that is the case.
7. **The Turtles:** Their only other hit 'Elenore' was in 1968.

HARD (3 Points)

8. **Lizard Point:** Lizard Point is in Cornwall and unsurprisingly is also the site of a lighthouse.
9. **Frog:** The triangular inner part of a horse's hoof is also called a frog.
10. **Alligator (Pear):** Alligators have broader U-shaped snouts whereas crocodiles have narrower V-shaped snouts.

QUIZ No. 25: **GUESS THE LINK**

EASY (1 Point)

1. **TV:** What was the name of the members' club frequented by Arthur Daley in *Minder*?
2. **Art & Literature:** Which collection of 24 stories by Geoffrey Chaucer starts with 'The Knight's Tale' and 'The Miller's Tale'?
3. **Sport & Games:** Which then non-League team beat Newcastle United 2-1 in the 1972 FA Cup third round?

MEDIUM (2 Points)

4. **People:** Which Royals' photographer, who was an earl and a cousin of the Queen, died in 2005 aged 66?
5. **Art & Literature:** Who is the master of Thornfield Hall whom the eponymous *Jane Eyre* falls in love with?
6. **Sport & Games:** Which Scottish sprinter won the 100 metres in the 1980 Moscow Olympics?
7. **People:** Who was the first person to sail around the world single-handedly in his yacht *Gipsy Moth IV* in 1967?

HARD (3 Points)

8. **Places:** Which city was known as Verulamium to the Romans?
9. **History:** Who was the prime minister on the death of Queen Victoria in 1901, then in his third non-consecutive term?
10. **TV:** Which actor starred as *Tarzan* in the NBC TV series that ran from 1966 to 1968?

WHAT IS THE LINK BETWEEN ALL OF THE ANSWERS?

EASY (1 Point)

1. **Winchester Club:** Jane Austen and William II are buried here.
2. *Canterbury Tales*: St Augustine established the first cathedral in 597 and the Archbishop Thomas Becket was murdered here in 1170 by Henry II's men.
3. **Hereford United:** The cathedral is the home of *Mappa Mundi*, a medieval world map from the 13th century.

MEDIUM (2 Points)

4. **Patrick Lichfield:** Lichfield is the only medieval cathedral with three spires.
5. **Mr (Edward) Rochester:** Rochester was founded in 604 and is the second-oldest cathedral in England after Canterbury.
6. **Allan Wells:** Wells is the smallest city in England and the cathedral houses the second-oldest clock in Britain.
7 **Sir Francis Chichester:** Chichester is home to the Goodwood Estate which includes the racecourse and the Festival of Speed motor racing circuit.

HARD (3 Points)

8. **St Albans:** St Albans is the oldest site of continuous Christian worship in Britain, being where St Alban became the first Christian martyr in Britain.
9. **Marquess of Salisbury:** Salisbury has the tallest spire in England at 404 ft. It is home to one of the four surviving copies of the Magna Carta (Lincoln also has one).
10. **Ron Ely:** The cathedral is known as the 'Ship of the Fens'.

1. **Films:** Vivien Leigh played which character in the 1939 film *Gone with the Wind*?
2. **TV:** Which TV presenter hosted the shows *Double Your Money* and *Opportunity Knocks*?
3. **Food & Drink:** James Martin presented which Saturday morning cookery show from 2006 to 2016?

MEDIUM (2 Points)

4. **Music:** What was the title of the biggest hit for the Fratellis which got to No. 5 in the UK charts in 2006?
5. **Places:** Which famous building's address is at 1600 Pennsylvania Avenue, Washington?
6. **TV:** Frank Thornton played which character in *Are You Being Served?*
7. **Films:** Diane Keaton won the Best Actress Oscar for playing the eponymous character in which 1977 Woody Allen film?

HARD (3 Points)

8. **Music:** In which 1973 song by the Sweet do the lyrics 'Oh yeah! It was like lightning, everybody was fighting' appear?
9. **Art & Literature:** Sherlock Holmes first appeared in which 1887 Arthur Conan Doyle novel?
10. **Music:** The Beatles songs 'Eleanor Rigby' and 'Got to Get You into My Life' appear on which 1966 album?

WHAT IS THE LINK BETWEEN ALL OF THE ANSWERS?

ANSWERS QUIZ No. 26: LINK – CLUEDO

EASY (1 Point)

1. **Scarlett O'Hara:** *Gone with the Wind* was a 1936 novel by Margaret Mitchell, the only one published in her lifetime.
2. **Hughie Green:** After his death, a tabloid story exposed him as the biological father of TV presenter Paula Yates.
3. *Saturday Kitchen*: The first two regular presenters of the show were Gregg Wallace (2002–03) and Antony Worrall Thompson (2003–06).

MEDIUM (2 Points)

4. **'Chelsea Dagger':** The Fratellis' only other UK Top 10 hit was 'Whistle for the Choir', also in 2006.
5. **The White House:** Although George Washington oversaw the building of the White House, second president John Adams was the first to live in it in 1800.
6. **Captain Peacock:** Frank Thornton also played Truly in *Last of the Summer Wine* from 1997.
7. *Annie Hall*: Woody Allen also won the 1978 Best Director Oscar for *Annie Hall*.

HARD (3 Points)

8. **'The Ballroom Blitz':** The Sweet only had one No. 1 hit, with 'Blockbuster', also in 1973. 'Hell Raiser' and 'The Ballroom Blitz' both reached No. 2 in the same year.
9. *A Study in Scarlet*: The second Sherlock Holmes novel was *The Sign of the Four* which followed in 1890.
10. *Revolver*: 'Yellow Submarine' was also on the same album, featuring lead vocals by Ringo Starr.

QUIZ No. 27: **GUESS THE LINK**

1. **TV:** Which actress played Pat Butcher in *EastEnders* from 1986 until 2012?
2. **Sport & Games:** Which Scotland manager died shortly after the end of a World Cup qualifying game v Wales in 1985?
3. **Films:** Who starred as one of *Charlie's Angels* alongside Cameron Diaz and Drew Barrymore in the 2000 film?

MEDIUM (2 Points)

4. **TV:** John Ratzenberger starred as which character, a postman, in the US comedy series *Cheers*?
5. **Music:** Which Australian group had a UK No. 6 hit in 1989 with 'Beds Are Burning'?
6. **Sport & Games:** Which snooker player, nicknamed 'Dracula', won the last of his six World titles in 1978?
7. **TV:** Which female TV presenter has co-presented *Countryfile* since 2009 and *Secret Britain* from 2015?

HARD (3 Points)

8. **Animals & Nature:** What was the name of the Skye Terrier that guarded his owner's grave for 14 years until his own death in 1872?
9. **Music:** Who is the bass guitarist with the group U2?
10. **TV:** In the 1983 Yellow Pages TV advert, who was the author of the book *Fly Fishing*, turning out to be the maker of the telephone call searching for his own book?

WHAT IS THE LINK BETWEEN ALL OF THE ANSWERS?

ANSWERS QUIZ No. 27: **LINK – *DALLAS***

1. **Pam St Clement:** Pam Barnes Ewing, played by Victoria Principal, was the sister of Cliff Barnes.
2. **Jock Stein:** John Ross (Jock) Ewing Sr was the father of the brothers J.R., Gary and Bobby. He was played by Jim Davis until his death from cancer in 1981.
3. **Lucy Liu:** Lucy Ewing, the daughter of Gary Ewing (the main character in *Knots Landing)* was played by Charlene Tilton.

MEDIUM (2 Points)

4. **Cliff (Clavin):** Cliff Barnes was J.R. Ewing's main rival and was played by Ken Kercheval.
5. **Midnight Oil:** The family business was Ewing Oil but there has been a company of that name in Maryland since 1965.
6. **Ray Reardon:** Ray Krebbs was the illegitimate son of Jock Ewing and was played by Steve Kanaly.
7. **Ellie Harrison:** Miss Ellie was played by Barbara Bel Geddes for all but one series. Donna Reed replaced her in 1984 but Bel Geddes returned in 1985.

HARD (3 Points)

8. **Greyfriars Bobby:** Bobby Ewing was played by Patrick Duffy who also played the *Man from Atlantis.*
9. **Adam Clayton:** Clayton Farlow was played by Howard Keel, a star in several musicals especially *Seven Brides for Seven Brothers.*
10. **J R Hartley:** J R Ewing was played by Larry Hagman who died in 2012.

1. **History:** Which Roman general first invaded Britain in 55 BC?
2. **Pot Luck:** What is the alternative name for the Christian day of the Epiphany, consequently called because of the number of days after Christmas?
3. **TV:** In the TV adverts, 'Happiness was a cigar called...'?

4. **Music:** Which Dire Straits song includes the lyrics: 'When you can fall for chains of silver, you can fall for chains of gold'?
5. **History:** Which English king was successful at the Battle of Agincourt in 1415?
6. **Music:** Which Christmas song reached No. 2 in the 1982 UK charts for David Essex?
7. **Sport & Games:** Which Mattel board game, played using double-sided black and white discs, is a variant of the traditional game of Reversi?

8. **History:** Which English king was the last to die in battle when killed at the Battle of Bosworth Field in 1485?
9. **Music:** The traditional 'Wedding March' played in churches when the married couple leave the church is from which piece of music by Felix Mendelssohn?
10. **Sport & Games:** Which horse won the 1973 Champion Hurdle and was the first to regain the title in 1975?

WHAT IS THE LINK BETWEEN ALL OF THE ANSWERS?

1. **Julius Caesar:** Caesar was assassinated on the Ides (15th) of March in 44 BC.
2. **Twelfth Night:** The play is set in Illyria which was an ancient area of the western Balkans.
3. **Hamlet:** The full title is *The Tragedy of Hamlet, the Prince of Denmark.*

MEDIUM (2 Points)

4. **'Romeo and Juliet':** The surnames of the two families are the Montagues and the Capulets.
5. **Henry V:** Henry was the son of Henry IV and reigned from 1413 to 1422.
6. **'A Winter's Tale':** The play is called *The Winter's Tale* and features Antigonus being chased by a bear.
7. **Othello:** Othello was also known as The Moor of Venice and was married to Desdemona.

HARD (3 Points)

8. **Richard III:** His lost remains were found under a car park in Leicester in 2012 and he was reburied at Leicester Cathedral in 2015.
9. **'A Midsummer Night's Dream':** The play includes the characters Oberon, Titania, Bottom and Puck, also known as Robin Goodfellow.
10. **Comedy of Errors:** The 1988 Bette Midler film *Big Business* was broadly based on the play.

QUIZ No. 29: GUESS THE LINK

1. **Pot Luck:** What did Queen Victoria celebrate in 1887 and Queen Elizabeth II in 2002?
2. **Entertainment:** What was the maiden name of David Beckham's wife?
3. **TV:** What is the name of the New York coffee shop in *Friends*?

4. **History:** In which 1815 battle did the Duke of Wellington defeat Napoleon Bonaparte?
5. **Sport & Games:** In Monopoly, which property completes the yellow set with Leicester Square and Coventry Street?
6. **Maths & Numbers:** The formula 2πr calculates the radius of what?
7. **Science & Medicine:** The Aurora Borealis is more commonly known as what?

8. **Places:** What does the D.C. stand for in Washington D.C.?
9. **Entertainment:** Which Art Deco music venue on Queen Caroline Street, London W6 used to be called the Odeon?
10. **Food & Drink:** Which cocktail is made with blackcurrant vodka, triple sec, cranberry juice and lime juice?

WHAT IS THE LINK BETWEEN ALL OF THE ANSWERS?

EASY (1 Point)

1. **Golden Jubilee:** Queen Elizabeth II overtook Victoria as the longest reigning monarch in 2015.
2. **Victoria Adams:** She was born in 1974 and they married in 1999.
3. **Central Perk:** *Friends* ran for ten seasons from 1994 to 2004.

MEDIUM (2 Points)

4. **Waterloo:** The town of Waterloo is based in Belgium.
5. **Piccadilly:** Piccadilly is also one of the two Manchester railway stations along with Victoria.
6. **Circle:** The formula πr^2 calculates the area of a circle.
7. **Northern Lights:** The Southern Lights is the Aurora Australis.

HARD (3 Points)

8. **District of Columbia:** The city was named after the first president George Washington (1789–97).
9. **Hammersmith Apollo:** It opened in 1932 and was renamed the Hammersmith Odeon in 1962.
10. **Metropolitan:** This is a variant of the Cosmopolitan cocktail which contains lemon vodka.

EASY (1 Point)

1. **Music:** Which 1984 Madonna hit starts with the line 'I made it through the wilderness'...
2. **Films:** Which 1988 comedy film starred Arnold Schwarzenegger and Danny DeVito?
3. **Sport & Games:** What is the nickname of Derby County Football Club?

MEDIUM (2 Points)

4. **Art & Literature:** Which author wrote *Kane and Abel* and *The Prodigal Daughter*?
5. **TV:** Which actress, married to actor Timothy West, played Sybil in *Fawlty Towers*?
6. **Music:** Who was the lead singer with the group Marillion?
7. **Art & Literature:** Which was the first of the seven *Chronicles of Narnia* books written by C S Lewis?

HARD (3 Points)

8. **Places:** What is the name of the island in the middle of Niagara Falls?
9. **Sport & Games:** Robbie Paul scored 224 tries in 241 games for which rugby league Super League team?
10. **Places:** What is the deepest lake in the Lake District?

WHAT IS THE LINK BETWEEN ALL OF THE ANSWERS?

EASY (1 Point)

1. **'Like a Virgin':** Virgo is an earth sign ruled by Mercury (Aug 23 to Sep 22).
2. **Twins:** Gemini is an air sign ruled by Mercury (May 21 to Jun 20).
3. **The Rams:** Aries is a fire sign ruled by Mars (Mar 21 to Apr 19).

MEDIUM (2 Points)

4. **Jeffrey Archer:** Sagittarius is a fire sign ruled by Jupiter (Nov 22 to Dec 21).
5. **Prunella Scales:** Libra is an air sign ruled by Venus (Sep 23 to Oct 22).
6. **Fish:** Pisces is a water sign ruled by Neptune (Feb 19 to Mar 20).
7. **The Lion, The Witch and the Wardrobe:** Leo is a fire sign ruled by the Sun (Jul 23 to Aug 22).

HARD (3 Points)

8. **Goat Island:** Capricorn is an earth sign ruled by Saturn (Dec 22 to Jan 19).
9. **Bradford Bulls:** Taurus is an earth sign ruled by Venus (Apr 20 to May 20).
10. **Wastwater:** Aquarius is an air sign ruled by Uranus (Jan 20 to Feb 18).

Cancer is a water sign ruled by the Moon (Jun 21 to Jul 22).
Scorpio is a water sign ruled by Mars (Oct 23 to Nov 21).

1. **TV:** Which actress played Maddie Hayes in the '80s TV show *Moonlighting*?
2. **Films:** Which character is voiced by Eddie Murphy in the *Shrek* films?
3. **Science & Medicine:** Au is the chemical symbol for which element?

MEDIUM (2 Points)

4. **Sport & Games:** Which British athlete won the gold medal in the 1964 Olympics long jump?
5. **Music:** Which 1997 Robbie Williams song starts with the line 'I sit and wait...'?
6. **Theatre:** The song 'Any Dream Will Do' is from which stage musical?
7. **Science & Medicine:** The Polaris star is commonly called the Pole Star or which other name?

HARD (3 Points)

8. **Films:** Ingrid Bergman stars as the missionary Gladys Aylward in which 1958 film?
9. **TV:** The traditional carol service shown on BBC2 every Christmas Eve comes from the chapel of which Cambridge college?
10. **Music:** George Michael secretly donated the proceeds of which 1996 single to the charity Childline?

WHAT IS THE LINK BETWEEN ALL OF THE ANSWERS?

1. **Cybill Shepherd:** Bruce Willis co-starred as David Addison and it ran for five seasons from 1985 to 1989.
2. **Donkey:** Mike Myers voiced Shrek and Cameron Diaz voiced Princess Fiona.
3. **Gold:** Gold is atomic number 79 in the periodic table in between platinum (78) and mercury (80).

MEDIUM (2 Points)

4. **Mary Rand:** She broke the world record and also won a silver in the pentathlon and a bronze in the 4 x 100m relay.
5. **'Angels':** It is Williams's biggest-selling single but only reached No. 4 in the UK charts.
6. *Joseph and the Amazing Technicolor Dreamcoat*: The Andrew Lloyd Webber and Tim Rice musical starred Jason Donovan and Phillip Schofield in the 1990s.
7. **North Star:** The star is in the constellation Ursa Minor.

HARD (3 Points)

8. *Inn of the Sixth Happiness*: Gladys Aylward was a Christian missionary to China but the film was filmed in North Wales and England.
9. **King's College:** The BBC2 service is pre-recorded but there is a live carol service on Christmas Eve from King's broadcast on Radio 4.
10. **'Jesus to a Child':** His generosity only came to light after his death in 2016 when Childline's founder Esther Rantzen revealed his secret.

QUIZ No. 32: **GUESS THE LINK**

1. **TV:** Which 1980s TV show hosted by Kenneth Kendall featured Anneka Rice as the 'Skyrunner'?
2. **Entertainment:** Which actor starred in *The Saint* and *The Persuaders* before becoming James Bond?
3. **Sport & Games:** Which London-based football team play at The Valley?

4. **Films:** Which actor's most famous films were *Ben-Hur* and *The Ten Commandments*?
5. **Politics:** Who was British prime minister between 1964 and 1970 and then again between 1974 and 1976?
6. **Science & Medicine:** In the human body, the hip joint and the shoulder joint are what types of joint?
7. **Sport & Games:** Which British athlete won a gold medal in the women's pentathlon at the 1972 Munich Olympics?

8. **Films:** Which 2013 film about the creation of *Mary Poppins* starred Tom Hanks as Walt Disney?
9. **Music:** Who wrote the song 'Hallelujah' covered by Jeff Buckley and latterly Alexandra Burke after winning the *X Factor* in 2008?
10. **TV:** Which comedian was a regular on David Gower's team for the first 3 series of the sports quiz *They Think It's All Over*?

WHAT IS THE LINK BETWEEN ALL OF THE ANSWERS?

EASY (1 Point)

1. **Treasure Hunt:** Annabel Croft took over from Anneka Rice when she left to have a baby.
2. **Roger Moore:** Simon Templar was *The Saint* and he played Lord Brett Sinclair in *The Persuaders* alongside Tony Curtis as Danny Wilde.
3. **Charlton Athletic:** The club nickname is the Addicks.

MEDIUM (2 Points)

4. **Charlton Heston:** He won the Best Actor Oscar in 1959 for *Ben-Hur*.
5. **Harold Wilson:** He was born in Huddersfield in 1916 and was the MP for Huyton for 33 years.
6. **Ball and Socket:** The hip and shoulder are the only true ball and socket joints – the ankle, elbow and knee are all hinge joints.
7. **Mary Peters:** She moved to N Ireland when she was 11 and won the BBC Sports Personality of the Year Award in 1972.

HARD (3 Points)

8. **Saving Mr Banks:** Emma Thompson starred as Pamela 'P.L.' Travers who wrote the *Mary Poppins* books.
9. **Leonard Cohen:** Cohen was Canadian and died aged 82 in November 2016.
10. **Lee Hurst:** Rory McGrath was the regular comedian on Gary Lineker's team.

1. **Music:** Who was the fourth member of Bucks Fizz besides Mike Nolan, Bobby Gee and Jay Aston?
2. **Sport & Games:** Which 20-times Champion Jockey won his only Grand National in 2010 on Don't Push It?
3. **TV:** Which TV presenter has presented *Blue Peter*, *Countryfile* and *The One Show*?

MEDIUM (2 Points)

4. **Politics:** Who was leader of the Labour Party from 1992 until his sudden death in 1994?
5. **Music:** The Pet Shop Boys were formed in 1981 by Chris Lowe and which other singer / songwriter?
6. **History:** Which suffragette was killed by the King's horse when she walked onto the track in the 1913 Epsom Derby?
7. **TV:** Who played the role of Charlie Burrows, the housekeeper in the 1990s TV comedy *The Upper Hand*?

HARD (3 Points)

8. **Shopping & Fashion:** Which royal fashion designer designed the wedding and coronation dresses for Queen Elizabeth II?
9. **TV:** Which actor played the part of ARP Warden Hodges in *Dad's Army*?
10. **Music:** Which former member of Traffic had a solo UK No. 4 hit in 1975 with 'Love Hurts'?

WHAT IS THE LINK BETWEEN ALL OF THE ANSWERS?

EASY (1 Point)

1. **Cheryl Baker:** Tom Baker was the fourth doctor between 1974 and 1981.
2. **Tony McCoy:** Sylvester McCoy was the seventh doctor between 1987 and 1989.
3. **Matt Baker:** Colin Baker was the sixth doctor between 1984 and 1986.

MEDIUM (2 Points)

4. **John Smith:** Matt Smith was the eleventh doctor between 2010 and 2013.
5. **Neil Tennant:** David Tennant was the tenth doctor between 2005 and 2010, taking over from Christopher Eccleston who did just one series.
6. **Emily Davison:** Peter Davison was the fifth doctor between 1981 and 1984.
7. **Joe McGann:** Paul McGann was the eighth doctor appearing in just 2 episodes in 1996 – he is the brother of Joe McGann.

HARD (3 Points)

8. **Norman Hartnell:** William Hartnell was the first doctor between 1963 and 1966, followed by Patrick Troughton from 1966 to 1969.
9. **Bill Pertwee:** Jon Pertwee was the third doctor between 1970 and 1974 – he was also a distant cousin of Bill Pertwee.
10. **Jim Capaldi:** Peter Capaldi was the twelfth doctor between 2013 and 2017, before Jodie Whittaker became the first female doctor.

QUIZ No. 34: GUESS THE LINK

EASY (1 Point)

1. **People:** What is the name of David and Victoria Beckham's eldest child?
2. **Places:** Which US building was the tallest in the world from 1931 until 1970?
3. **Sport & Games:** Which West Kensington venue in London hosts the traditional men's warm-up tournament for Wimbledon?

MEDIUM (2 Points)

4. **Pot Luck:** On which famous landmark would you find the quote 'Give me your tired, your poor, your huddled masses yearning to break free'?
5. **TV:** The TV show *Mad Men* was set in an advertising agency located on which street famous for advertising?
6. **Music:** What was Joni Mitchell's only solo hit to make the UK charts?
7. **Sport & Games:** What was the name of Wigan's rugby league ground before they moved to the JJB Stadium in 1999?

HARD (3 Points)

8. **Music:** Which female singer's biggest UK hit was 'I Try', reaching No. 6 in 1999?
9. **Food & Drink:** Which cocktail consists of whiskey, sweet vermouth and Angostura bitters?
10. **Theatre:** Which musical includes the songs 'We're in the Money' and 'Keep Young and Beautiful'?

WHAT IS THE LINK BETWEEN ALL OF THE ANSWERS?

ANSWERS QUIZ No. 34: **LINK – NEW YORK**

EASY (1 Point)

1. **Brooklyn:** Brooklyn is the most populous borough in New York.
2. **Empire State Building:** The World Trade Center was then tallest until 1973 when Sears Tower was built in Chicago.
3. **Queen's (Club):** Queens is the largest borough in New York.

MEDIUM (2 Points)

4. **Statue of Liberty:** The statue was a gift from France and its building was overseen by Gustave Eiffel, famous for the Paris tower.
5. **Madison Avenue:** From the 1920s, many US advertising agencies were based on the street named after the fourth US President.
6. **'Big Yellow Taxi':** In 2013 some green taxis were introduced into New York but only in certain areas.
7. **Central Park:** The park contains Cleopatra's Needle (there are two others in Paris and London) and Strawberry Fields (dedicated to John Lennon).

HARD (3 Points)

8. **Macy Gray:** Macy's is a chain of stores that started in New York – now in the same group as Bloomingdale's.
9. **Manhattan:** Manhattan is the most densely populated borough in New York.
10. ***42nd Street***: Between Seventh and Eighth Avenues, seven theatres are on a stretch now called New 42nd Street.

1. **TV:** Which TV series written by Carla Lane about the Boswell family ran from 1986 to 1991?
2. **Music:** Which English singer / songwriter created an alter ego called Ziggy Stardust in 1972?
3. **Pot Luck:** What is cockney rhyming slang for 'look'?

4. **Animals & Nature:** What is the name for a female swan?
5. **History:** Who is the only prime minister to have served under three monarchs?
6. **Music:** Which 1983 song was the follow-up single to Eddy Grant's only No. 1 'I Don't Wanna Dance', this time reaching No. 2?
7. **TV:** Which specific dairy product is the favourite food of Wallace in the *Wallace and Gromit* films?

8. **Films:** For which 1997 film did Robin Williams win his only Oscar, as supporting actor playing a therapist treating maths genius Matt Damon?
9. **Food & Drink:** Lima beans, also sometimes known as sieva beans, are sold commercially in tins under what name?
10. **TV:** What was the name of the founding member and choreographer of the dance troupe Pan's People on *Top of the Pops*?

WHAT IS THE LINK BETWEEN ALL OF THE ANSWERS?

EASY (1 Point)

1. *Bread*: Carla Lane also wrote the sitcoms *The Liver Birds*, *Bless This House* and *Butterflies*, amongst others.
2. **David Bowie:** He was born David Robert Jones on 8 Jan 1947 and died on 10 Jan 2016 aged 69.
3. **Butcher's Hook:** This is often abbreviated to a 'butcher's'.

MEDIUM (2 Points)

4. **Pen:** A male swan is a cob and a baby swan is a cygnet.
5. **Stanley Baldwin:** He served under George V, Edward VIII and George VI and was also prime minister 3 times – 1923–24, 1924–29 and 1935–37.
6. **'Electric Avenue':** Eddy Grant was a founding member of the Equals and wrote their No. 1 hit 'Baby Come Back'.
7. **Wensleydale Cheese:** The cheese is from the town of Hawes in North Yorkshire and sales were struggling until mentioned in the films, which arguably saved the brand.

HARD (3 Points)

8. *Good Will Hunting*: The film also starred Ben Affleck and Minnie Driver.
9. **Butter Beans:** They are called lima beans as some types originated in Peru, the capital of which is Lima.
10. **Flick Colby:** She was also the choreographer of the subsequent dance troupes Ruby Flipper, Legs & Co and Zoo.

1. **Music:** What kind of bird was Orville, the chief puppet of ventriloquist Keith Harris?
2. **Films:** Which actress starred in the 1970 film *The Railway Children* before appearing from 2012 as Sister Julienne in *Call The Midwife* on TV?
3. **TV:** Who was the female presenter of *Crimewatch* from 1995 until her murder in 1999?

MEDIUM (2 Points)

4. **Science & Nature:** Bovine spongiform encephalopathy (BSE) was commonly known as what?
5. **Sport & Games:** Which Scottish football club plays in Dumfries?
6. **Pot Luck:** What generic name is given to an unidentified person in the US and Canada?
7. **Films:** Which 1979 film starring Joan Collins was a sequel to the 1978 film *The Stud*?

HARD (3 Points)

8. **TV:** Jo Frost starred in which eponymous TV role from 2004 to 2012, helping parents deal with difficult or unruly children?
9. **Places:** Which Somerset seaside town on the Bristol Channel was the setting for the TV series *The Café*?
10. **TV:** What is the nickname of Jenny Ryan, one of the 'chasers' on *The Chase*?

WHAT IS THE LINK BETWEEN ALL OF THE ANSWERS?

1. **Duck:** The male equivalent of the duck is a drake.
2. **Jenny Agutter:** A jenny is a female donkey, and even a female wren.
3. **Jill Dando:** A jill is a female ferret.

MEDIUM (2 Points)

4. **Mad Cow Disease:** Besides cattle, a cow is the name for a female elephant, camel and whale, amongst others.
5. **Queen of the South:** As well as female bees and wasps, a queen is the name of a female cat.
6. **John (Jane) Doe:** A doe is the female name for several animals including deer, rabbits, hamsters and mice.
7. *The Bitch:* A bitch is a female wolf as well as a dog.

HARD (3 Points)

8. *Supernanny:* A nanny is a female goat.
9. **Weston-super-Mare:** A mare is a female horse over 3 years old (it is a filly until then) but also the female of the zebra.
10. **The Vixen:** A vixen is a female fox.

EASY (1 Point)

1. **Sport & Games:** Which tennis player won the men's Olympics singles title in 2012 and 2016 as well as Wimbledon in 2013 and 2016?
2. **Pot Luck:** Pounds, pints and inches are examples of what type of measurements?
3. **Art & Literature:** In Charles Dickens' *A Christmas Carol*, what word follows 'Bah' when Scrooge refers to Christmas?

MEDIUM (2 Points)

4. **Sport & Games:** Which club won the FA Cup in 1984, beating Watford, and again in 1995, beating Manchester United?
5. **TV:** Which actress plays Dr Nikki Alexander in *Silent Witness?*
6. **Pot Luck:** What type of weapon is an assegai?
7. **Sport & Games:** The Hurlingham Club is famous for the playing of which sport?

HARD (3 Points)

8. **Music:** The first three singles of Cockney Rebel reached the Top 10 – 'Judy Teen', 'Make Me Smile (Come Up and See Me)' and which other?
9. **TV:** Angie Dickinson starred as which character in *Police Woman* from 1974 to 1978?
10. **Pot Luck:** By what is the game noughts and crosses known in North America?

WHAT IS THE LINK BETWEEN ALL OF THE ANSWERS?

ANSWERS QUIZ No. 37: **LINK – MINTS**

EASY (1 Point)

1. **Andy Murray:** Murray won his first major title when he won the US Open in 2012.
2. **Imperial:** The USA still use many imperial measurements rather than metric, although the UK pint is about 20% more than the US pint.
3. **Humbug:** Ebenezer Scrooge's business partner, now deceased, was Jacob Marley and his clerk is Bob Cratchit, whose son is Tiny Tim.

MEDIUM (2 Points)

4. **Everton:** The club won the double of the First Division and European Cup Winners' Cup in the 1984–85 season.
5. **Emilia Fox:** She took over from Amanda Burton in *Silent Witness* and is the daughter of actor Edward Fox.
6. **Spear:** The assegai gets its name from the southern African tree of the same name, a member of the dogwood family.
7. **Polo:** The game is played with four players on each team and a match consists of four chukkas of seven minutes each.

HARD (3 Points)

8. **'Mr Soft':** Steve Harley was the lead singer with Cockney Rebel and 'Make Me Smile (Come Up and See Me)' reached No. 1 in 1975.
9. **Pepper Anderson:** Angie Dickinson was married for 15 years to songwriter Burt Bacharach.
10. **Tic Tac Toe:** The game is also known as X's and O's in some countries.

1. **Music:** Which 1990 song was the only UK No. 1 for the Steve Miller Band?
2. **Pot Luck:** In what does a troglodyte live?
3. **Transport & Travel:** What was the make and model of the yellow three-wheeled car driven by the Trotters in *Only Fools and Horses*?

MEDIUM (2 Points)

4. **Animals & Nature:** Emperor, King and Rockhopper are types of which bird?
5. **Films:** Which legendary actor's last film was *The Shootist* in 1976?
6. **Music:** Which 1984 Nik Kershaw song has a chorus that starts, 'Near a tree by a river, there's a hole in the ground'?
7. **TV:** Who presented *The Generation Game* from 1978 to 1981, taking over from Bruce Forsyth, although Bruce did return to present a new version of the show in 1990?

HARD (3 Points)

8. **History:** Who was the King of Wessex from 871 to 899?
9. **Places:** Which city is the legislative capital of South Africa?
10. **Animals & Nature:** What type of creature is a flying fox?

WHAT IS THE LINK BETWEEN ALL OF THE ANSWERS?

ANSWERS QUIZ No. 38: LINK – *BATMAN*

EASY (1 Point)

1. **'The Joker':** The Joker was played on TV by Cesar Romero and famously in films by Jack Nicholson in the first *Batman* film and Heath Ledger in *The Dark Knight*.
2. **Cave:** The location for the Batcave in the 2012 film *The Dark Knight Rises* is at Henrhyd Falls in the Brecon Beacons.
3. **(Reliant) Robin:** Robin was originally played by Burt Ward in the TV series.

MEDIUM (2 Points)

4. **Penguin:** The Penguin (Oswald Chesterfield Cobblepot) was played by Burgess Meredith on TV and famously by Danny DeVito in *Batman Returns*.
5. **John Wayne:** Batman's secret identity is Bruce Wayne, a wealthy American playboy and philanthropist.
6. **'The Riddle':** The Riddler was played on TV by Frank Gorshin and in *Batman Forever* by Jim Carrey.
7. **Larry Grayson:** Robin's real name is Dick Grayson.

HARD (3 Points)

8. **Alfred the Great:** Alfred Pennyworth is Bruce Wayne's butler, famously played by Michael Caine in the three *Batman* films with Christian Bale in the lead role.
9. **Cape Town:** The cape helped the 'Caped Crusader' fly around Gotham City.
10. **(Fruit) Bat:** The title character was originally known as the 'Bat-Man'.

QUIZ No. 39: GUESS THE LINK

EASY (1 Point)

1. **Sport & Games:** What is the name of the oldest Championship belt awarded in boxing?
2. **Religion:** What is the name of the tall headdress worn by bishops and senior abbots?
3. **Animals & Nature:** A cougar is an alternative North American name for which animal?

MEDIUM (2 Points)

4. **Music:** Which singer had a 1984 UK hit with 'One Night in Bangkok'?
5. **Pot Luck:** What is the equivalent naval rank to a General in the Army and an Air Chief Marshal in the RAF?
6. **Sport & Games:** Who took over as manager of the Republic of Ireland football team in 2013 from Giovanni Trapattoni?
7. **Mythology:** Who was the Greek goddess of victory?

HARD (3 Points)

8. **TV:** What is the name of the character played by Simon Baker in TV's *The Mentalist*?
9. **Pot Luck:** What is the tenth letter of the Greek alphabet, roughly representing the letter 'k'?
10. **Sport & Games:** Which motorcyclist from Northern Ireland, who won a record 26 Isle of Man TT races, was killed in a race in Estonia in 2000, aged 48?

WHAT IS THE LINK BETWEEN ALL OF THE ANSWERS?

1. **Lonsdale Belt:** Henry Cooper was the first boxer to win three Lonsdale Belts outright.
2. **Mitre:** A mitre is also a name for a 90° joint, especially between two pieces of wood.
3. **Puma:** A puma is also called a mountain lion in North America.

4. **Murray Head:** The song was from the musical *Chess* and Murray Head had also famously sung the title song in *Jesus Christ Superstar*.
5. **Admiral:** After sponsoring the Leeds United kit in 1973/74, Admiral then became the first to sponsor the England football team kit from 1974.
6. **Martin O'Neill:** O'Neill was part of Brian Clough's European Cup-winning Nottingham Forest sides of 1979 and 1980 and won 64 caps for Northern Ireland.
7. **Nike:** She was the child of Pallas and Styx and her Roman equivalent was Victoria.

8. **Patrick Jane:** The series also stars Robin Tunney who plays Special Agent Teresa Lisbon.
9. **Kappa:** The first ten letters are alpha, beta, gamma, delta, epsilon, zeta, eta, theta, iota and kappa.
10. **Joey Dunlop:** His brother Robert Dunlop was also killed in 2008 during a practice lap for a race in Northern Ireland.

1. **Art & Literature:** What is the name of the trilogy of novels written by J R R Tolkien?
2. **Sport & Games:** Which cricket ground is home to Middlesex?
3. **TV:** What is the name of the Norfolk-based radio and TV presenter played by Steve Coogan?

MEDIUM (2 Points)

4. **Music:** Which song by the unusual duo of Bing Crosby and David Bowie got to No. 3 in 1982?
5. **Places:** Which river flows through the city of Perth in Australia?
6. **Films:** Which 1978 mercenary war film starred Richard Burton, Roger Moore and Richard Harris?
7. **Music:** What is the name of the greatest hits album released by George Michael in 1998?

HARD (3 Points)

8. **Pot Luck:** What was the name of the North Sea oil rig destroyed by fire in 1988, killing 167 people?
9. **Films:** Which 2002 romcom starred Jennifer Lopez as the titular character and also starred Ralph Fiennes and Natasha Richardson?
10. **Music:** Which band were originally called Sub Sub but changed their name and music style in 1998 after their music studio burnt down?

WHAT IS THE LINK BETWEEN ALL OF THE ANSWERS?

EASY (1 Point)

1. *Lord of the Rings*: The three parts were *The Fellowship of the Ring*, *The Two Towers* and *The Return of the King*.
2. **Lord's:** Lord's is based in St John's Wood, is owned by the MCC (Marylebone Cricket Club) and is home to the Ashes urn.
3. **Alan Partridge:** The character was originally created for the Radio 4 comedy programme *On the Hour* in 1991.

MEDIUM (2 Points)

4. **'Peace on Earth – Little Drummer Boy':** Terry Wogan and Aled Jones did a version for Children in Need in 2008 under the name 'Bandaged' which got to No. 3.
5. **Swan:** Melbourne is on the Yarra, Adelaide is on the Torrens and Sydney is on the Hawkesbury and the Parramatta.
6. *The Wild Geese*: None of the stars featured in the sequel *Wild Geese II*, although Richard Burton was due to but died days before filming started.
7. *Ladies and Gentlemen*: George's first two solo singles, 'Careless Whisper' in 1984 and 'A Different Corner' in 1986 both went to No. 1 in the UK.

HARD (3 Points)

8. **Piper Alpha:** Even the legendary 'Red' Adair's team could not put the fire out for three weeks.
9. *Maid in Manhattan*: The film was originally titled *The Chambermaid* and *Uptown Girl*.
10. **Doves:** Sub Sub had a No. 3. UK hit in 1993 with 'Ain't No Love (Ain't No Use)'

My Website

HAS YOUR WEBSITE BEEN PROPERLY CHECKED?
If not, then contact the experts TODAY!

- Does your website contain spelling, punctuation or grammatical errors?
- Does it contain text or layout inconsistencies?
- Does it contain web pages that don't work properly or link to the wrong page?
- If the answer to any of these questions could be **YES**, then contact info@correctmywebsite.co.uk for a **FREE REVIEW!**

Your website is your window to the world and your chance to stand out above the competition. However, unfortunately it is also an opportunity for you to show that your company is not quite up to the mark.

The average amount of time a visitor will stay on your site before making a judgement is **ONLY 8 SECONDS** and poorly written English on an otherwise good quality website can then lead to the unfair perception of a company being **unprofessional, unreliable** or even **untrustworthy**. Basic website errors are therefore costing UK businesses **millions of pounds each year** as customers choose to use an alternative company instead.

We will proofread every page on your website to ensure that it is **100% ACCURATE**, ensuring there are no more embarrassing or even costly mistakes. CONTACT US TODAY!

81

QUIZ No. 41: GUESS THE LINK

1. **Music:** Who was trying to contact Ground Control in the 1969 David Bowie song 'Space Oddity'?
2. **Sport & Games:** Which footballer features on the statue of the 'United Trinity' outside Old Trafford alongside George Best and Bobby Charlton?
3. **Films:** Which actor married Jennifer Aniston in 2000 and Angelina Jolie in 2014?
4. **Art & Literature:** Which children's author, who was Children's Laureate between 2005 and 2007, wrote the *Tracy Beaker* series of novels?
5. **Places:** What is the name of the multiple greenhouse complex based just outside St. Blazey in Cornwall?
6. **Music:** Which single, released with 'Reason to Believe', was Rod Stewart's first UK No. 1?

7. **Entertainment:** Which actor was married to Kim Basinger between 1993 and 2002?
8. **Films:** Which actor won a posthumous Academy Award for Best Supporting Actor for his performance as The Joker in *The Dark Knight*?
9. **Music:** Who is the lead singer with the band The Stone Roses?
10. **Entertainment:** Which Radio 1 DJ, who died in 2004, had the real name John R P Ravenscroft?
11. **Places:** Which Australian city is the capital of the state of Victoria?

12. **Films:** Which actress starred in *My Best Friend's Wedding* and *There's Something About Mary* and is the voice of Princess Fiona in *Shrek*?

13. **TV:** Which insurance company, sold to the Direct Line Group in 2012, is well known for its TV adverts featuring a nodding bulldog?

14. **Places:** Which city is the capital of New Zealand?

HARD (3 Points)

---

15. **Sport & Games:** Which player holds the record for the number of league appearances for Liverpool Football Club with 640 appearances between 1960 and 1978?

16. **Art & Literature:** What was the real name of the author George Orwell?

17. **TV:** Which actor played Father Ralph de Bricassart in the mini-series *The Thorn Birds* in the 1970s?

18. **History:** Which woman helped Bonnie Prince Charlie escape from Scotland after the defeat at Culloden in 1746?

19. **Places:** Old Sarum is an Iron Age hill fort close to which English city?

20. **TV:** What was the name of the 1970s TV series that starred Rock Hudson and Susan Saint James in the title roles?

WHAT IS THE LINK BETWEEN ALL OF THE ANSWERS?

---

1. **Major Tom:** John Major (Con) was MP for Huntingdon and was PM 1990–97. He was PM during the Gulf War, the Maastricht Treaty and Black Wednesday.
2. **Denis Law:** Andrew Bonar Law (Con) was MP for Glasgow Central and PM 1922–23, only 211 days.
3. **Brad Pitt:** William Pitt the Younger (Tory) was MP mainly for Cambridge University and was PM from 1783–1801. His father (the Elder) was PM 1766–68.
4. **Jacqueline Wilson:** Harold Wilson (Lab) was MP for Huyton and PM 1964–70 and 1974–76. He oversaw devaluation of the pound and the EEC referendum.
5. **The Eden Project:** Anthony Eden (Con) was MP for Warwick and Leamington and PM 1955–57. He was PM during the Suez Crisis and introduced Premium Bonds.
6. **Maggie May:** Theresa May (Con) is MP for Maidenhead and became PM in 2016. Maggie was the nickname of Margaret Thatcher, MP for Finchley and PM 1979–90.

7. **Alec Baldwin:** Stanley Baldwin (Con) was MP for Bewdley and was PM from 1923–24, 1924–29 and 1935–37. He was PM during the General Strike of 1926.
8. **Heath Ledger:** Edward Heath (Con) was MP for Bexley and was PM from 1970–74. He was PM during decimalisation and introduced VAT; he also had a yacht called *Morning Cloud*.
9. **Ian Brown:** Gordon Brown (Lab) was MP for Kirkcaldy & Cowdenbeath and was PM 2007–10.
10. **John Peel:** Robert Peel (Con) was MP for Tamworth and was PM 1834–35 and 1841–46. He repealed the Corn Laws after the Great Irish Potato Famine.

11. **Melbourne:** Lord Melbourne (William Lamb – Whig) was well known for mentoring a young Queen Victoria and was PM 1834 and 1835–41.
12. **Cameron Diaz:** David Cameron (Con) was MP for Witney and PM 2010–16.
13. **Churchill:** Winston Churchill (Con) was heavily influential during the Second World War and was MP for Epping when PM 1940–45 and MP for Woodford when PM 1951–55.
14. **Wellington:** The Duke of Wellington (Tory) was famous for his defeat of Napoleon at Waterloo in 1815 and was PM 1828–30 and briefly as caretaker in 1834.

HARD (3 Points)

15. **Ian Callaghan:** James Callaghan (Lab) was MP for Cardiff SE and PM 1976–79. He is the only PM ever to have also been Chancellor, Home Secretary and Foreign Secretary.
16. **Eric Blair:** Tony Blair (Lab) was MP for Sedgefield and PM 1997–2007. He was PM during the attacks on the Twin Towers in 2001 and the invasion of Iraq in 2003.
17. **Richard Chamberlain:** Neville Chamberlain (Con) was MP for Birmingham Edgbaston and PM 1937–40. Infamously tried to get 'Peace of Our Time' through appeasement with Germany.
18. **Flora MacDonald:** Ramsay MacDonald (Lab) was MP for Aberavon when PM in 1924 and MP for Seaham when PM 1929–35.
19. **Salisbury:** The Marquess of Salisbury (Robert Gascoyne-Cecil – Con) was PM 1885–86, 1886–92 and 1895–1902. He was PM on the death of Queen Victoria in 1901.
20. *McMillan & Wife*: Harold Macmillan (Con) was MP for Bromley and was PM 1957–63, made the 'Wind of Change' speech, was PM during the Cuban Missile Crisis and the Profumo Affair.

QUIZ No. 42: GUESS THE LINK

1. **TV:** What is the name of the pub on *Coronation Street*?
2. **Politics:** Which colloquial term refers to a press and PR officer, a position once held by Alastair Campbell in the Tony Blair government?
3. **TV:** Which TV quiz show has been presented by Bamber Gascoigne and Jeremy Paxman?
4. **Pot Luck:** In business, what is calculated by subtracting all operating expenses from gross profit?
5. **Sport & Games:** What is the name for the person who officiates in a game of cricket?
6. **TV:** Which comedy entertainer plays Frank in *Not Going Out* and Barry in *Mount Pleasant*?

7. **Places:** Which palace in Richmond was originally built for Cardinal Thomas Wolsey?
8. **Sport & Games:** Which game has six players per team and each team can only touch the ball three times before returning the ball over the net?
9. **Food & Drink:** Which brand of instant potato was advertised in the '70s and '80s using Martian puppets?
10. **TV:** Which character in the TV series *M*A*S*H* had the full name Benjamin Franklin Pierce?
11. **Music:** What was the name of the 2008 No. 2 duet by James Morrison and Nelly Furtado?
12. **Films:** What was the name of the 'pet detective' played by Jim Carrey?

13. **Places:** What is the name of the main mountain route between Afghanistan and Pakistan?
14. **TV:** What is the name of the HBO fantasy series based on the series of books *A Song of Ice and Fire*?

HARD (3 Points)

---

15. **Sport & Games:** In bridge, what term is used for the successful contract of winning all 13 tricks?
16. **Films:** Which 1942 film starring John Mills, Celia Johnson and Noel Coward was the first film directed by David Lean and was the first film role for a young Richard Attenborough?
17. **TV:** Which TV series, first shown in 2005 starred Wentworth Miller as Michael Scofield who intentionally got sent to prison in order to try to help his brother Lincoln escape?
18. **Music:** Which group had hits in 1967 with 'Simon Smith and his Amazing Dancing Bear' and 'The House That Jack Built'?
19. **Sport & Games:** What word can be used for the number two on dice or playing cards?
20. **Music:** Which female duo had a No. 5 hit in 1984 with 'Since Yesterday'?

WHAT IS THE LINK BETWEEN ALL OF THE ANSWERS?

---

1. **Rovers Return:** The pub was built by the brewery Newton and Ridley but is now a free house.
2. **Spin Doctor:** There was a group called the Spin Doctors whose highest hit was 'Two Princes' that got to No. 3 in 1993.
3. *University Challenge*: Bamber Gascoigne presented the show from 1962 to 1987 and it was revived in 1994 to be presented by Jeremy Paxman.
4. **Net Profit:** This figure is also usually after tax and is sometimes called 'the bottom line'.
5. **Umpire:** There is only one umpire in tennis but three in cricket, including the third umpire who reviews decisions made on the field via TV replays.
6. **Bobby Ball:** His real name is Robert Harper and his partner Tommy Cannon is called Thomas Derbyshire.

MEDIUM (2 Points)

7. **Hampton Court:** Building commenced in 1515 but the palace passed to Henry VIII in 1530.
8. **Volleyball:** The game originated in Massachusetts and was originally called 'Mintonette'.
9. **Smash:** It was launched by Cadbury in 1960 and later had the slogan 'For Mash Get Smash'.
10. **Hawkeye:** Hawkeye was played on TV by Alan Alda but in the film by Donald Sutherland.

11. **'Broken Strings':** James Morrison is from the UK and Nelly Furtado is from Canada.
12. **Ace Ventura:** There was also a film sequel called *Ace Ventura: When Nature Calls*.
13. **Khyber Pass:** The pass cuts through the Hindu Kush range of mountains.
14. *Game of Thrones*: The series was first shown in 2011.

15. **Grand Slam:** In bridge, winning 12 tricks is called a 'small slam'.
16. *In Which We Serve*: Coward also co-directed and composed the music. It was based on the true story of Lord Louis Mountbatten's ship HMS *Kelly*, sunk in the Battle of Crete.
17. *Prison Break*: Wentworth Miller also starred in two Mariah Carey music videos as her love interest.
18. **Alan Price Set:** Alan Price also had a hit called 'Rosetta' in 1971 with Georgie Fame.
19. **Deuce:** There is also a solitaire card game called 'Deuces' or 'Big Two'.
20. **Strawberry Switchblade:** They were Jill Bryson and Rose McDowall from Glasgow.

QUIZ No. 43: **GUESS THE LINK**

EASY (1 Point)

1. **Sport & Games:** Who took over as manager of Liverpool FC after Bill Shankly?
2. **Music:** Which song was the first to enter the UK charts for Thin Lizzy, getting to No. 6 in 1973?
3. **TV:** In which series did Ronnie Barker star as Norman Stanley Fletcher?
4. **Sport & Games:** What is the name of Birmingham City's home ground?
5. **Music:** Who was the lead singer with the group Ultravox?
6. **TV:** Which Simpsons' character is the evil owner of the Springfield Nuclear Plant and is Homer Simpson's boss?

MEDIUM (2 Points)

7. **Places:** Which city is the capital of the Australian state of Western Australia?
8. **Theatre:** Which Shakespeare tragedy features the characters Macduff, Duncan and Banquo?
9. **Music:** What was the title of the Peter Gabriel song that referenced the TV show *It's a Knockout*?
10. **Sport & Games:** Which former Wasps and England fly-half was made director of rugby at Newcastle Falcons in 1995, where he is credited with discovering Jonny Wilkinson?
11. **Films:** Which 1986 action fantasy film stars Christopher Lambert as the title character and Sean Connery as Ramirez, both of them immortal warriors?
12. **TV:** Who took over presenting the *Antiques Roadshow* from Michael Aspel in 2008?

13. **Sport & Games:** Which British racing driver finished runner-up in the World Championship four times and was third three times between 1955 and 1961 but never won the title?

14. **Music:** Which group's first chart entry was 'If You Think You Know How To Love Me' in 1975?

15. **Sport & Games:** What was the previous name of the Scottish football team Livingston FC when they played in Edinburgh before they moved to Livingston in 1995?

16. **Films:** Which was the first book in the series of books by James Patterson about the forensic psychologist Alex Cross which also led to a 2001 film starring Morgan Freeman?

17. **TV:** On ITV's *The Chase*, which chaser is known as the 'Dark Destroyer'?

18. **Sport & Games:** Which former Luton Town, Newcastle United and Arsenal centre-forward was known as 'Supermac' and in 1975 scored all five goals against Cyprus at Wembley?

19. **Films:** Which 2003 film starred Charlize Theron as real-life serial killer Aileen Wuornos, for which she won a Best Actress Oscar?

20. **Sport & Games:** Which American-owned horse won the 1980 Grand National ridden by the American amateur jockey Charlie Fenwick?

WHAT IS THE LINK BETWEEN ALL OF THE ANSWERS?

ANSWERS QUIZ No. 43: **LINK – SCOTLAND**

1. **Bob Paisley:** He won 3 European Cups as Liverpool manager and is one of only 5 men to have won the First Division as a player and a manager with the same club. St. Mirren FC is based in Paisley.
2. **'Whiskey in the Jar':** The song was originally a traditional Irish folk song, hence the 'whiskey' spelling with 'whisky' being the correct spelling for Scotch whisky.
3. *Porridge*: The series ran from 1974 to 1977 and there were only 21 episodes in total. Samuel Johnson's dictionary of 1755 disparagingly referred to oats being given to horses in England but being used to support the people in Scotland.
4. **St Andrew's:** The town of St Andrews, with its famous golf course, doesn't have an apostrophe and is where Prince William and Kate went to university.
5. **Midge Ure:** He also had brief spells with Slik, Thin Lizzy, Rich Kids and Visage. Scotland is of course plagued by midges in the Highlands and the Western Isles in particular.
6. **Mr Burns:** His full name is Charles Montgomery Burns. Burns Night is on 25 January, the anniversary of the birth of Robert Burns.

7. **Perth:** The Australian city is on the River Swan and the Scottish city lies on the River Tay.
8. *Macbeth*: Macbeth is known as the 'Scottish Play'.
9. **'Games Without Frontiers':** There are many Highland Games in Scotland but the one at Braemar is the one traditionally attended by the Royal Family.

10. **Rob Andrew:** Andrew is the patron saint of Scotland and his feast day is on 30 November.
11. *Highlander:* The Great Glen runs from Inverness to Fort William separating the Northwest Highlands to the south east and the Grampian Mountains to the north west.
12. **Fiona Bruce:** Robert the Bruce was King of Scotland from 1306 to 1329 and led the Scots to a famous victory over the English at Bannockburn in 1314.
13. **Stirling Moss:** Stirling – 'The Gateway to the Highlands' – lies on the River Forth and was once the capital of Scotland.
14. **Smokie:** Arbroath smokies are a type of smoked haddock.

HARD (3 Points)

15. **Meadowbank Thistle:** The thistle is the national emblem of Scotland.
16. *Along Came a Spider:* It was whilst watching a spider keep trying to form its web, despite several failed attempts, that inspired Robert the Bruce to carry on fighting the English.
17. **Shaun Wallace:** William Wallace led the Scots to victory at Stirling Bridge in 1297 but lost the Battle of Falkirk in 1298. He was captured and executed in 1305 and was portrayed by Mel Gibson in the film *Braveheart.*
18. **Malcolm Macdonald:** In 1692 thirty-eight members of the MacDonald clan were massacred at Glencoe by members of the Campbell clan.
19. *Monster:* Despite many reported sightings, no hard evidence has been found of the Loch Ness monster.
20. **Ben Nevis:** Ben Nevis is the tallest mountain in the UK at 4,409 ft. followed by Ben Macdui at 4,294 ft.

1. **Music:** The signature tune to the 1957 Broadway musical *The Music Man* was 'Seventy-Six......' what?
2. **Science & Medicine:** What is the generic name for the body parts with a vital function like the heart, lungs and kidneys?
3. **Music:** What was the name of the 1973 debut album by Mike Oldfield released on Virgin Records?
4. **TV:** What is the name of the leader of the dance troupe Diversity who won *Britain's Got Talent* in 2009?
5. **Food & Drink:** How is a cone-shaped wafer filled with ice cream better known?
6. **Music:** What is the lowest singing voice?

7. **Animals & Nature:** What is the noise made by an elephant called?
8. **Films:** Holly Hunter won a Best Actress Oscar for her performance as a mute Scottish musician who moved to New Zealand in which 1993 film, also starring Harvey Keitel and Sam Neill?
9. **Music:** What is the name of the last opera composed by Wolfgang Amadeus Mozart?
10. **Food & Drink:** Which brand of lager was created by Guinness in 1960 and named after a musical instrument historically associated with Brian Boru?
11. **Places:** What is the name of the area broadly between Florida, Bermuda and Puerto Rico where a number of ships and planes have mysteriously disappeared over the years?

12. **Music:** Which 1965 song was the only UK No. 1 hit for the Byrds?

13. **Films:** Which 2001 film, starring Nicolas Cage and Penélope Cruz, is set on the Greek island of Cephalonia and tells the story of the execution of Italian soldiers by the Germans?

14. **Pot Luck:** What was the name of Simon Le Bon's yacht that capsized in the 1985 Fastnet race?

HARD (3 Points)

---

15. **Music:** Which song did Justin Hayward and John Lodge take to No. 8 in the UK charts in 1975?

16. **Art & Literature:** Who wrote the series of novels featuring the master criminal Dr Fu Manchu?

17. **Music:** Which singer had a 1979 No. 8 hit in the UK with 'Gonna Get Along Without You Now'?

18. **Entertainment:** What was the name of the British comedy magician who performed his act as the 'Shriek of Araby'?

19. **Sport & Games:** Which horse ridden by Frankie Dettori won the Epsom Derby and Prix de l'Arc de Triomphe in 2015?

20. **Music:** Which group had a UK hit in 1979 with 'Clog Dance'?

WHAT IS THE LINK BETWEEN ALL OF THE ANSWERS?

---

1. **Trombones:** A sackbut was a type of trombone from the Renaissance and Baroque eras.
2. **Organs:** Johann Sebastian Bach's 'Toccata and Fugue in D minor' was written for the organ and famously appears in the 1940 Walt Disney animation *Fantasia*.
3. ***Tubular Bells:*** The album gained global attention when its introduction was used in the horror film *The Exorcist*.
4. **Ashley Banjo:** Diversity beat Susan Boyle into second place in the 2009 final.
5. **Cornet:** A cornet is a smaller version of the trumpet, predominantly used as the lead instrument in brass bands.
6. **Bass:** Women are typically classed as either soprano, mezzo-soprano or contralto with men being either countertenor, tenor, baritone or bass.

7. **Trumpet:** The piece 'Trumpet Voluntary' is often wrongly attributed to Henry Purcell rather than Jeremiah Clarke and is actually called the 'Prince of Denmark's March'.
8. ***The Piano:*** Anna Paquin also won the Best Supporting Actress for the film, aged just 11, to become the second youngest winner after Tatum O'Neal for *Paper Moon* who was aged ten.
9. ***The Magic Flute:*** Mozart was born in Salzburg in 1756 but died in Vienna aged just 35.
10. **Harp:** The coat of arms of Ireland is traditionally a gold harp with silver strings on a blue background.

11. **Bermuda Triangle:** Barry Manilow had a UK hit of that name that got to No. 15 in 1981.
12. **'Mr Tambourine Man':** The song was written by Bob Dylan and was also released in 1965 on his album *Bringing It All Back Home*.
13. ***Captain Corelli's Mandolin:*** The film is based on the novel by Louis de Bernières.
14. **Drum:** In 1988 the yacht was sold to Sir Arnold Clark, famous for his car dealerships, but he loaned the yacht back to Le Bon in 2005 to compete in the Fastnet race, 20 years after its accident.

HARD (3 Points)

---

15. **'Blue Guitar':** Justin Hayward and John Lodge were both members of the Moody Blues.
16. **Sax Rohmer:** He was friends with Harry Houdini and based his magician character Bazarada on Houdini.
17. **Viola Wills:** She was discovered in 1965 by Barry White who changed her name to Viola Wills.
18. **Ali Bongo:** His real name was William Wallace and he was made president of the Magic Circle on 8 Sep 2008, exactly six months before he died.
19. **Golden Horn:** It was Dettori's second Derby win after he first won on Authorized in 2007 at his fifteenth attempt. In 1996 he rode seven winners in a day at Ascot but in 2000 was lucky to survive a light plane crash, being rescued by fellow jockey Ray Cochrane.
20. **Violinski:** The Grimethorpe Colliery Brass Band performed a version of this song in the 1996 film *Brassed Off*.

1. **Films:** What is the name of the character played by Gene Hackman in the *French Connection* films?
2. **TV:** Which comedian wrote and starred in TV shows between 1969 and 1980 called *Q5, Q6, Q7, Q8* and *Q9*?
3. **Music:** Which Jamaican singer's first UK release, 'Oh Carolina', reached No. 1 in 1993?
4. **Films:** What is the name of the cowboy doll in the *Toy Story* films?
5. **Science & Medicine:** Which planet was discovered in 1930 by Clyde Tombaugh, although its classification was reduced in 2006 to a dwarf planet?
6. **Films:** Which 1963 film was the first of the series of films starring Peter Sellers as Inspector Jacques Clouseau?

7. **TV:** Which Scottish actor followed Colin Baker to play the seventh Doctor Who from 1987 to 1989, the last of its original run before its relaunch in 2005?
8. **Music:** What was the first UK hit for Jonathan Richman and the Modern Lovers which reached No. 11 in 1977?
9. **Films:** Which 1981 film, which spawned two sequels, revolves around a group of Florida high school students trying to lose their virginity at a nightclub, after which the film is named?
10. **Art & Literature:** Which Greek poet was the author of *The Iliad* and *The Odyssey*?

11. **Music:** What is the common forename of the German composer Mendelssohn?
12. **Entertainment:** Who composed the music and lyrics for the musical *Oliver!*?
13. **Films:** Which actress was nominated for an Oscar for her role as Skylar in *Good Will Hunting* and also appeared in *Grosse Point Blank* and *Sleepers*?
14. **Music:** Which song did Toni Basil take to No. 2 in the UK charts in 1982?

HARD (3 Points)

---

15. **Sport & Games:** What was the nickname of former England, Leicestershire, Lancashire and Derbyshire all-rounder Phillip DeFreitas?
16. **TV:** In the 1970s sitcom *The Good Life*, what were the Christian names of the characters played by Richard Briers and Paul Eddington?
17. **Music:** Which song reached No. 4 in 1973 for the Hotshots, their only chart hit?
18. **History:** What was the name of the second US president to be assassinated?
19. **Sport & Games:** Which US golfer won the US Masters in 1970 and the US Open in 1959 and 1966, in the latter coming back from seven strokes down to Arnold Palmer with nine holes to play?
20. **Music:** The first top 30 hit for the Fun Lovin' Criminals was the 1996 hit '...... Snacks'?

WHAT IS THE LINK BETWEEN ALL OF THE ANSWERS?

---

1. **(Jimmy) 'Popeye' Doyle:** Popeye originally appeared in a comic strip but most famously in the TV cartoons alongside Olive Oyl, Bluto, Wimpy and Swee'Pea amongst others.
2. **Spike Milligan:** Spike is the bulldog in the *Tom and Jerry* cartoons, often appearing with his young son Tyke.
3. **Shaggy:** Norville 'Shaggy' Rogers appears in *Scooby-Doo* alongside Fred Jones, Daphne Blake and Velma Dinkley.
4. **(Sheriff) Woody:** Woody Woodpecker first appeared in 1940, originally voiced by Mel Blanc, and even had a cameo role in the 1988 film *Who Framed Roger Rabbit?*
5. **Pluto:** Pluto is Mickey Mouse's pet and first appeared in 1930, named after the then newly discovered ninth planet.
6. ***The Pink Panther:*** In the original film, the Pink Panther was the name of a valuable pink diamond. The cartoon character used in most of the films' credits later featured in its own cartoon series.

7. **Sylvester McCoy:** Sylvester was a cat who could usually be found chasing either the bird Tweety Pie or the mouse Speedy Gonzales.
8. **'Roadrunner':** Wile E Coyote repeatedly tried to catch the Road Runner but without success.
9. ***Porky's:*** Porky Pig had an unfortunate stutter and was an early Warner Brothers character, first appearing in 1935.

10. **Homer:** Homer Jay Simpson is married to Marge (Marjorie Jacqueline – née Bouvier). The Simpsons first appeared on the *Tracey Ullman Show* in 1987.
11. **Felix:** In 1929, when television was at the experimental stage, the very first image to be seen was an illustration of Felix the Cat.
12. **Lionel Bart:** Bart Simpson's character is actually voiced by Nancy Cartwright. She also voices Nelson Muntz and Ralph Wiggum, amongst others.
13. **Minnie Driver:** Minnie Mouse is the girlfriend of Mickey Mouse and her full name is Minerva.
14. **'Mickey':** Mickey Mouse first appeared in the short film *Steamboat Willie* in 1928.

HARD (3 Points)

15. **Daffy:** Daffy Duck was voiced by Mel Blanc, who also voiced Bugs Bunny, Porky Pig, Sylvester and Tweety Pie amongst many others.
16. **Tom and Jerry:** The cartoon *Tom and Jerry* first appeared in 1940 and it was also the original name of Simon & Garfunkel.
17. **'Snoopy vs the Red Baron':** Snoopy is Charlie Brown's pet beagle in the *Peanuts* comic strip by Charles M Schulz.
18. **James Garfield:** Garfield the cat, created by Jim Davis, was born in the kitchen of an Italian restaurant which explains his love of lasagne and pizza.
19. **Billy Casper:** The film *Casper the Friendly Ghost* revealed his full name to have been Casper McFadden.
20. **Scooby:** Scooby-Doo was a Great Dane and his nephew was called Scrappy-Doo.

1. **Music:** Who was the lead singer with the group Marillion?
2. **Food & Drink:** What was the name of the traditional aniseed-flavoured chews, often available as 'penny tray' sweets with fruit salads?
3. **Sport & Games:** On which racecourse are the 1000 Guineas and 2000 Guineas run?
4. **Pot Luck:** What is Italian for the number one?
5. **TV:** Robert Vaughn played which character in the 1960s TV series *The Man from U.N.C.L.E.*?
6. **Music:** Which Take That song contains the lyrics: 'My heart is numb, has no feeling, so while I'm still healing'?

7. **Entertainment:** Which singer, who married an England footballer, was originally a member of S Club Juniors before joining the Saturdays?
8. **Animals & Nature:** The kniphofia or tritoma plant is commonly known as a 'red-hot....'?
9. **Food & Drink:** Which spirit is flavoured with juniper berries?
10. **Music:** Adele's first album was *19* but what was the title of her second?
11. **Pot Luck:** If you get down on the floor on your hands and knees, you are said to be on what?

12. **Sport & Games:** What is the name of the raised fine wool fibres of a snooker table baize cloth which cause the balls to move slightly when played slowly?
13. **Places:** What is the name of the two separate rivers that flow through Aberdeen and Sheffield?
14. **Music:** Which group had UK No. 1's in 1990 with 'The Power' and in 1992 with 'Rhythm is a Dancer'?

HARD (3 Points)

---

15. **Films:** In which 1949 Ealing comedy did Alec Guinness play nine different characters?
16. **Pot Luck:** What name is given to a mainly temporary floating bridge, often used in wartime?
17. **Music:** Which Spanish duo had a 1977 UK No. 1 with 'Yes Sir I Can Boogie'?
18. **Films:** Which 1978 film starred Joan Collins with Oliver Tobias, later to be followed by its sequel *The Bitch*, both written by her sister Jackie Collins?
19. **Food & Drink:** What is the name of the small round or slightly oval pies, usually containing minced beef and jelly, especially popular in the north-west of England?
20. **Music:** Which singer / songwriter wrote the song 'A New England', a No. 7 hit in the UK for Kirsty MacColl in 1985?

WHAT IS THE LINK BETWEEN ALL OF THE ANSWERS?

---

1. **Fish:** The game requires players to collect sets of four cards of the same value and is also called Go Fish.
2. **Black Jacks:** Blackjack is also called 21 and each player tries to beat the dealer with a score as close to 21 as possible without exceeding that number.
3. **Newmarket:** Players bet on the four kings as 'horses' and the cards are dealt with an extra 'dummy' hand. Cards are played in turn, lowest first, and whoever plays the queen of the 'horse' gets the money.
4. **Uno:** UNO is a card game with a special pack of coloured numbered cards which include special cards to change direction, make players miss a turn etc.
5. **Napoleon Solo:** Solo is a type of whist for four players but where often one player plays against the other three, hence the name.
6. **'Patience':** Patience is a game for one player which the Americans call Solitaire.

7. **Frankie Bridge:** Contract bridge is for four players (2v2) and the game is preceded by bidding for the number of tricks likely to be won. The suits in descending order are no trumps, spades, hearts, diamonds and clubs.
8. **Poker** Texas Hold 'Em is the most common form of poker, although there are other variants like seven-card stud, five-card draw and Omaha.
9. **Gin:** Gin rummy is a game for two players where the aim is to collect sets of cards e.g. of the same number value or a run of three or more cards of the same suit etc.

10. ***21***: See blackjack above and note that aces can count as one or eleven.

11. **All Fours:** The game is also called High-Low-Jack-Game as points go to the players who played the highest and the lowest trumps, the winner of the trick with the jack of trumps and to the one with the most card points.

12. **Nap:** Short for Napoleon and played usually with just aces and face cards. Bidding 'nap' means all five tricks, 'Napoleon' means all five tricks leading with the lowest trump and the top bid is 'Wellington' leading with the lowest card.

13. **Don:** The most popular version is nine-card don with each player having nine cards.

14. **Snap!:** This game is simply about turning over cards and placing onto a pile of cards in the centre and the first to shout 'Snap' when the cards match takes the cards.

HARD (3 Points)

---

15. ***Kind Hearts and Coronets***: Hearts is a game ideally for four players and the objective is not to win tricks containing hearts or the queen of spades, although if you can win all of the tricks with those cards in then that is even better.

16. **Pontoon:** Pontoon is a variant of blackjack but uses the terms 'twist' and 'stick'.

17. **Baccara:** One variant of baccarat is called 'chemin de fer' which means railway in French.

18. ***The Stud***: Stud is a variant of poker and seven-card stud is the most popular.

19. **Whist Pies:** Whist is most often played in pairs and players have to follow suit but can use a trump if that is not possible.

20. **Billy Bragg:** Three-card brag is the most common game, usually played for money.

QUIZ No. 47: **GUESS THE LINK**

1. **Places:** What is the former name of the city in India now called Mumbai?
2. **Pot Luck:** Which two letters follow the name of a barrister during the reign of a queen?
3. **Music:** Which Christmas song starts 'Dashing through the snow, on a one-horse open sleigh'?
4. **TV:** John Alderton in *Please Sir!* and Barry Evans in *Mind Your Language* were both members of which profession?
5. **Pot Luck:** Yeomen Warders at the Tower of London are more commonly known as what?
6. **Places:** Which beach city in Los Angeles County is nicknamed 'The 'Bu'?

7. **Music:** Which singer had a UK No. 1 hit in 1979 with 'One Day at a Time'?
8. **Entertainment:** Which former Radio Caroline DJ has presented 'Sounds of the '70s' on Radio 2 on Sunday afternoons since 2009?
9. **History:** Marengo was the name of the horse of which military leader?
10. **Buildings:** Newgate Prison was on the site of which current day Criminal Court?
11. **TV:** In *Thunderbirds*, which of the Tracy brothers pilots the submarine Thunderbird 4?

12. **Music:** Who was the lead singer with the group East 17?
13. **History:** Which leader of the Union Army during the American Civil War became president of the USA in 1869?
14. **Pot Luck:** The shooting season for which bird starts on 12 August?

HARD (3 Points)

---

15. **Politics:** What was the name of the inaugural First Minister of Scotland who died in 2000 after a fall?
16. **Sport:** Which Newbury race had been sponsored by the same company for 60 years since 1957 until its last running under that name in 2016?
17. **Music:** Which group had a UK No. 1 hit in 1970 called 'Woodstock'?
18. **TV:** Who was the other team captain with Henry Cooper in the first five series of *A Question of Sport*?
19. **Entertainment:** Which former cockney Fleet Street editor hosted the Radio 2 breakfast show from 1986 to 1991?
20. **History:** Which lover of Lord Byron called him 'mad, bad and dangerous to know'?

WHAT IS THE LINK BETWEEN ALL OF THE ANSWERS?

EASY (1 Point)

1. **Bombay:** Mumbai is the capital of the state of Maharashtra and Bombay Sapphire is a brand of gin.
2. **QC:** It stands for Queen's Counsel (KC if the monarch is a king) and QC is a brand of sherry.
3. **'Jingle Bells':** The song was originally written for Thanksgiving and Bell's is a brand of Scotch whisky.
4. **Teachers:** *The Fenn Street Gang* was a sequel to *Please Sir!* (named after the school) and Teacher's is also a brand of Scotch whisky from Glasgow.
5. **Beefeaters:** They are not Yeomen of the Guard, who are bodyguards of the monarch, and Beefeater is a brand of gin.
6. **Malibu:** It is about 30 miles west of Los Angeles and Malibu is a rum liqueur.

MEDIUM (2 Points)

7. **Lena Martell:** It was the only hit for Helen Thomson – her real name – and Martell is a brand of brandy.
8. **Johnnie Walker:** His real name is Peter Waters Dingley and Johnnie Walker is a brand of Scotch whisky originally from Kilmarnock.
9. **Napoleon (Bonaparte):** The horse was named after the Battle of Marengo in 1800 and Napoleon is a blend of brandy (also called XO – extra old) that is at least six years old.
10. **Old Bailey:** Newgate was the first prison established by King Henry II in 1188 and Baileys Irish Cream is an Irish whiskey liqueur.
11. **Gordon:** He also co-pilots Thunderbird 2 with Virgil and Gordon's is a brand of gin.

12. **Brian Harvey:** E17 is the postcode of Walthamstow, their home town, and Harveys Bristol Cream is a brand of sherry.
13. **Ulysses S Grant:** The S stands for Simpson (his mother's maiden name) but it was added to his name in error at West Point. Grant's is a Scotch whisky and William Grant also built the Glenfiddich distillery in Dufftown.
14. **Grouse:** It is called the 'Glorious Twelfth' and The Famous Grouse is a brand of Scotch whisky originally from Perth.

HARD (3 Points)

---

15. **Donald Dewar:** He was just 63 years old and Dewar's is a brand of Scotch whisky now owned by Bacardi.
16. **Hennessy Gold Cup:** It became the Ladbrokes Trophy from 2017 and Hennessy (the sponsors) is a brand of cognac.
17. **Matthews' Southern Comfort:** The song was written by Joni Mitchell about the famous 1969 Woodstock music festival in New York state and Southern Comfort is a US whiskey-based liqueur flavoured with fruit and spice.
18. **Cliff Morgan:** He was made captain of the Welsh rugby union team in 1956 and another Welsh captain, Gareth Edwards, later became a team captain on *A Question of Sport*, in 1979. Captain Morgan is a brand of dark rum named after the 17th century privateer, Sir Henry Morgan... from Wales.
19. **Derek Jameson:** He also hosted a TV show called *Do They Mean Us?* – with his catchphrase 'Do they mean us? They surely do!' – and Jameson is a brand of Irish whiskey.
20. **Lady Caroline Lamb:** She was the wife of future prime minister Viscount Melbourne, Queen Victoria's first prime minister, and Lamb's Navy is a brand of dark rum.

1. **Places:** Which London street was once the location of most of Britain's national newspapers?
2. **People:** Which model and photographer became Rod Stewart's third wife in 2007?
3. **Entertainment:** Which ex-Radio 1 and Radio 2 DJ was nicknamed 'Diddy' by comedian Ken Dodd?
4. **Pot Luck:** According to the nursery rhyme, where did Doctor Foster go to in a shower of rain?
5. **Food & Drink:** Which celebrity chef owns the Fat Duck restaurant in Bray, Berkshire?
6. **Music:** Which singer had her biggest hit in the UK when 'Heartbreaker' reached No. 2 in 1982?

7. **Sport & Games:** Which cricket county did Paul Collingwood captain to the County Championship title in 2013, following their earlier wins in 2008 and 2009?
8. **Places:** In which English university is the Bodleian Library housed?
9. **TV:** With whom did Susannah Constantine present the first five series of the TV makeover show *What Not to Wear*?
10. **History:** Which battle of 1685 was the last skirmish of the Monmouth Rebellion, an attempt to overthrow the new king James II?
11. **Sport & Games:** Which Leicestershire motorsport circuit was home to MotoGP from 1987 until 2009 and held its only F1 Grand Prix in 1993, the European Grand Prix, which was won by Ayrton Senna?

12. **Art & Literature:** What is the name of the poem by Oscar Wilde written during his incarceration for 'gross indecency'?
13. **People:** Which Scottish civil engineer and architect designed the Caledonian Canal and the Menai Bridge, amongst other projects?
14. **Sport & Games:** Which Football League club play at St James Park and are nicknamed the Grecians?

HARD (3 Points)

15. **Politics:** Which Labour politician was Chancellor of the Exchequer from 1947 to 1950 in the government of Clement Attlee?
16. **Places:** On which Kent river are the towns of Tonbridge, Maidstone and Rochester?
17. **Sport & Games:** Which yachtsman was the first man to sail single-handedly around the world non-stop westwards, doing so in 1971 in his yacht *British Steel*?
18. **History:** Queen Victoria appointed Benjamin Disraeli the Earl of where in 1876?
19. **TV:** What was the surname of the character played by David Ogden Stiers in *M*A*S*H*? He was Major Charles Emerson .... III?
20. **Pot Luck:** Which form of corporal punishment involved the use of a wooden rod or a bunch of bound twigs, and was still used in the Isle of Man until the mid-1970s?

WHAT IS THE LINK BETWEEN ALL OF THE ANSWERS?

1. **Fleet Street:** Fleet Services are on the M3 between J4A and J5 near Basingstoke.
2. **Penny Lancaster:** Lancaster Forton Services are on the M6 between J32 and J33 near Lancaster.
3. **David Hamilton:** Hamilton Services are on the M74 between J6 and J5 near Hamilton.
4. **Gloucester:** Gloucester Services are on the M5 between J11A and J12 near Whaddon, Gloucester.
5. **Heston Blumenthal:** Heston Services are on the M4 between J2 and J3 near Heston.
6. **Dionne Warwick:** Warwick Services are on the M40 between J12 and J13 near Warwick.

MEDIUM (2 Points)

7. **Durham:** Durham Services are on the A1(M) between J61 and J62 near Durham.
8. **Oxford:** Oxford Services are on the M40 between J7 and J8 near Wheatley, Oxfords.
9. **Trinny Woodall:** Woodall Services are on the M1 between J31 and J32 near Sheffield.
10. **Sedgemoor:** Sedgemoor Services are on the M5 between J21 and J22 near Rooks Bridge, Somerset.
11. **Donington Park:** Donington Park Services are on the M1 between J23A and J24 near Kegworth.
12. *The Ballad of Reading Gaol*: Reading Services are on the M4 between J11 and J12 near Reading.

13. **Thomas Telford:** Telford Services are on the M54 between J3 and J4 near Telford.
14. **Exeter City:** Exeter Services are on the M5 between J30 and J31 near Exeter.

HARD (3 Points)

15. **Stafford Cripps:** Stafford Services are on the M6 between J14 and J15 near Stone in Staffs.
16. **Medway:** Medway Services are on the M2 between J4 and J5 near Farthing Corner, Kent.
17. **Chay Blyth:** Blyth Services are on the A1(M) at J34 near Blyth, Notts.
18. **Beaconsfield:** Beaconsfield Services are on the M40 between J1A and J2 near Beaconsfield.
19. **Winchester:** Winchester Services are on the M3 between J8 and J9 near Winchester.
20. **Birching (or The Birch):** Birch Services are on the M62 between J18 (M60 / M66) and J19 for Heywood.

1. **Places:** What is the name of the children's hospital in Liverpool?
2. **Music:** In 'The Christmas Song' made famous by Nat King Cole, what were 'roasting on an open fire'?
3. **Sport & Games:** What is the name of the horse race run at Epsom in June over a mile and a half that is the equivalent of the Derby for three-year-old fillies?
4. **Films:** Which 1984 Wes Craven horror film first introduced the character Freddy Krueger?
5. **TV:** Which TV presenter has presented both *This Morning* and *Dancing on Ice* with Phillip Schofield?
6. **Pot Luck:** What red symbol appears in the middle of the Canadian flag?

7. **Music:** Which 1982 song did Paul McCartney and Stevie Wonder take to No. 1?
8. **Religion:** Who was the Archbishop of Canterbury from 2002 until he retired in 2012, handing over to Justin Welby?
9. **Films:** In which 1975 film did Diana Ross star as fashion designer Tracy Chambers. She also sang the theme tune which was subtitled 'Do You Know Where You're Going To'?
10. **Places:** What is the second largest city in the Republic of Ireland by population?
11. **Music:** Which John Denver song was the biggest hit for Peter, Paul & Mary, reaching No. 2 in 1970?

114

12. **People:** What is the name of Will Smith's daughter who made her acting debut in the 2007 film *I Am Legend* alongside her father?
13. **Sport & Games:** Who was the first British Formula One World Champion in 1958?
14. **Religion:** What is the name of the first day of Lent?

HARD (3 Points)

15. **Films:** Which 1965 film stars John Wayne and Dean Martin as two of four brothers who reunite back at their home town of Clearwater, Texas for their mother Katie's funeral?
16. **Music:** Which female singer's biggest hits were 'Eighth Day' in 1980 and 'Will You' in 1981?
17. **Sport & Games:** Which horse trained by Gordon Elliott and ridden by Robbie Power won the 2007 Grand National?
18. **Animals & Nature:** What food source do silkworms rely on to survive?
19. **Films:** Which actor plays Captain James T Kirk in the *Star Trek* films of 2009, 2013 and 2016?
20. **TV:** Billy Murray played which corrupt detective in *The Bill* from 1995 to 2004?

WHAT IS THE LINK BETWEEN ALL OF THE ANSWERS?

EASY (1 Point)

1. **Alder Hey:** The hospital was first established as a military hospital in 1914 for the US Army.
2. **Chestnuts:** About 80% of the world's chestnuts come from China, not to be confused with horse chestnuts that come from conkers.
3. **The Oaks:** The Oaks and the Derby make up the five Classics along with the 1,000 Guineas, 2,000 Guineas and the St Leger.
4. *A Nightmare on Elm Street*: Freddy Krueger was played by Robert Englund who also starred in the science-fiction series *V* as Willie, one of the 'visitors'.
5. **Holly Willoughby:** Holly Willoughby also presented *Surprise Surprise* from 2012 to 2015, originally presented by Cilla Black from 1984 to 2001.
6. **Maple Leaf:** The NHL ice hockey team from Toronto are also called the Toronto Maple Leafs.

MEDIUM (2 Points)

7. **'Ebony & Ivory':** Paul McCartney also had two hits with Michael Jackson, 'The Girl is Mine' which got to No. 8 in 1982 and 'Say Say Say' which got to No. 2 in 1983.
8. **Rowan Williams:** Rowan Williams was preceded by George Carey (1991–2002) and Robert Runcie (1980–1991).
9. *Mahogany*: Diana Ross had previously made her debut in the 1972 film biopic *Lady Sings the Blues* where she plays the jazz singer Billie Holiday.
10. **Cork:** Cork is in the province of Munster and is situated on the River Lee.

11. **'Leaving on a Jet Plane':** John Denver was born Henry John Deutschendorf Jr. and was killed while piloting his own aircraft when it crashed in 1997 – he was 53.

12. **Willow:** Her brother Jaden Smith also starred alongside his father Will Smith in the 2006 film *The Pursuit of Happyness.*

13. **Mike Hawthorn:** Hawthorn won the 1958 World title by just one point from Stirling Moss, who never won the title, helped by Moss who convinced stewards to reverse Hawthorn's disqualification in Portugal. After winning the title, Hawthorn never raced again but was killed in a car crash the following year.

14. **Ash Wednesday:** It is preceded by Shrove Tuesday and followed by Maundy Thursday and Good Friday.

HARD (3 Points)

15. ***The Sons of Katie Elder*:** John Wayne also starred with Dean Martin in the 1959 film *Rio Bravo*, which featured another singer Ricky Nelson as well as Angie Dickinson.

16. **Hazel O'Connor:** Both songs featured in the 1980 film *Breaking Glass* in which she starred. The film was co-produced and part-financed by Dodi Fayed.

17. **Silver Birch:** The horse had only moved from the English champion trainer Paul Nicholls in December 2006 and won the Grand National four months later. It took Gordon Elliott another eleven years to win it again, with Tiger Roll in 2018 and again in 2019.

18. **Mulberry Leaves:** The leaves are the sole source of food for silkworms, although some types of moth also eat mulberry leaves.

19. **Chris Pine:** James 'Tiberius' Kirk was played by William Shatner in the original *Star Trek* TV series from 1966 to 1969. He also starred as *T.J. Hooker* from 1982 to 1986.

20. **Don Beech:** Billy Murray also starred as Johnny Allen in *EastEnders* from 2005 to 2006.

QUIZ No. 50: GUESS THE LINK

1. **Sport & Games:** What shape is both the playing field and the ball in Australian rules football?
2. **Places:** The Government Communications Headquarters (GCHQ) is based in which English spa town in the south-west?
3. **Politics:** Which chamber of the UK Parliament is split into two groups – Spiritual and Temporal?
4. **Sport & Games:** Which team of underdogs beat Liverpool 1-0 in the 1988 FA Cup final?
5. **Music:** Which 1998 song was the first No. 1 for Robbie Williams?
6. **Religion:** Who is the patron saint of Scotland, celebrated annually on 30 November?

7. **Places:** What is the state capital of the US state of Maine?
8. **Art & Literature:** Which 1953 play by Arthur Miller is based on the Salem witch trials?
9. **History:** Which 1066 battle to repel the Norwegian army of Harald Hardrada took place in Yorkshire about three weeks before King Harold Godwinson's troops were subsequently defeated by the Normans at the Battle of Hastings?
10. **Food & Drink:** Which south-east Asian soup is made from the solidified saliva of swiftlets?
11. **Sport & Games:** In 1995, the Scottish football club now known as Livingston FC relocated there from Edinburgh – under what name did they play in Edinburgh?
12. **Transport & Travel:** Based in Dubai, which is the largest airline in the Middle East?

13. **Places:** Which is the easternmost and the largest in area of the five New York boroughs?
14. **Sport & Games:** Which team lost to Manchester United in both the 1990 and 2016 FA Cup finals?

HARD (3 Points)

15. **History:** From which venue did the BBC broadcast the first TV programme in 1936?
16. **Sport & Games:** Which team won the first two FA Cup finals and also won six out of the first nine finals?
17. **Films:** Which actress played Batgirl in the 1997 film *Batman & Robin*, with George Clooney as Batman, Uma Thurman as Poison Ivy and Arnold Schwarzenegger as Mr Freeze?
18. **Places:** The Colosseum is the main entertainment venue at which Las Vegas hotel, where Celine Dion has made the most residency appearances, playing over 1,100 shows?
19. **Transport & Travel:** What was the name of the third sister ship – built by Harland & Wolff for the White Star Line – to the Britannic and the ill-fated Titanic?
20. **Food & Drink:** Which food item was reputedly 'invented' by John Montagu, the 4th Earl of the place after which it was named?

WHAT IS THE LINK BETWEEN ALL OF THE ANSWERS?

1. **Oval:** The Oval is the home of Surrey County Cricket Club. Originally known as the Kennington Oval, it hosted England's first international football match vs. Scotland in 1870 and also the first FA Cup final in 1872.
2. **Cheltenham:** The Cheltenham Festival is horse racing's premier jumps fixture in March, featuring the Gold Cup.
3. **House of Lords:** Lord's is the home of Middlesex County Cricket Club and is owned by the MCC (Marylebone Cricket Club). It is also home to the world's oldest sporting museum.
4. **Wimbledon:** Wimbledon is one of the four tennis majors, along with the US, French and Australian Opens, held at the All England Lawn Tennis and Croquet Club.
5. **'Millennium':** The Millennium Stadium is the national stadium of Wales in Cardiff, home to the Wales RU team. It hosted the FA Cup finals from 2001 to 2006.
6. **St Andrew:** The Royal and Ancient Golf Club of St Andrews is regarded as the 'Home of Golf'. St Andrew's is also the name of Birmingham City's football ground.

7. **Augusta:** Augusta National, Georgia has been the home of the US Masters since 1934. The winner receives a green jacket.
8. ***The Crucible***: The World Snooker Championship has been held at the Crucible Theatre in Sheffield since 1977, the first winner there being John Spencer.
9. **Stamford Bridge:** Stamford Bridge is the home of Chelsea Football Club with no connection to the battle site near York.

10. **Bird's Nest:** This name was given to the Beijing National Stadium used for the 2008 Olympics due to its design.
11. **Meadowbank Thistle:** Meadowbank Stadium is also an athletics stadium and hosted the Commonwealth Games in 1970 and 1986, the first venue to host the Games twice.
12. **Emirates:** The Emirates Stadium has been the home of Arsenal FC since 2006 when they moved from Highbury.
13. **Queens:** Queen's Club in London hosts an annual grass court tennis tournament which players often use as a warm-up event before Wimbledon.
14. **Crystal Palace:** Crystal Palace National Sports Centre is an athletics stadium built close to the original Great Exhibition building destroyed by fire in 1936 and is on the site where the FA Cup final was played until 1914.

HARD (3 Points)

15. **Alexandra Palace:** It has hosted the PDC World Darts since 2007 and the Masters Snooker since 2012.
16. **Wanderers:** Wanderers Stadium is in Johannesburg. It hosted the 2003 Cricket World Cup final, in 2006 South Africa chased down a record ODI score of 434, and AB de Villiers scored the fastest ODI 50 off 16 balls in 2015.
17. **Alicia Silverstone:** Silverstone has hosted the British Grand Prix since 1987, having alternated the hosting with Brands Hatch from 1963 to 1986.
18. **Caesar's Palace:** Caesar's Palace in Las Vegas used to be the main US boxing venue for the top fights, including Ali v Holmes, Leonard v Hearns and Hagler v Duran.
19. **Olympic:** The Olympic Stadium was built for the London 2012 Olympics. It is now called London Stadium and has been the home of West Ham United since 2016.
20. **Sandwich:** Sandwich in Kent is home to the Royal St George's Golf Club, home to the Open in 2011 when Darren Clarke won his only major.

QUIZ No. 51: GUESS THE LINK

1. **Sport & Games: The** New York Mets are one of the Major League Baseball teams based in New York – what's the name of the other one?
2. **Places:** Which city is the capital of Peru?
3. **Art & Literature:** Which Shakespeare play revolves around the family feud between the Montagues and the Capulets?
4. **Maths & Numbers:** What metric unit is equal to 35.274 ounces?
5. **Films:** Which actor made his film debut in 1992 as Wayne Campbell in *Wayne's World*?
6. **TV:** Which TV drama stars Derek Jacobi and Anne Reid as Alan and Celia, two former childhood sweethearts now in their seventies?

7. **Music:** Which Liverpool band had Top 10 hits with 'The Cutter' in 1983 and 'The Killing Moon' in 1984?
8. **Films:** Which actor starred as Bud Fox, a young stockbroker who ends up working for Gordon Gekko, played by Michael Douglas in the 1987 film *Wall Street*?
9. **Places:** Which is the largest of Canada's ten provinces and the only one with a mainly French-speaking population?
10. **Pot Luck:** Topaz is the birthstone for which month?
11. **Art & Literature:** Which poet and playwright's only novel was *The Picture of Dorian Gray*, written in 1890?
12. **Transport & Travel:** Which is the best-selling Volkswagen model of all time?

13. **Films:** Which 2011 film about a group of British pensioners moving to a retirement hotel in India, starred Judi Dench, Bill Nighy and Maggie Smith, amongst others?

14. **Art & Literature:** Which French novelist and dramatist wrote the 1831 novel *The Hunchback of Notre Dame*?

HARD (3 Points)

---

15. **Pot Luck:** What was the name of the North Sea oil and gas rig off Aberdeen that was destroyed by fire in 1988, killing 167 people?

16. **Music:** With which Madonna single did Kelly Osbourne have a UK No. 3 hit in 2002?

17. **TV:** What was the name of the US cartoon series featuring a muscular, narcissistic womaniser with a blond, rockabilly haircut, sunglasses and an Elvis Presley-like voice?

18. **Sport & Games:** Which Formula 1 team were formed in 2008 when Vijay Mallya and Michiel Mol bought the Spyker (previously Jordan) team?

19. **Places:** Freetown is the capital city of which West African country?

20. **Music:** Which female Australian singer's first two UK singles in 2003 were 'Born to Try' and 'Lost Without You', both reaching the UK Top 5?

WHAT IS THE LINK BETWEEN ALL OF THE ANSWERS?

---

1. **New York Yankees:** The Yankees play in the American League and the Mets play in the National League. They played each other in the World Series for the only time in 2000, the Yankees winning 4-1.
2. **Lima:** Lima is on a desert strip between the Andes and the Pacific Ocean with a coast of about 80 km, home to around a third of Peruvians and gets no proper rain.
3. *Romeo and Juliet*: The play is set in Verona and the 1961 film *West Side Story* is loosely based on the play with the Jets representing the Montagues and the Sharks the Capulets.
4. **Kilo(gram):** Kilo is derived from the Greek word 'khilioi' meaning a thousand. Mega- is used for a million, but milli- for a thousandth and micro- for a millionth.
5. **Mike Myers:** Dana Carvey co-stars as Garth Algar and the film also features a cameo from Meat Loaf as a doorman and Alice Cooper as himself playing in concert.
6. *Last Tango in Halifax*: The series was written by Sally Wainwright who also wrote *Happy Valley* (starring Sarah Lancashire) and *Unforgiven* (starring Nicola Walker) and they play the daughters of Celia and Alan.

7. **Echo & the Bunnymen:** Lead singer Ian McCulloch started off in a band with Julian Cope and Pete Wylie who went on to form The Teardrop Explodes and Wah! respectively.
8. **Charlie Sheen:** He is the son of actor Martin Sheen, but his real name is Carlos Estévez, his brother being actor Emilio Estévez. He also went to school with Robert Downey Jr.

9. **Quebec:** From east to west they are British Columbia, Alberta, Saskatchewan, Manitoba, Ontario, Quebec, Newfoundland and Labrador, New Brunswick, Nova Scotia and Prince Edward Island. Yukon, Northwest Territories and Nunavut are the territories to the north.

10. **November:** The 12 in calendar order are garnet, amethyst, aquamarine, diamond, emerald, pearl, ruby, peridot, sapphire, opal, topaz and turquoise.

11. **Oscar Wilde:** His most famous play is *The Importance of Being Earnest* and his last work was *The Ballad of Reading Gaol*.

12. **Golf:** The VW Golf first appeared in the UK in 1974 but was launched in the US in 1975 as the VW Rabbit!

13. ***The Best Exotic Marigold Hotel:*** The film, and its 2015 sequel, also starred Dev Patel, Celia Imre and Penelope Wilton with the sequel also featuring Richard Gere.

14. **Victor Hugo:** He also wrote the 1862 novel *Les Misérables*. It opened in the West End in 1985 and is now its longest-running musical.

HARD (3 Points)

15. **Piper Alpha:** It opened in 1976 and in 1988 accounted for around 10% of North Sea oil and gas production.

16. **'Papa Don't Preach':** The song was a 1986 UK No. 1 for Madonna, her second after 'Into the Groove' in 1985.

17. **Johnny Bravo:** There were appearances by Donny Osmond, Adam West and Shaquille O'Neal, as well as animated guests like Fred Flintstone and Scooby-Doo.

18. **Force India:** The team is based in Silverstone and gained their first points when Giancarlo Fisichella came second in the 2009 Belgian Grand Prix.

19. **Sierra Leone:** The name of Freetown originated when it became a settlement in 1787 for repatriated slaves.

20. **Delta Goodrem:** She also played Nina Tucker in *Neighbours*.

1. **Art & Literature:** Which author wrote the novels *Animal Farm* in 1945 and *1984* in 1949?
2. **Life & Lifestyle:** Which direct-selling beauty company was founded in 1886 by David H McConnell and is the second-biggest direct-selling company after Amway?
3. **Music:** Who became the lead singer with Ultravox after spells with Slik, Thin Lizzy, Rich Kids and Visage?
4. **Religion:** What do you call a notice read out on three successive Sundays in a parish church, announcing an intended marriage and giving the opportunity for objections?
5. **Places:** Which London street is traditionally associated with the newspaper industry?
6. **Sport & Games:** The BDO and the PDC are the governing bodies in which sport?

7. **Entertainment:** What was the maiden name of Cheryl before she married Ashley Cole?
8. **People:** Parker and Barrow were the surnames of which notorious American criminals during the early 1930s?
9. **TV:** In the 1980s TV series *Cagney & Lacey*, Sharon Gless played Christine Cagney but who played Mary Beth Lacey?
10. **Music:** Which female singer's first UK chart hit was 'Amoureuse' in 1973, which got to No. 13?
11. **Politics:** Who was British prime minister from 1955 to 1957 and was later known as Lord Avon?

12. **TV:** What was the name of the ITV franchise serving the London area on weekdays from 1968 to 1992?
13. **Technology:** In computing, which three letters follow the file name and the dot in an executable file?
14. **Music:** Which Gerry & the Pacemakers song starts with the line, 'Life, goes on day after day; hearts, torn in every way'?

HARD (3 Points)

---

15. **Places:** The Cumbrian market town of Keswick is close to which of the Lake District lakes?
16. **Music:** The 1970s group Slade comprised Noddy Holder, Dave Hill, Don Powell and who else?
17. **TV:** Jon Hamm played which character in the TV series *Mad Men*?
18. **Animals & Nature:** Which is the largest breed of terrier, also known as the 'King of the Terriers'?
19. **Entertainment:** Which singer/songwriter was married to composer/producer Tony Hatch for over 30 years and wrote the lyrics to the theme tune for the TV show *Neighbours*?
20. **Art & Literature:** Which Welsh market town in Powys hosts an annual Literary Festival and is sometimes referred to as the 'town of books'?

WHAT IS THE LINK BETWEEN ALL OF THE ANSWERS?

---

1. **George Orwell:** The River Orwell flows through Suffolk and forms an estuary at Ipswich before joining with the River Stour at Felixstowe and then flowing into the North Sea.
2. **Avon:** There are a number of River Avons including the Bristol Avon, 'Shakespeare's' Avon in Warwickshire and also the Salisbury Avon which joins the River Stour in Christchurch Harbour.
3. **Midge Ure:** The River Ure is the main river of Wensleydale in N Yorkshire and it flows into the Ouse.
4. **Banns:** The River Bann is the longest river in Northern Ireland, the two sections (Upper and Lower Bann) being either side of Lough Neagh, the largest lake in the British Isles.
5. **Fleet Street:** The River Fleet is the longest of London's subterranean rivers and it gives its name to Fleet Street.
6. **Darts:** The River Dart is a river in Devon which rises on Dartmoor and flows into the sea at Dartmouth.

7. **Tweedy:** The River Tweed forms part of the border between England and Scotland and tweed cloth is named after it.
8. **Bonnie and Clyde:** The River Clyde is the second longest river in Scotland after the River Tay, with the third longest being the River Spey.
9. **Tyne Daly:** The North Tyne and South Tyne converge near Hexham before flowing into the North Sea with Newcastle upon Tyne, Wallsend and North Shields on the north bank and Gateshead, Jarrow and South Shields on the south bank.

10. **Kiki Dee:** One River Dee flows through Chester and forms part of the England / Wales border and another flows close to Balmoral Castle in Aberdeenshire.
11. **Anthony Eden:** The River Eden flows through Carlisle into the Solway Firth after merging with the River Esk.
12. **Thames Television:** The River Severn is the longest river in the UK, the Thames is the longest entirely in England and the Tay is the longest in Scotland.
13. **exe:** The River Exe is the main river in Devon and flows south for over 50 miles, reaching the sea at Exmouth.
14. **'Ferry Cross The Mersey':** The River Mersey starts at the confluence of the River Tame and the River Goyt in Stockport before flowing through the Manchester Ship Canal.

HARD (3 Points)

15. **Derwent Water:** Besides the River Derwent in Cumbria, there are others in Derbyshire, Northumberland and N. Yorkshire.
16. **Jim Lea:** The River Lea originates near Luton in the Chilterns before flowing into the River Thames, being its easternmost tributary.
17. **Don Draper:** There is a River Don that flows into the North Sea at Aberdeen and one in South Yorkshire flowing through Sheffield, Rotherham and Doncaster.
18. **Airedale:** The River Aire rises at Malham Tarn, flows through Leeds then meets the River Calder at Castleford before emptying into the River Ouse.
19. **Jackie Trent:** The River Trent is the third longest in the UK and flows through Stoke, Burton and Nottingham before joining the River Ouse to form the Humber Estuary.
20. **Hay-on-Wye:** The River Wye forms much of the border between England and Wales and meets the Severn estuary near Chepstow.

QUIZ No. 53: **GUESS THE LINK**

EASY (1 Point)

1. **Music:** Who was the bass guitarist with the group Queen until 1991?
2. **TV:** Which Liverpool comedian hosts the TV show *In Conversation With...*?
3. **Sport & Games:** What is the original name of the home ground of AFC Bournemouth?
4. **People:** Lambeth Palace is the London residence of whom?
5. **Music:** Which Welsh rock group had a UK No. 2 hit in 1996 called 'A Design For Life'?
6. **TV:** Which 1980s political satire sitcom starred Paul Eddington, Nigel Hawthorne and Derek Fowlds?

MEDIUM (2 Points)

7. **Sport & Games:** Which Sussex wicketkeeper kept wicket in both of England's victorious Ashes teams in 2009 and 2011?
8. **Music:** Which reggae singer's highest chart entry was 'Wild World' which reached No. 5 in 1988?
9. **TV:** Which character did Sid James play in the TV sitcom *Bless This House*?
10. **Sport & Games:** Which former Swansea City centre-back was appointed the club's player-manager after the sacking of Michael Laudrup before going on to manage Leeds United, Middlesbrough and Birmingham City?
11. **Maths & Numbers:** If first, second, third etc. are known as ordinal numbers, what are the actual numbers one, two, three etc. called?

12. **TV:** Who hosted the TV show *Sale of the Century* from 1971 to 1983?
13. **Sport & Games:** Which former Chelsea and Queens Park Rangers manager took over at Manchester United in 1977 after Tommy Docherty was sacked?
14. **TV:** What is the name of the TV sitcom starring Tom Hollander as an Anglican priest in a London church which also features Olivia Colman as his wife?

HARD (3 Points)

---

15. **Art & Literature:** Which 18th century English poet wrote *Essay on Criticism* and *The Rape of the Lock* and was known for his translations of Homer?
16. **Sport & Games:** Which grey horse, ridden by Pat Eddery, won the 1997 St Leger at Doncaster?
17. **Music:** Which singer had a UK No. 7 hit in 1963 with 'Dominique'?
18. **Pot Luck:** What phrase, originating in an 1895 *Punch* cartoon, is given to something bad that is called good out of politeness or timidity?
19. **Sport & Games:** Which company were the first sponsors of the English Football League?
20. **Films:** Which 1980 film starring The Who's Roger Daltrey is initially set in Durham prison and then in London after he escapes?

WHAT IS THE LINK BETWEEN ALL OF THE ANSWERS?

---

1. **John Deacon:** Deacon was upset by the death of Freddie Mercury in 1991 and largely retired after that.
2. **John Bishop:** His first guest was James Corden in 2016.
3. **Dean Court:** The ground's first sponsored name was the Fitness First Stadium from 2001 and it was named the Vitality Stadium after promotion to the Premier League in 2015.
4. **Archbishop of Canterbury:** The palace is on the south bank of the Thames next to St Thomas' Hospital and across the river from the Houses of Parliament.
5. **Manic Street Preachers:** The group's lead singer and lead guitarist is James Dean Bradfield.
6. *Yes Minister: Yes Minister* ran for three series from 1980 to 1984 followed by two series of *Yes Prime Minister* from 1986 to 1988.

7. **Matt Prior:** Prior was the first wicketkeeper to make a century (126) on his Test debut in 2007 and was the second-fastest to reach 1,000 Test runs behind Les Ames.
8. **Maxi Priest:** The song 'Wild World' was written by Cat Stevens and was also a No. 8 hit for Jimmy Cliff in 1970.
9. **Sid Abbott:** Sid James starred in six series from 1971 to 1976 alongside Diana Coupland, Robin Stewart and Sally Geeson. James died on stage in Sunderland in 1976 just after the last episode was aired.
10. **Garry Monk:** He played for Swansea City in all four divisions from 2004 to 2014 and was part of the 2013 League Cup-winning team against Bradford City.

11. **Cardinal Numbers:** Hampton Court Palace was built for Cardinal Wolsey and it is one of only two surviving palaces of Henry VIII along with St James's Palace.
12. **Nicholas Parsons:** He has also famously presented the Radio 4 show *Just a Minute* in six decades, since 1967.
13. **Dave Sexton:** He had also previously taken over from Tommy Docherty at Chelsea in 1967, going on to win the FA Cup in 1970 and the Cup Winners' Cup in 1971.
14. *Rev*: It ran for three series from 2010 to 2014 with Miles Jupp as Nigel and Simon McBurney as Archdeacon Robert.

HARD (3 Points)

15. **Alexander Pope:** His *Essay on Criticism* included the famous quotations 'To err is human; to forgive, divine' and 'Fools rush in where angels fear to tread'.
16. **Silver Patriarch:** The horse was only beaten a short head in the 1997 Derby by Benny The Dip and this race also provided Pat Eddery with his 4,000th career winner, joining Sir Gordon Richards and Lester Piggott.
17. **The Singing Nun:** The song reached No. 1 in the US for Jeanine Deckers, also known as Sister Smile, who was a Belgian Dominican nun.
18. **Curate's Egg:** The cartoon described a timid curate who had been served a bad egg while dining with his bishop and said that parts of the egg were excellent.
19. **Canon:** Canon sponsored the Football League for 3 seasons (1983–86) followed by Today for 1 season (1986–87) and Barclays for 6 seasons (1987–93) who went on to sponsor the Premier League after the initial sponsorship by Carling.
20. *McVicar*: The film also stars singer Adam Faith, Steven Berkoff, Billy Murray (who played Don Beech in *The Bill*) and Brian Hall (who played the chef Terry in *Fawlty Towers*).

QUIZ No. 54: **GUESS THE LINK**

1. **Music:** Which singer, who had a hit with 'Walk On By' in 1964, had her biggest hit in the UK in 1982 with 'Heartbreaker' which reached No. 2?
2. **Food & Drink:** Which sauce made by Lea & Perrins is used to flavour a Bloody Mary cocktail?
3. **Places:** Which city is the capital of Western Australia?
4. **Entertainment:** Which former Radio 1 and Radio 2 DJ was nicknamed 'Diddy' by Ken Dodd when he appeared on *Doddy's Music Box* in the late 1960s?
5. **Sport & Games:** Molineux is the home ground of which football club?
6. **Music:** Which US singer's first UK hit was 'Heaven is a Place on Earth' which got to No. 1 in 1987?

7. **Films:** Which English actor played Austin Powers' controller Basil Exposition in all three of the *Austin Powers* films?
8. **Food & Drink:** Which cracker-type biscuit, often eaten with cheese, was invented by the physician William Oliver around 1750?
9. **History:** The Royal Pavilion is a pleasure palace built for King George IV, then Prince Regent, in which seaside resort in East Sussex?
10. **TV:** Stratford Johns played DCI (later DCS) Charlie Barlow in *Z Cars* and its spin-off *Softly, Softly*, but who played his sidekick DS (later DI/DCI) John Watt in both series?
11. **Science & Medicine:** What is the more common name of magnesium sulphate, a common ingredient of bath salts, named after a town in Surrey?

12. **Places:** In which south-west spa town is GCHQ located?
13. **Music:** Fiddler's Dram had a UK No. 3 hit in 1979 with which song?
14. **Food & Drink:** Pomfret cakes are an alternative name for which circular liquorice-flavoured sweets originally made in the West Yorkshire town after which they are named?

HARD (3 Points)

---

15. **Entertainment:** England football captain Billy Wright married Joy in 1958 who was one of the three sisters who made up which British trio of the 1950s?
16. **Sport & Games:** Which card game includes an element where the four kings are removed from the game and used as 'horses' on which to place money? There is also a pot to pay into for the first person to get rid of all their cards and a dummy hand which players can bid for?
17. **Places:** Which seaside town on the Isle of Wight, just up the coast from Shanklin, is the location of the main airport for light aircraft?
18. **History:** Who was the British prime minister when Queen Victoria died in 1901?
19. **Sport & Games:** Who was the Everton manager when they were League Champions in 1963 and 1970 and also when they won the 1966 FA Cup?
20. **Entertainment:** Which radio and television comedian of the 1940s and 1950s was nicknamed 'Cheerful Charlie'?

WHAT IS THE LINK BETWEEN ALL OF THE ANSWERS?

---

1. **Dionne Warwick:** She is the cousin of Whitney Houston but neither are related to the singer Thelma Houston.
2. **Worcester(shire) Sauce:** The sauce was first introduced in 1837 and Lea & Perrins was bought by Heinz (later Kraft Heinz) in 2005.
3. **Perth:** Perth lies on the River Swan and is home to the WACA cricket ground.
4. **David Hamilton:** He was born David Pilditch in Manchester in 1938 and changed his name to Hamilton after his mother's maiden name.
5. **Wolverhampton Wanderers:** Three of the ground's four stands are named after former players (Stan Cullis, Billy Wright and Steve Bull) and the fourth is named after Sir Jack Hayward (former owner and chairman who died in 2015).
6. **Belinda Carlisle:** She originally gained fame as the lead singer with the all-girl group The Go-Go's, which also featured Jane Wiedlin who tasted solo success in 1988 with the single 'Rush Hour'.

7. **Michael York:** The character is a spoof character based on M in the James Bond films, whilst Dr Evil is similarly based on the villain Ernst Stavro Blofeld.
8. **Bath Oliver:** It was called a Bath Oliver simply because William Oliver was from Bath.
9. **Brighton:** It was redesigned and rebuilt from 1815 in an Indian style with domes and minarets and is the work of architect John Nash.

10. **Frank Windsor:** *Z Cars* also provided early roles for Brian Blessed, Colin Welland and Joss Ackland, among others.
11. **Epsom Salts:** The Epsom Derby was first run in 1780, but The Oaks for three-year-old fillies only was first run the year before in 1779.
12. **Cheltenham:** GCHQ stands for Government Communications Headquarters.
13. **'Day Trip to Bangor':** The song is subtitled (Didn't We Have a Lovely Time).
14. **Pontefract Cakes:** The alternative name Pomfret cakes comes from the Norman word for Pontefract.

HARD (3 Points)

---

15. **Beverley Sisters:** Their three biggest UK hits all had a Christmas theme: 'I Saw Mommy Kissing Santa Claus' in 1953 and 'Little Drummer Boy' and 'Little Donkey', both in 1959.
16. **Newmarket:** The money on each king goes to the person who plays the queen of the same suit but if any queen isn't played during the game then that king's money carries over to the next game.
17. **Sandown:** It also the location of the island's zoo.
18. **The Marquess of Salisbury:** His birth name was Robert Gascoyne-Cecil and he served on three separate occasions as prime minister.
19. **Harry Catterick:** Catterick died in 1985 of a heart attack just after watching a game at Goodison Park, almost five years after club legend Dixie Dean had died of a heart attack at the ground whilst watching them play Liverpool.
20. **Charlie Chester:** His famous phrase used to be 'This is Cheerful Charlie, your Chin-up Boy Chester'.

QUIZ No. 55: GUESS THE LINK

1. **Sport & Games:** Which football club play their home games at Craven Cottage?
2. **TV:** Which comedian is responsible for the characters Kevin the Teenager and Tim Nice-But-Dim?
3. **Entertainment:** Which Art Deco entertainment venue opened in 1932 as the Gaumont Palace and has been familiarly known over the years as the 'Hammy-O'?
4. **Pot Luck:** What is the name of the clock time at the Royal Observatory in London abbreviated to GMT?
5. **Transport & Travel:** The traditional name for a cab or taxi was a ....carriage, named after a place in London?
6. **TV:** Who has been the opposite team captain to Ian Hislop on *Have I Got News for You* since it started in 1990?

7. **Sport & Games:** In the board game Monopoly, what is the third property in the pale blue set with Euston Road and Pentonville Road?
8. **Places:** Old Harrovians formerly went to which London public school founded in 1572?
9. **Films:** *Kind Hearts and Coronets*, *Passport to Pimlico* and *The Ladykillers* are examples of which comedies, produced at the famous West London TV and film studios?
10. **TV:** Which character does Ricky Gervais play in the TV series *The Office*?
11. **Sport & Games:** Which football team won the First Division title in 1955 and the FA Cup in 1970 but then failed to win another domestic trophy until they won the FA Cup in 1997?

12. **Places:** What is the name of the official residence of the Archbishop of Canterbury?
13. **Pot Luck:** What is the Cockney rhyming slang for 'hair'?
14. **Music:** The follow-up to Suggs's debut solo single 'I'm Only Sleeping' was called '...... Town'?

HARD (3 Points)

---

15. **Films:** Which 2010 British film tells the story of female sewing machinists going on strike at a London Ford plant, demanding equal pay?
16. **Places:** Which market town in North Yorkshire near Scotch Corner is home to a Norman castle which overlooks the River Swale?
17. **People:** Gerald Cavendish Grosvenor, one of the richest men in Britain when he died in 2016, was better known as the Duke of where?
18. **Sport & Games:** In Blackburn Rovers' 1995 Premier League-winning team, who formed the so-called 'SAS' striking partnership with Alan Shearer?
19. **Pot Luck:** From which prison did the Great Train Robber Ronnie Biggs escape in 1965?
20. **Music:** Which song from the musical *Me and My Girl* was named after a London street which then gave its name to a Cockney dance?

WHAT IS THE LINK BETWEEN ALL OF THE ANSWERS?

EASY (1 Point)

1. **Fulham:** Hammersmith and Fulham is the only borough with three professional football clubs – Fulham, QPR and Chelsea.

2. **Harry Enfield:** He also played Dermot in the first series of *Men Behaving Badly* before Neil Morrissey took over as Tony.

3. **Hammersmith Odeon:** It was known as the Hammersmith Odeon from 1962 to 1992 and since then has been known as the Hammersmith Apollo with a variety of sponsors.

4. **Greenwich Mean Time:** Greenwich is also home to the O2 Arena, National Maritime Museum and *Cutty Sark*.

5. **Hackney:** The Hackney Empire opened in 1901 and Charlie Chaplin, WC Fields and Stan Laurel all performed there before it began hosting TV shows in the 1950s and 1960s such as *Take Your Pick* and *Oh! Boy*.

6. **Paul Merton:** His real name is Paul Martin and he hosted *Room 101* between Nick Hancock and Frank Skinner and has been a regular on the Radio 4 show *Just a Minute* since 1989.

MEDIUM (2 Points)

7. **The Angel Islington:** Islington had two prisons before the women's prison HMP Holloway, where Ruth Ellis was hanged, closed in 2016. That left HMP Pentonville where Dr Crippen and John Christie were hanged.

8. **Harrow:** Old Harrovians include prime ministers Winston Churchill and Robert Peel, poet Lord Byron, actor Benedict Cumberbatch and singer James Blunt.

9. **Ealing Comedies:** Other famous Ealing comedies include *The Lavender Hill Mob* and *The Man in the White Suit*.

10. **David Brent:** The series was based in the office of Wernham Hogg in Slough and also starred Martin Freeman as Tim and Mackenzie Crook as Gareth.
11. **Chelsea:** Chelsea did beat Real Madrid in the 1971 European Cup Winners' Cup final after a replay.
12. **Lambeth Palace:** Across the Thames from the Houses of Parliament, it was acquired for the archbishop around 1200 and part of it was used to imprison the Lollards, the followers of John Wycliffe, in the 17th century.
13. **Barnet (Fair):** It is often abbreviated to just 'Barnet' but is named after Barnet Fair, an annual horse and pleasure fair over three days in September.
14. **'Camden (Town)':** The area is probably best known for its street markets and in 2004, Chris Evans famously opened a stall there and sold many of his possessions.

HARD (3 Points)

15. *Made in Dagenham:* Sally Hawkins stars with Bob Hoskins, Miranda Richardson and Rosamund Pike.
16. **Richmond:** Scotch Corner is where the A1(M) crosses the A66 which goes from Middlesbrough to Workington.
17. **(Duke of) Westminster:** Westminster is home to not just the Houses of Parliament, Westminster Abbey and Westminster Cathedral, but also to Tate Britain and the London Eye.
18. **Chris Sutton:** He started his professional career with Norwich City before moving to Blackburn in 1994 and then played for Chelsea and Celtic.
19. **Wandsworth:** Wandsworth used to be called 'the hanging prison' and both Derek Bentley and William 'Lord Haw-Haw' Joyce were executed there.
20. **'The Lambeth Walk':** The musical is also known for the songs 'The Sun Has Got His Hat On' and 'Leaning on a Lamp-post', made famous by George Formby.

QUIZ No. 56: GUESS THE LINK

1. **Sport & Games:** Which golfer, who won seven Majors in the 1960s, had a following called Arnie's Army, a name he later used to set up his charitable foundation?
2. **Music:** Bucks Fizz were originally made up of Mike Nolan, Bobby Gee, Jay Aston and which female singer?
3. **Films:** Which then young actress played Velvet Brown in the 1944 film *National Velvet* alongside Mickey Rooney?
4. **TV:** Which character did Shane Richie play in *EastEnders*?
5. **Sport & Games:** Which Northern Irish footballer got the nickname 'El Beatle' during his playing career?
6. **Entertainment:** Which comedian and impressionist was famously the subject of a fake headline in the *Sun* about eating a hamster?

7. **TV:** Lee Mack is one of the team captains on *Would I Lie To You?* but who is the other?
8. **Sport & Games:** Which boxing commentator was also presenter of the midweek sports programme *Sportsnight* from 1975 to 1985?
9. **Music:** Which female singer had a UK No. 1 hit in 1985 with 'Move Closer'?
10. **TV:** Kevin Kennedy played which character in *Coronation Street* from 1983 to 2003?
11. **Sport & Games:** Jamie Vardy moved to Leicester City in 2012 from which club who had just secured promotion to the Football League for the first time?

12. **Entertainment:** After a relationship with DJ Bruno Brookes, Anthea Turner was married for eight years to which other DJ, who was also her manager at the time?
13. **Films:** Which actress, who was married to Kenneth Branagh from 1994 to 1999 and Tim Burton from 2001 to 2014, starred as Queen Elizabeth, the Queen Mother in the 2010 film *The King's Speech*?
14. **Sport & Games:** Which British racing driver, who was Formula 1 World Champion in 1963 and 1965, was killed in 1968 at Hockenheim in Germany?

HARD (3 Points)

15. **Food & Drink:** Which cocktail consists of gin, lemon juice, sugar and soda and is traditionally served in a tall glass?
16. **TV:** Raymond Burr starred as which criminal defence lawyer in a series that originally ran from 1957 to 1966?
17. **Sport & Games:** Which Australian driver was the Formula 1 World Champion in 1980?
18. **Films:** Which Taiwanese film director directed the films *Crouching Tiger, Hidden Dragon, Brokeback Mountain* and *Life of Pi*?
19. **Music:** Which US country singer had UK hits in 1973 with 'Behind Closed Doors' and 'The Most Beautiful Girl'?
20. **TV:** Which character did Todd Carty play in *Grange Hill*?

WHAT IS THE LINK BETWEEN ALL OF THE ANSWERS?

ANSWERS QUIZ No. 56: LINK – DRUMMERS

1. **Arnold Palmer:** Carl Palmer was the drummer with The Crazy World of Arthur Brown, Atomic Rooster, Emerson, Lake & Palmer and Asia.
2. **Cheryl Baker:** Ginger Baker was the drummer with Cream, Blind Faith and the Baker Gurvitz Army.
3. **Elizabeth Taylor:** Roger Taylor was the drummer with Queen although another Roger Taylor was the drummer with Duran Duran.
4. **Alfie Moon:** Keith Moon was the drummer with the Who and briefly played with the Plastic Ono Band and the Jeff Beck Group.
5. **George Best:** Pete Best was the original drummer of The Beatles, often called 'the fifth Beatle', before he was replaced by Ringo Starr.
6. **Freddie Starr:** Ringo Starr became the drummer of The Beatles after leaving Rory Storm and the Hurricanes.

7. **David Mitchell:** Mitch Mitchell was the drummer with the Jimi Hendrix Experience after leaving Georgie Fame and the Blue Flames.
8. **Harry Carpenter:** Karen Carpenter played drums in the Carpenters with her brother Richard playing keyboards.
9. **Phyllis Nelson:** Sandy Nelson was a US drummer who had a UK No. 3 hit in 1961 with 'Let There Be Drums'.
10. **Curly Watts:** Charlie Watts joined the Rolling Stones in 1963 after a spell with Alexis Korner's Blues Incorporated.
11. **Fleetwood Town:** Mick Fleetwood was the drummer for Fleetwood Mac, the other members being John and Christine McVie, Stevie Nicks and Lindsey Buckingham.

12. **Peter Powell:** Cozy Powell had his biggest hit in 1973 with 'Dance With The Devil' which got to No. 3 and the drummer in Slade was called Don Powell.
13. **Helena Bonham Carter:** John Bonham joined Led Zeppelin, originally called the New Yardbirds, in 1968, joining Jimmy Page and Robert Plant. He died at the age of 32 in 1980.
14. **Jim Clark:** Dave Clark was the singer and drummer with the Dave Clark Five who had a UK No. 1 in 1963 with 'Glad All Over'. He was very close friends with Freddie Mercury and was with him when he died.

HARD (3 Points)

15. **Tom Collins:** Phil Collins was the drummer with Genesis and took over lead vocals when Peter Gabriel left in 1975. He also starred as Buster Edwards in the 1988 film *Buster* about the Great Train Robbery, with Julie Walters starring as his wife.
16. **Perry Mason:** Nick Mason was the drummer and a founding member of Pink Floyd. He is the only member to have featured on every one of their albums.
17. **Alan Jones:** Kenney Jones was the drummer with the Small Faces. When Steve Marriott was replaced by Rod Stewart and Ronnie Wood, they became the Faces. He then joined the Who in 1978, replacing Keith Moon after his death.
18. **Ang Lee:** Tommy Lee was the drummer and founding member of Mötley Crüe. He married Pamela Anderson in 1995 just four days after they met.
19. **Charlie Rich:** Buddy Rich was an American jazz drummer who performed with Tommy Dorsey and Count Basie.
20. **Tucker (Jenkins):** Mick Tucker was the drummer with the Sweet alongside Brian Connolly, Steve Priest and Andy Scott.

QUIZ No. 57: **GUESS THE LINK**

1. **Pot Luck:** A Cockney is said to be someone born within the sound of what?
2. **Transport & Travel:** The two main train stations in Manchester are Victoria and which other?
3. **Sport & Games:** Which football team won the Premier League title in 2016 for the first time?
4. **Entertainment:** Who took over the Radio 2 lunchtime show from Jimmy Young in 2003 and started presenting the TV show *Eggheads* in 2008?
5. **TV:** Which comedian has starred in *A League of Their Own* since 2012 and played a teacher in the TV series *Bad Education* from 2012 to 2014?
6. **Pot Luck:** What is the highest rank in the British Royal Navy?

7. **History:** What title is given to a prince who rules in place of a monarch due to absence or incapacity e.g. due to illness or minority?
8. **Transport & Travel:** Which London mainline train station is the terminus for services from Glasgow Central, Manchester Piccadilly, Liverpool Lime Street and Birmingham New Street?
9. **Buildings:** Sir Basil Spence is most closely associated with the rebuilding of which Midlands cathedral after it was destroyed by bombing during the Second World War?
10. **Places:** Which is the most northerly county in England and the least densely populated?

11. **Sport & Games:** In cricket, which club has the initials MCC?

12. **Pot Luck:** Which London prison is informally known as 'The Ville'?

13. **History:** In which naval battle of 1805 off the coast of southern Spain did the British Royal Navy commanded by Nelson defeat Napoleon's French and Spanish fleets?

14. **Places:** In which area of London did serial killer Jack the Ripper kill his victims?

HARD (3 Points)

15. **Sport & Games:** Which football club won the League Cup in 1986, the last time it was known as the Milk Cup, beating Queens Park Rangers 3-0 in the Wembley final?

16. **Pot Luck:** According to a famous 1959 advert for a brand of cigarettes, 'You're never alone with a ......'?

17. **History:** Blenheim Palace in Oxfordshire, commissioned after victory at the Battle of Blenheim in 1704, was originally a reward for John Churchill, 1st Duke of where?

18. **TV:** What was the name of Russ Abbot's character who played a spoof of James Bond?

19. **Places:** On which Westminster street in central London is The Reform Club, a former gentlemen's club that was the first to open its doors to women in 1981?

20. **Sport & Games:** What was the name of ITV's primary wrestling commentator from 1955 to 1988?

WHAT IS THE LINK BETWEEN ALL OF THE ANSWERS?

1. **Bow Bells:** The Bow Street Runners were founded in 1749 by Henry Fielding and were the first professional police force.
2. **Piccadilly:** Landmarks on Piccadilly include the Ritz Hotel, Fortnum & Mason and the Royal Academy of Arts.
3. **Leicester City:** Maurice Micklewhite changed his name to Michael Caine when he was in a phone box on Leicester Square and saw *The Caine Mutiny* being shown at the Odeon.
4. **Jeremy Vine:** He is the brother of stand-up comedian Tim Vine who also appeared in the first five series of the TV sitcom *Not Going Out*.
5. **Jack Whitehall:** The Palace of Whitehall was the main residence of monarchs from 1530 to 1698 until it was largely destroyed by fire, and Charles I was executed there in 1649.
6. **Admiral of the Fleet:** Fleet Street used to be the centre of the newspaper industry.

MEDIUM (2 Points)

7. **Prince Regent:** Regent Street starts at Piccadilly Circus and is the location of the famous toy shop Hamleys.
8. **Euston:** Euston Road is home to University College Hospital and the British Library.
9. **Coventry:** Coventry Street runs from Piccadilly Circus to Leicester Square and is home to the Prince of Wales Theatre.
10. **Northumberland:** Northumberland Avenue runs from Victoria Embankment to Charing Cross and is home to the Playhouse Theatre.

11. **Marylebone Cricket Club:** The MCC are the owners of Lord's cricket ground and its members wear scarlet and gold striped ties and blazers, affectionately known as 'egg and bacon'.

12. **Pentonville:** John Christie was hanged in the prison in 1953 and several celebrities including George Best, Boy George and George Michael have served short sentences there.

13. **Trafalgar:** Nelson's Column was built to commemorate the battle and Trafalgar Square is named after the battle where a Christmas tree donated by Norway is erected each year.

14. **Whitechapel:** The Royal London Hospital has been based on Whitechapel Road since the 18th century.

HARD (3 Points)

15. **Oxford United:** Oxford Street runs from Marble Arch to Tottenham Court Road and is where Selfridges and John Lewis opened their first department stores.

16. **Strand:** There was a music hall song called 'Let's All Go Down the Strand' and Somerset House is on The Strand which housed all birth, marriage and death certificates until 1970.

17. **Duke of Marlborough:** The palace is also famously the birthplace of Sir Winston Churchill.

18. **Basildon Bond:** He was named after a brand of stationery.

19. **Pall Mall:** Pall Mall is also home to other members' clubs including the Royal Automobile Club and the Oxford and Cambridge Club.

20. **Kent Walton:** The wrestling was part of ITV's *World of Sport* programme for 20 years of that period.

QUIZ No. 58: GUESS THE LINK

1. **Music:** Who was the lead singer with the Doors?
2. **People:** What was the name of the American socialite whose relationship with Edward VIII led to his abdication in 1936?
3. **Places:** In which country is the world's most northerly capital city?
4. **TV:** MasterChef was relaunched in 2005 with two new judges – John Torode and who else?
5. **People:** Which member of the Royal Family married the former England rugby union player Mike Tindall in 2011?
6. **Politics:** Who was the US President between 1993 and 2001, after George H W Bush and before George W Bush?

7. **Sport & Games:** Which British figure skater became both Olympic and World Champion in 1976?
8. **TV:** Which former member of the group Mis-Teeq has been a judge on both *Strictly Come Dancing* and *Britain's Got Talent*?
9. **Films:** Which Welsh actor starred in the 1959 film *Look Back in Anger*, the 1968 film *Where Eagles Dare* and the 1984 film *1984*?
10. **Music:** What was the only UK No. 1 hit for The Sweet, reaching the top spot in 1973?
11. **Sport & Games:** Michael Schumacher won the first of his seven Formula 1 world titles in 1994 driving for which team?
12. **Places:** Alicante and Benidorm are located on which of the Spanish Costas?

13. **Geography:** Which word has come to refer to the rainy season of a seasonally affected area, with most of its annual rainfall falling during that period?
14. **TV:** Which actor played Captain Peacock in *Are You Being Served?* and Herbert 'Truly' Truelove in *Last of the Summer Wine*?

15. **Sport & Games:** Who was the manager of Liverpool Football Club who took over from Graeme Souness in 1994 and was manager until 1998 when Gerard Houllier took sole charge?
16. **Music:** Victoria Hesketh from Blackpool, whose best-known UK hit is 'Remedy' which got to No. 6 in 2009 is better known by what stage name?
17. **People:** Which Canadian-born publisher and politician, elevated to the peerage in 1917, had bought the *Daily Express* in 1916, launched the *Sunday Express* in 1918 and bought the *Evening Standard* in 1923?
18. **Pot Luck:** The original names of Santa Claus's eight reindeer – Rudolph was not in the original eight – are traditionally Dasher, Dancer, Prancer, Vixen, Cupid, Donner, Blitzen and which other?
19. **Politics:** Which MP for Richmond Park was the Conservative candidate for the 2016 London mayoral election which he lost to Sadiq Khan representing Labour?
20. **Sport & Games:** Which female tennis player turned professional in 1979 at age 14 and lost to Martina Navratilova in the Wimbledon final of 1983, having inflicted the largest ever Wimbledon defeat on Billie Jean King in the semi-finals by a score of 6-1, 6-1?

WHAT IS THE LINK BETWEEN ALL OF THE ANSWERS?

1. **Jim Morrison:** Morrisons was founded in 1899 by William Morrison and has its head office in Bradford.
2. **Wallis Simpson:** Wallis is a chain of women's fashion stores, the first store being opened in Islington in 1923 and part of the Arcadia group since 1999.
3. **Iceland:** The first Iceland store was opened in Oswestry in 1970 and its head office is in Deeside in Wales.
4. **Gregg Wallace:** Greggs is the largest bakery chain in the UK with its head office in Newcastle upon Tyne, and the first shop was opened nearby in Gosforth in 1951.
5. **Zara Phillips:** Zara is a Spanish clothing and accessories retailer with over 6,500 stores in 88 countries.
6. **Bill Clinton:** Clinton Cards opened its first shop in Epping in Essex in 1968 but went into administration in 2012 with 350 shop closures before being bought by US company American Greetings.

7. **John Curry:** Currys' first shop opened in Leicester in 1888 but was taken over by Dixons in 1984, later merging with PC World shops in 2015.
8. **Alesha Dixon:** Dixons started out as a photographic studio in Southend in 1937.
9. **Richard Burton:** Burton Menswear began in Chesterfield in 1903, eventually becoming part of the Arcadia Group with Dorothy Perkins, Miss Selfridge and Topshop, among others.
10. **'Blockbuster':** Blockbuster was a US-based movie and game rentals business with over 9,000 stores worldwide in 2004.

11. **Benetton:** Benetton was founded in 1965 in Belluno, Italy and its core brand became United Colors of Benetton.
12. **Costa Blanca:** Costa Coffee's head office is in Dunstable and it was acquired by Whitbread in 1995.
13. **Monsoon:** The first Monsoon shop opened in 1973 and its sister company Accessorize opened its first store in 1984.
14. **Frank Thornton:** Thorntons is a British chocolate brand established in Sheffield in 1911.

HARD (3 Points)

15. **Roy Evans:** Evans is a women's clothing retailer founded in 1930 which was bought by the Arcadia Group in 1971.
16. **Little Boots:** Boots was founded in 1849 in Nottingham and its head office has always been there.
17. **Lord Beaverbrook:** Beaverbrooks opened its first jewellers in Belfast in 1919 and has its head office in Lytham St Annes near Blackpool.
18. **Comet:** Comet was an electrical retail chain founded in Hull in 1933 but went into administration in 2012.
19. **Zac Goldsmith:** Goldsmiths jewellers opened its first shop in 1778 in Newcastle upon Tyne and still trades from the same address.
20. **Andrea Jaeger:** The fashion chain Jaeger was originally founded in 1884 specialising in woollen undergarments, even worn by the explorer Ernest Shackleton.

1. **Sport & Games:** Which British driver won the Formula 1 World Championship in 1996?
2. **Music:** Which singer's UK debut hit 'Bailamos' reached No. 4 in 1999 and then had a No. 1 hit with 'Hero' in 2002?
3. **Entertainment:** Louise Nurding from the girl group Eternal married which footballer in 1998?
4. **Sport & Games:** Which Italian jockey rode his first Derby winner on Authorized in 2007 and followed that with another win on Golden Horn in 2015?
5. **TV:** Which actress and singer starred as the title character in the US TV series *Hannah Montana*?
6. **Films:** Which actor starred as Gordon Gekko in the 1987 film *Wall Street* and reprised the role in the 2010 sequel?

7. **Music:** Whose debut hit was 'Too Late for Goodbyes' which got to No. 6 in the UK in 1984?
8. **Sport & Games:** Who is England's second-highest wicket-taker in Test matches after James Anderson?
9. **People:** Who followed Bill Clinton as US president in 2001?
10. **Music:** Which singer had a 1966 UK No. 1 hit with 'These Boots are Made for Walkin''?
11. **Sport & Games:** Which Chelsea player became Chelsea's all-time top scorer in 2013, breaking Bobby Tambling's record which had stood for over 40 years?

12. **TV:** Which actor stars as Jack Bauer in all the series of *24*, each series unfolding in real time, set over a 24-hour period on one day?
13. **Music:** Which singer's UK debut hit was 'Kids in America' in 1981?
14. **Films:** Which actress starred as Anastasia Steele in the *Fifty Shades* series of films?

HARD (3 Points)

15. **Films:** The 1969 film *Easy Rider* stars Dennis Hopper and which other actor as bikers riding across the southern states of the USA?
16. **Music:** Which female singer's first album, released in 2002, was the critically acclaimed *Come Away With Me*, which reached No. 1 in the UK, the US and five other countries?
17. **Sport & Games:** Who trained the horse Ballabriggs to win the 2011 Grand National?
18. **Art & Literature:** Which Oxford-born author's most famous novels include *Money* (1984), *London Fields* (1989) and *Time's Arrow* (1991)?
19. **Music:** Which singer's biggest hits in the UK were 'Pink Cadillac' in 1988 and 'Miss You Like Crazy' in 1989?
20. **Sport & Games:** Having been player-manager at Burton Albion from 1998 to 2009, who returned to manage the club in 2015 after spells with Derby County and Sheffield United?

WHAT IS THE LINK BETWEEN ALL OF THE ANSWERS?

EASY (1 Point)

1. **Damon Hill:** Graham Hill won the Formula 1 World Championship twice, in 1962 and 1968, but died in a plane crash in 1975 aged just 46.
2. **Enrique Iglesias:** Julio Iglesias was a goalkeeper at Real Madrid until a car accident left him unable to walk for two years, so he learned to play guitar and started to sing. His 'Begin the Beguine' was a 1981 UK No. 1.
3. **Jamie Redknapp:** Harry Redknapp played most of his career for West Ham and then Bournemouth and his first two managerial jobs were for Bournemouth and then West Ham. He is also Frank Lampard's uncle.
4. **Frankie Dettori:** Gianfranco Dettori won the 2000 Guineas in 1975 and 1976 riding for Henry Cecil. His son's full name is Lanfranco, shortened to Frankie.
5. **Miley Cyrus:** Her father Billy Ray Cyrus also starred as her father in the series. He had a UK No. 3 hit in 1992 with 'Achy Breaky Heart'.
6. **Michael Douglas:** Kirk Douglas starred in many films but famously as Vincent van Gogh in *Lust for Life* (1956) and as the title character in *Spartacus* (1960).

MEDIUM (2 Points)

7. **Julian Lennon:** John Lennon wrote 'Lucy in the Sky With Diamonds' about a drawing of Julian's and 'Hey Jude' was originally written as 'Hey Jules'.
8. **Stuart Broad:** Chris Broad played 26 Test matches for England and was part of the 1986/87 Ashes-winning team, scoring centuries in three successive Tests.
9. **George W Bush:** He and George HW Bush are only the second father and son to serve after John and John Quincy Adams.

10. **Nancy Sinatra:** She also had a 1967 UK No. 1 with her father Frank with 'Somethin' Stupid'.
11. **Frank Lampard:** He is the son of Frank Lampard Sr. who played most of his career at West Ham United where Frank Jr. started, playing for his uncle, Harry Redknapp.
12. **Kiefer Sutherland:** He was born in London but both he and his father Donald now reside in Canada.
13. **Kim Wilde:** Her father Marty had several hits in the '50s and '60s including 'Donna' and 'Teenager in Love'.
14. **Dakota Johnson:** Her mother is Melanie Griffith and her father is Don Johnson. In turn, Melanie Griffith's mother was Tippi Hedren who starred in Hitchcock's *The Birds*.

HARD (3 Points)

15. **Peter Fonda:** His father Henry Fonda won his only Best Actor Oscar for his final film role in *On Golden Pond*, in which his real-life daughter Jane Fonda also played his daughter.
16. **Norah Jones:** Her father is Indian musician Ravi Shankar who was a big influence on George Harrison, who subsequently bought a sitar and used it on the track 'Norwegian Wood'.
17. **Donald McCain:** His father Donald 'Ginger' McCain won the Grand National 4 times, 3 with Red Rum in 1973, 1974 and 1977 and in 2004 with Amberleigh House.
18. **Martin Amis:** His father was Kingsley Amis, whose first and probably most famous novel was *Lucky Jim*.
19. **Natalie Cole:** She died on New Year's Eve 2015 aged 65 but her father Nat King Cole died in 1965 at the age of just 45.
20. **Nigel Clough:** Brian Clough scored a remarkable 251 goals in 274 games for Middlesbrough and Sunderland and won the First Division as a manager with both Derby County and Nottingham Forest, as well as two European Cups with Forest.

QUIZ No. 60: **GUESS THE LINK**

1. **Sport & Games:** What is the nickname of Derby County Football Club?
2. **History:** Thomas Wolsey held which religious position in the Catholic Church from 1515?
3. **Films:** Which 1994 animated film tells the story of Simba?
4. **Pot Luck:** Up until October 2015, when the number of balls increased to 59, how many balls were there in total in the main Lotto draw of the National Lottery?
5. **Art & Literature:** Which US author wrote *Angels & Demons* and *The Da Vinci Code*?
6. **Music:** Which group, with Gerry Rafferty on vocals, had their biggest UK hit in 1973 with 'Stuck in the Middle with You'?

7. **TV:** Roger Moore starred as Simon Templar in which 1960s TV series based on the novels by Leslie Charteris?
8. **Transport & Travel:** Which car company was acquired by Ford in 1990, then sold to Tata Motors along with Land Rover in 2008?
9. **Entertainment:** In the *Toy Story* film franchise, what type of toy is Woody, voiced by Tom Hanks?
10. **Sport & Games:** Which Australian media tycoon founded the controversial 'World Series Cricket' in 1977?
11. **TV:** Which 1980s US TV soap revolved around the feuding Gioberti and Channing families in the wine industry?

12. **Films:** What was the title of the first film in which Harrison Ford played Jack Ryan, the CIA analyst from the Tom Clancy series of novels?
13. **Pot Luck:** Which birds reside in the Tower of London and superstition says that if they leave then the British Crown will fall?
14. **Sport & Games:** The original nickname of Crystal Palace Football Club was 'the Glaziers', after the original Crystal Palace, but was changed to which current nickname by Malcolm Allison in 1973?

HARD (3 Points)

---

15. **Animals & Nature:** Which specific animal is the national animal of both India and Bangladesh, also being most commonly found in those two countries?
16. **TV:** What was the name of the stuntman played by Lee Majors in the 1980s TV series *The Fall Guy*?
17. **Music:** Besides the title track, what was the other single released from the famous Wings album *Band on the Run*?
18. **People:** Which British adventurer became the youngest-ever Chief Scout, aged 35, in 2009?
19. **Politics:** What is the collective name for the first ten amendments to the US Constitution?
20. **People:** What was the alias given to the armed robber, kidnapper and murderer Donald Neilson?

WHAT IS THE LINK BETWEEN ALL OF THE ANSWERS?

---

1. **The Rams:** The Los Angeles Rams moved to St Louis in 1994 after 48 years in LA, but moved back to LA in 2016.
2. **Cardinal:** The Arizona Cardinals spent 28 years in St Louis before moving to Phoenix in 1988.
3. ***The Lion King*:** The Detroit Lions moved to Detroit in 1934 and the name was chosen due to the baseball team being called the Detroit Tigers.
4. **49:** The San Francisco 49ers started in the NFL in 1946 and are named after the 'Forty-Niners', the people who went to seek their fortune in the California Gold Rush of 1849.
5. **Dan Brown:** The Cleveland Browns were named after first coach Paul Brown and their colours are brown and orange but are the only NFL team not to have a logo on their helmets.
6. **Stealers Wheel:** The Pittsburgh Steelers originally used the same name as the baseball team, the Pirates, but changed it in 1940 when steelworker Joe Santoni won the competition to rename the team.

7. ***The Saint*:** The New Orleans Saints were awarded a franchise on All Saints' Day, 1 November 1966, and the name is also derived from the jazz song 'When the Saints Go Marching In'.
8. **Jaguar:** Although jaguars aren't native to Jacksonville, the oldest living jaguar in North America was housed in Jacksonville Zoo.
9. **Cowboy:** The Dallas Cowboys' debut season was in 1960 and they were originally going to be called the Steers, then the Rangers, before deciding on the Cowboys.

10. **Kerry Packer:** The Green Bay Packers play at Lambeau Field, named after their founder Earl 'Curly' Lambeau and are based in Green Bay, Wisconsin.
11. *Falcon Crest*: The Atlanta Falcons joined the NFL in 1965 and play at the Mercedes-Benz Stadium.
12. *Patriot Games*: The New England Patriots changed their name from the Boston Patriots when they moved to Foxborough, Massachusetts in 1971.
13. **Ravens:** The Baltimore Ravens took their name from the Edgar Allan Poe poem *The Raven* as Poe died and is buried there.
14. **The Eagles:** The Philadelphia Eagles' first season was in 1933 but they only won their first Super Bowl in the 2017 season, beating the New England Patriots.

HARD (3 Points)

15. **Bengal Tiger:** The Cincinnati Bengals were also named by founder Paul Brown and now play in the Paul Brown Stadium.
16. **Colt Seavers:** The Indianapolis Colts were originally the Baltimore Colts, after the area's link to horse breeding.
17. **'Jet':** The New York Jets share the MetLife Stadium with the New York Giants, which is actually in East Rutherford, New Jersey.
18. **Bear Grylls:** The Chicago Bears have played at Soldier Field since 1971 but previously played at Wrigley Field, home to the Chicago Cubs baseball team.
19. **The Bill of Rights:** The Buffalo Bills actually play in New York and their name references Buffalo Bill Cody.
20. **The Black Panther:** The Carolina Panthers play in Charlotte which is the largest city in North Carolina.

QUIZ No. 61: WHO LET THE DOGS OUT?

1. **Music:** Which family group had hits in the 1980s with 'Slow Hand', 'Automatic' and 'Jump (For My Love)'?
2. **TV:** Which children's TV character had a ship called the *Black Pig* and an enemy called Cut-Throat Jake?
3. **Places:** The towns of Leek and Uttoxeter are in which English county?
4. **Transport & Travel:** Which US bus company has its HQ in Dallas but was taken over by FirstGroup in 2007?
5. **History:** What regnal name did the two monarchs share who ruled either side of the Interregnum period of 1649 to 1660?
6. **Films:** Which 1941 film starring Humphrey Bogart as Sam Spade centres on the pursuit of a jewel-encrusted statuette?

MEDIUM (2 Points)

7. **Sport & Games:** Which ex-Gloucestershire wicketkeeper won 54 Test caps for England between 1988 and 1998 and became a full-time artist after retirement?
8. **Films:** Which 1973 film set on board a prison ship stars Steve McQueen and Dustin Hoffman as fellow prisoners?
9. **TV:** Which ex-mayor of Cincinnati has hosted a controversial talk show featuring relationship difficulties that often escalated into arguments and violence?
10. **Music:** Which British band had a No. 5 hit in 1980 called 'Everybody's Got to Learn Sometime'?

11. **Pot Luck:** Which cartoon strip about a dog first appeared in the *Daily Mail* in 1963?
12. **History:** What was the name of the ship that Charles Darwin sailed on as a naturalist for the trip primarily to South America?
13. **Music:** Which rapper featured on Alexandra Burke's 2010 hit 'All Night Long'?
14. **Sport & Games:** What was the nickname of ex-Manchester United goalkeeper Peter Schmeichel?

HARD (3 Points)

---

15. **Places:** What is the name of the most easterly province in Canada, its capital being St John's?
16. **History:** What was the popular name for the anti-foreign and anti-Christian uprising in China between 1899 and 1901?
17. **Music:** Which American rock group had a UK No. 3 hit in 1999 with 'The Bad Touch'?
18. **Art & Literature:** What is the name of the British fictional character, a First World War veteran, created by H C McNeile under his pen name 'Sapper'?
19. **Religion:** Who is the patron saint of mountaineers, skiers and the Alps?
20. **Places:** What was the fourth historical region of Croatia, alongside Croatia Proper, Slavonia and Istria?

1. **Pointer Sisters:** The Pointer Sisters were sisters and during their heyday in the '80s they were Ruth, Anita and June. Bonnie was part of the original group but she opted for a solo career.
2. **Captain Pugwash:** The show was victim of some urban myths created around some risqué character names that never existed – they were in fact invented by a student rag.
3. **Staffordshire:** The county has three professional football clubs – Stoke City, Port Vale and Burton Albion – although Wolves, WBA and Walsall all used to be in Staffordshire.
4. **Greyhound:** The Greyhound bus memorably features in the 1969 film *Midnight Cowboy* and the Rod Stewart 1976 song 'The Killing of Georgie'.
5. **King Charles:** Charles I was beheaded in 1649 and his son Charles II regained the throne in 1660.
6. *The Maltese Falcon*: This film was the first directed by John Huston.

7. **Jack Russell:** Russell coached Geraint Jones before the Ashes series of 2005 and was briefly the goalkeeping coach at Forest Green Rovers.
8. *Papillon*: Papillon is French for butterfly (Steve McQueen's character had a butterfly tattoo).
9. **Jerry Springer:** Springer was mayor of Cincinnati for the calendar year 1977.
10. **The Korgis:** Their only other Top 20 hit was 'If I Had You' which reached No. 13 in 1979.

11. **Fred Basset:** The cartoon strip was designed by Scottish cartoonist Alex Graham.
12. **HMS *Beagle*:** Darwin was aboard the ship on its second voyage from 1831 to 1836.
13. **Pitbull:** He had a UK No. 1 hit in 2011 with 'Give Me Everything' feat. Ne-Yo and Nayer.
14. **The Great Dane:** Chesney Brown had a dog called Schmeichel in *Coronation Street* who was a Great Dane.

HARD (3 Points)

15. **Newfoundland and Labrador:** Newfoundland is an island separated from the Labrador peninsula by the Gulf of St Lawrence.
16. **Boxer Rebellion:** The leading force of the Boxer Rebellion was a secret society called the Righteous and Harmonious Fists.
17. **The Bloodhound Gang:** 'The Bad Touch' was the group's only Top 10 hit in the UK.
18. **Hugh 'Bulldog' Drummond:** H C McNeile was given the name 'Sapper' by the owner of the *Daily Mail*, Lord Northcliffe, based on the nickname of his corps, the Royal Engineers.
19. **St Bernard:** In the 1970s, Bernie Winters used to have a St Bernard called Schnorbitz as his 'comedy partner' after he split from his brother, Mike.
20. **Dalmatia:** *101 Dalmatians* was a 1996 film, based on the 1961 Walt Disney animated version, starring Glenn Close as Cruella de Vil.

QUIZ No. 62: **TOOLS OF THE TRADE**

1. **Music:** Whose debut UK hit 'U Can't Touch This' reached No. 3 in 1990?
2. **TV:** Which 1980s US-based TV crime drama series starred Don Johnson and Philip Michael Thomas as two undercover detectives?
3. **Films:** Which 2004 film, which has spawned several sequels, revolves around the character John Kramer, known as the 'Jigsaw Killer'?
4. **Sport & Games:** In the game of Cluedo, the six weapons are revolver, dagger, rope, candlestick, lead piping and which other?
5. **Life & Lifestyle:** What is the name of the networking device used in homes and offices to connect to the Internet, often wirelessly?
6. **Music:** Which group's biggest UK hit was 'Lessons in Love' in 1986?

7. **Words:** What word can relate to a series of exercises in either military training or sports coaching?
8. **Films:** Which 1987 comedy film stars Steve Martin and John Candy trying to get home to Chicago for Thanksgiving?
9. **Music:** Which group had a No. 9 hit in the UK in 1975 with 'Sky High'?
10. **Places:** Which town is capital of the Falkland Islands?

11. **People:** Which captain in the Army did Princess Anne marry in 1973?
12. **Music:** Peter Gabriel's highest UK singles chart position was No. 4 which he achieved in 1986 with which song?
13. **Food & Drink:** Which cocktail is broadly vodka and orange juice?
14. **Films:** Which 1974 US slasher film first featured the character Leatherface?

HARD (3 Points)

---

15. **Music:** Dave & Ansil Collins had both of their UK hits in 1971 with 'Double Barrel' which reached No. 1 and which other song which got to No. 7?
16. **Art & Literature:** What was Len Deighton's first spy novel, later turned into a 1965 film starring Michael Caine as Harry Palmer?
17. **Places:** The address of the building known colloquially as 'The Gherkin' is on which London thoroughfare?
18. **TV:** Which children's TV presenter fronted the show *Wacaday* from 1985 until 1992, a spin-off of the earlier TV show *Wide Awake Club*, of which he was also a key presenter?
19. **Entertainment:** Which traditional puppet character is derived from a Neapolitan character called Pulcinella?
20. **Music:** Which Jamaican singer had several UK hits with his countryman Chaka Demus?

1. **M C Hammer:** He was born in Oakland, California in 1962 and his real name is Stanley Kirk Burrell.
2. *Miami Vice*: Don Johnson starred as James 'Sonny' Crockett and Philip Michael Thomas starred as Ricardo 'Rico' Tubbs.
3. *Saw*: Donnie Wahlberg, who starred as a detective in the next four *Saw* films, was a founding member of the boy band New Kids on the Block.
4. **Spanner:** In the USA, a spanner is called a wrench.
5. **Router:** A router (pronounced rowter) is a tool used for hollowing out an area, usually in woodworking.
6. **Level 42:** Lead singer Mark King also played bass and became famous for his slap style of playing.

7. **Drill:** A drill is also the name of a primate closely related to the mandrill and the baboon.
8. *Planes, Trains & Automobiles*: John Candy, whose many films included *Cool Runnings*, *Home Alone* and *Uncle Buck*, died in 1994 of a heart attack, aged just 43.
9. **Jigsaw:** They were named after a nightclub in Manchester and in Australia were known as British Jigsaw as there was another group of that name.
10. **(Port) Stanley:** The name of the town is officially Stanley, although often referred to outside the islands as Port Stanley, and was originally called Port Jackson.
11. **Mark Phillips:** He won an equestrian team Olympic gold medal in 1972 and a silver medal in 1988.

12. **'Sledgehammer':** He also reached No. 4 in 1980 with 'Games Without Frontiers'.
13. **Screwdriver:** There are many variants of the cocktail but the most popular is probably by simply adding orange soda.
14. ***The Texas Chainsaw Massacre:*** The 1974 film cast were largely local Texans and friends of director Tobe Hooper, though the franchise has now spawned a number of sequels.

HARD (3 Points)

15. **'Monkey Spanner':** Ansil Collins was his real name but Dave was actually called Dave Barker.
16. ***The Ipcress File:*** The novel involves Cold War brainwashing with IPCRESS standing for 'Induction of Psycho-neuroses by Conditioned REflex with Stress'.
17. **St Mary Axe:** The building was completed in 2003, has 41 floors and was designed by Norman Foster.
18. **Timmy Mallett:** He also formed the pop group Bombalurina with Dawn Andrews (Gary Barlow's wife) and Annie Dunkley and they had a UK No. 1 in 1990 with 'Itsy Bitsy Teeny Weeny Yellow Polka Dot Bikini'.
19. **Mr Punch:** Besides Punch and Judy, regular characters often include the baby, the constable, the doctor, the crocodile and Toby the dog.
20. **Pliers:** Their names were Everton Bonner and John Taylor and they had a 1993 UK No. 1 with a version of the Beatles' 'Twist and Shout'.

1. **Music:** Which singer's only UK No. 1 hit was 'My Ding-a-Ling' in 1972?
2. **Food & Drink:** Who was the other judge alongside Paul Hollywood for the first seven series of *The Great British Bake Off*?
3. **TV:** Which actor starred as Simon Wicks in *EastEnders* and PC Nick Rowan in *Heartbeat*?
4. **Pot Luck:** What name is sometimes given to a person who will tag along with a couple or a few couples, but they themselves are single?
5. **Films:** Who was the first black actress to win the Best Actress Oscar for the 2001 film *Monster's Ball*?
6. **Music:** What was the highest UK chart hit for Fats Domino, reaching No. 6 in 1956?

7. **TV:** Which Hanna & Barbera cartoon character was depicted as a blue dog with a Southern drawl, often singing the song 'Oh My Darling, Clementine'?
8. **Music:** Which track was the other track on the 1967 Beatles double A-side with 'Penny Lane'?
9. **Shopping & Fashion:** Which fashion house produces garments and accessories with its now famous tan, black and red check pattern known as Haymarket check?
10. **Films:** What is the full name of the Razzies, the annual awards 'celebrating' the worst in film?

11. **Music:** Which Irish group had Top 20 hits in 1994 with 'Linger' and 'Zombie'?
12. **Art & Literature:** Which literary character first appeared in the novel *The Adventures of Tom Sawyer* before being the subject and the narrator of its sequel?
13. **Music:** Which 1968 song was the only UK No. 1 hit for the Move?
14. **TV:** What was the name of the 1970s TV series and the 1976 film which was based on the principle of everybody being eliminated at the age of 30 in order to keep population levels under control?

HARD (3 Points)

---

15. **Music:** Which singer had a 1980 UK Top 10 hit with 'The Sunshine of Your Smile'?
16. **Animals & Nature:** What is the main food source of the silkworm?
17. **Music:** Which singer had Top 10 UK hits in the mid-1960s with 'The Crying Game', 'Little Things' and 'Mama'?
18. **Places:** What is the longest river in Scotland?
19. **Food & Drink:** From what does gin predominantly get its distinctive flavour?
20. **Music:** Which record producer founded the Tamla and Motown record labels?

EASY (1 Point)

1. **Chuck Berry:** He was famous for his rock 'n' roll songs like 'Maybellene', 'Roll Over Beethoven' and 'Johnny B Goode'.
2. **Mary Berry:** Prue Leith took over from Mary Berry when the programme moved to Channel 4 in 2017.
3. **Nick Berry:** He also had a UK No. 1 hit in 1986 with 'Every Loser Wins'.
4. **Gooseberry:** Jostaberry is a hybrid fruit created by interbreeding gooseberries and blackcurrants.
5. **Halle Berry:** She also played the Bond girl 'Jinx' in the 2002 James Bond film *Die Another Day*.
6. **'Blueberry Hill':** Fats Domino was born Antoine Domino Jr. in New Orleans to a French Creole family and Louisiana Creole was his first language.

MEDIUM (2 Points)

7. **Huckleberry Hound:** He first appeared in 1958 in the *Huckleberry Hound Show* which also introduced Yogi Bear, who was originally going to be called Huckleberry Bear.
8. **'Strawberry Fields Forever':** It was their first UK single not to get to No. 1 since their 1963 hit 'Please Please Me'. It was kept off the top spot by Engelbert Humperdinck's 'Release Me'.
9. **Burberry:** The company was founded in Basingstoke in 1856.
10. **Golden Raspberry Awards:** Sylvester Stallone has won the Worst Actor Razzie four times, for *Rhinestone*, *Rambo: First Blood Part II*, *Rambo III* and *Stop! Or My Mom Will Shoot*.

11. **The Cranberries:** Lead singer Dolores O'Riordan died of accidental drowning in her hotel room in January 2018.
12. **Huckleberry Finn:** Mark Twain's real name was Samuel Langhorne Clemens and he was raised in Hannibal, Missouri on the Mississippi River.
13. **'Blackberry Way':** Roy Wood, Jeff Lynne, Bev Bevan and Richard Tandy formed the Electric Light Orchestra when the Move broke up but Roy Wood left to form Wizzard in 1972.
14. *Logan's Run:* Michael York played the main character Logan 5 in the film version.

HARD (3 Points)

15. **Mike Berry:** He also starred as Mr Spooner in the TV series *Are You Being Served?* in series 8 to 10, replacing Trevor Bannister who played Mr Lucas.
16. **Mulberry Leaves:** They prefer white mulberry leaves although they do also eat other types of mulberry leaves.
17. **Dave Berry:** He was born David Holgate Grundy in Sheffield in 1941 and his backing band were called the Cruisers.
18. **Tay:** The river flows through Perth and Dundee lies on the north bank of the Firth of Tay where it enters the North Sea.
19. **Juniper Berries:** They can also be used for medicinal purposes, especially in the treatment of arthritis.
20. **Berry Gordy Jr:** He had earlier co-written the Jackie Wilson song 'Reet Petite' and in the same year discovered Smokey Robinson and the Miracles.

QUIZ No. 64: **ALL THE WORLD'S A STAGE MUSICAL**

1. **Music:** Which group had a UK No. 1 hit in 1976 with 'If You Leave Me Now'?
2. **Food & Drink:** Which chef made his TV debut in 1999 with *The Naked Chef*?
3. **Shopping & Fashion:** Harmony and Silvikrin are brand names of which styling product?
4. **Music:** Which 1979 song by Squeeze includes the lyrics 'And meanwhile at the station there's a couple of likely lads who swear like how's your father'?
5. **Pot Luck:** Which fictional character was alternatively known as 'The Demon Barber of Fleet Street'?
6. **Films:** Which 1994 animated Disney film revolved around the character Simba?

MEDIUM (2 Points)

7. **Places:** Tulsa is in which US state?
8. **TV:** What was the name of the TV series starring Richard O'Sullivan as widower Simon Harrap raising his adolescent daughter Samantha which ran from 1984 to 1988?
9. **Music:** ABBA's Eurovision-winning song 'Waterloo' went to No. 1 in 1974 but what was their second UK No. 1 hit in 1975?
10. **Films:** Which 1996 film, based on Roald Dahl's novel, starred Mara Wilson as the title character who uses telekinesis to deal with her parents and school principal?

11. **Pot Luck:** What is the name for the waxy substance used as make-up by actors?
12. **Music:** Which Queen song starts with the line 'Buddy you're a boy, make a big noise'?
13. **Places:** Tonga, Fiji and Tahiti are in which ocean?
14. **Films:** For which 1977 Woody Allen film did Diane Keaton win the Best Actress Oscar?

HARD (3 Points)

15. **Sport & Games:** Which horse trained by Aidan O'Brien won the 2012 Epsom Derby and 2000 Guineas but just failed to win the Triple Crown when he finished second in the St Leger?
16. **Music:** Which group's debut hit 'There's a Whole Lot of Loving' reached No. 2 in the UK charts in 1975?
17. **Pot Luck:** A trichologist specialises in the treatment of which part of the body?
18. **Art & Literature:** Which French historical novel by Victor Hugo culminates in the 1832 June Rebellion in Paris?
19. **Places:** Which famous New York thoroughfare is the location for the UN Headquarters, the Chrysler Building and Grand Central Station?
20. **Music:** What was the name of the debut album for Soft Cell which contained the hit singles 'Tainted Love', 'Bedsitter' and 'Say Hello, Wave Goodbye'?

EASY (1 Point)

1. **Chicago:** The main characters are Velma Kelly and Roxie Hart, played by Catherine Zeta-Jones and Renee Zellwegger in the 2002 film which won the Best Picture Oscar, the first musical to do so since *Oliver!* in 1968.

2. **Jamie Oliver:** Lionel Bart wrote the music and lyrics to *Oliver!*, the main characters including Oliver Twist, the Artful Dodger, Fagin, Bill Sikes and Nancy.

3. **Hairspray:** The musical spawned a 2007 film musical starring John Travolta and Michelle Pfeiffer.

4. **'Cool For Cats':** Elaine Paige starred as Grizabella in the original *Cats* production and had a UK No. 6 hit in 1981 with the song 'Memory' from the musical.

5. **Sweeney Todd:** The character first appeared in the penny dreadful serial *The String of Pearls*.

6. *The Lion King:* The music was written by Elton John and includes the Top 20 hits 'Can You Feel the Love Tonight' and 'Circle of Life'.

MEDIUM (2 Points)

7. **Oklahoma:** The musical *Oklahoma!* includes the song 'Oh, What a Beautiful Mornin'' sung by Howard Keel in the original West End musical, who also played Clayton Farlow in the TV series *Dallas*.

8. *Me and My Girl:* The musical includes the songs 'The Lambeth Walk', 'The Sun Has Got His Hat On' and 'Leaning on a Lamp-post'.

9. **'Mamma Mia':** Former ABBA members Benny Andersson and Bjorn Ulvaeus who originally wrote the songs were involved in the development of the show.

10. *Matilda*: The main character is Matilda Wormwood and in the film her parents are played by Rhea Perlman and Danny DeVito, who also directed it.

11. **Greasepaint**: The musical *Grease* is set in Rydell High School and the main characters Danny Zuko and Sandy Dumbrowski were part of the greaser gangs the T-Birds and the Pink Ladies.

12. **'We Will Rock You'**: The stage musical was written by Ben Elton and choreographed by Arlene Phillips, becoming the longest-running musical at London's Dominion Theatre.

13. **South Pacific:** The Rodgers and Hammerstein musical includes the songs 'Some Enchanted Evening', 'There is Nothing Like a Dame', 'Younger Than Springtime' and 'Happy Talk'.

14. *Annie Hall*: The musical *Annie* includes the songs 'Tomorrow' and 'It's a Hard Knock Life'.

HARD (3 Points)

15. **Camelot:** The Lerner and Loewe musical opened on Broadway in 1960 with Richard Burton as King Arthur and Julie Andrews as Queen Guinevere.

16. **Guys and Dolls:** Two main characters are Sky Masterson and Nathan Detroit, played in the 1955 film version by Marlon Brando and Frank Sinatra respectively.

17. **Hair (and scalp):** The song 'Aquarius' by the group Fifth Dimension got to No. 11 in the UK charts in 1969.

18. *Les Misérables*: The main protagonist in the book and musical is Jean Valjean.

19. **42nd Street:** The songs in the musical include 'We're in the Money', 'Keep Young and Beautiful' and 'I Only Have Eyes For You'.

20. *Non-Stop Erotic Cabaret*: The musical *Cabaret* was set in Berlin and starred Liza Minnelli as Sally Bowles in the 1972 film version.

1. **Music:** What was the debut hit for the Bangles in the UK, reaching No. 2 in the charts in 1986?
2. **Pot Luck:** What has now become the name of the day after Thanksgiving in the USA, regarded as the first day of the Christmas shopping season on which retailers make many special offers?
3. **TV:** Which weekend cookery programme on BBC1 was hosted by James Martin from 2006 until he left in 2016?
4. **Religion:** On which religious feast day do Christians traditionally eat pancakes?
5. **Music:** Which New Order song, originally released in 1983 but remixed twice in 1988 and 1995, is the biggest selling 12" single of all time?
6. **Art & Literature:** What is the name of the main character's companion in Daniel Defoe's 1719 novel *Robinson Crusoe*?

7. **TV:** Lisa Loring played which character in the 1960s TV series *The Addams Family*?
8. **Music:** Which group finally had a UK No. 1 hit in 2013 with Sean Paul with the song 'What About Us'?
9. **Religion:** In the Christian calendar, which day is the first day of Lent?
10. **TV:** What was the original name of the ITV weekend variety show that has always been transmitted from the same West End theatre and which originally ran from 1955 until 1967, although it has been revived several times subsequently?
11. **Pot Luck:** What is the literal translation of Mardi Gras?

12. **Entertainment:** The Three Tenors consisted of Luciano Pavarotti, José Carreras and which other singer?
13. **TV:** Which children's TV show succeeded *Multi-Coloured Swap Shop* when Noel Edmonds left and ran from 1982 until 1987 with presenters including Mike Read, Maggie Philbin, Sarah Greene, Keith Chegwin and John Craven?
14. **Music:** Blondie had two No. 1 hits in the UK in 1979 – 'Heart of Glass' was one, but what was the other?

HARD (3 Points)

---

15. **Films:** What is the name of the 1996 film starring Sean Bean, Emily Lloyd and Pete Postlethwaite that revolves around a factory worker going on to play for Sheffield United?
16. **Pot Luck:** What name is given to 24 October 1929 which was effectively the first day of the Wall Street Crash?
17. **Music:** The Australian group the Easybeats had a UK No. 6 hit in 1966 with which song?
18. **Films:** What was the name of the 1960 film starring Albert Finney as Arthur Seaton, a 'kitchen sink' drama about a young machinist having an affair with a married woman?
19. **Entertainment:** Marti Webb had a 1980 UK No. 3 hit with 'Take That Look Off Your Face' from which Andrew Lloyd Webber musical, a one-woman show in which she starred?
20. **Music:** Which Rolling Stones song was on a double A-side with 'Let's Spend the Night Together' on their 1967 No. 3 hit?

1. **'Manic Monday':** Their only No. 1 was 'Eternal Flame' in 1989.
2. **Black Friday:** The name Black Friday was first used to refer to that day in 1966 when originally referring to the amount of heavy traffic due to the number of shoppers.
3. *Saturday Kitchen:* Ainsley Harriott did a pilot show in 2001 before Gregg Wallace hosted from 2002 to 2003 followed by Antony Worrall Thompson for the next three years.
4. **Shrove Tuesday:** This is traditionally the day before the fasting period of Lent begins.
5. **'Blue Monday':** New Order had a UK No. 1 in 1990 with 'World in Motion' sung with the England World Cup squad, famously featuring a John Barnes rap.
6. **Friday:** Crusoe was on the island 25 years before he met Friday, so called because that was the day they met. They both returned to England four years later.

7. **Wednesday:** John Astin played Gomez, Carolyn Jones played Morticia and Ken Weatherwax played her brother Pugsley.
8. **The Saturdays:** The Saturdays are Frankie Bridge (Sandford), Rochelle Humes (Wiseman), Una Healy, Mollie King and Vanessa White.
9. **Ash Wednesday:** People often receive a cross on their foreheads made by using ashes, often obtained by burning palm leaves from last year's Palm Sunday.
10. *Sunday Night at the London Palladium:* The first compere was Tommy Trinder followed by Bruce Forsyth, Norman Vaughan and Jimmy Tarbuck.

11. **Fat Tuesday:** Mardi Gras celebrations vary from city to city and in New Orleans it runs from the Epiphany on 6 January right up until Ash Wednesday.

12. **Plácido Domingo:** Domingo is Spanish for Sunday and they first sang together in Rome on the eve of the World Cup in Italy in 1990 and also at the next three World Cups in Los Angeles, Paris and Yokohama.

13. *Saturday Superstore*: It was succeeded by *Going Live!* With Phillip Schofield and Sarah Greene from 1987 to 1993 and then *Live & Kicking* from 1993 to 2001 with Jamie Theakston and Zoe Ball amongst others.

14. **'Sunday Girl':** In 1980 they had three consecutive UK No. 1's with 'Atomic', 'Call Me' and 'The Tide is High' but they had to wait until 1999 for their last one, 'Maria'.

HARD (3 Points)

---

15. *When Saturday Comes*: Joe Elliott of Def Leppard sang two songs on the soundtrack and had a minor part as Bean's brother but his scenes were cut in the final edit.

16. **Black Thursday:** The following Tuesday, 29 October 1929, is also called Black Tuesday as that is when stocks bottomed out and it was the start of the Great Depression.

17. **'Friday on my Mind':** Although the band were from Australia, all their families had emigrated there from England, Scotland and the Netherlands.

18. *Saturday Night and Sunday Morning*: It was based on the first novel by British writer Alan Sillitoe published in 1958.

19. *Tell Me on a Sunday*: She had a No. 5 hit in 1985 with a cover of Michael Jackson's 'Ben' in memory of Ben Hardwick, Britain's youngest liver transplant patient.

20. **'Ruby Tuesday':** Melanie did a cover version of the song in 1970 which reached No. 9 in the UK charts.

181

QUIZ No. 66: AT THE BUILDERS' YARD

EASY (1 Point)

1. **TV:** Which comedienne and actress wrote and starred in the TV series *dinnerladies*, which ran for two series from 1998 to 2000?
2. **Pot Luck:** What is the name of the academic cap with a stiff, flat square top and a tassel attached, worn by students at graduation?
3. **Sport & Games:** What was the original name under which Muhammad Ali started his boxing career?
4. **Places:** What material is the Taj Mahal in India built from?
5. **TV:** Which actor starred as Leonard 'Oz' Osborne in the TV show *Auf Wiedersehen, Pet*?
6. **Music:** Which group had hits in the 1960s and 1970s with 'Light My Fire' and 'Riders on the Storm'?

MEDIUM (2 Points)

7. **History:** What name was given to the carved figures, including soldiers, horses and chariots, discovered in China in 1974 and dating from around 200 BC?
8. **TV:** What name did Jethro give to the swimming pool in the 1960s TV series *The Beverly Hillbillies*?
9. **Music:** Which group had hits in the 1990s that included 'Fool's Gold', 'Waterfall' and 'I Am The Resurrection'?
10. **Art & Literature:** What was the name of the debut novel of the Bangladeshi-born author Monica Ali, set in a London street at the heart of the capital's Bangladeshi community?
11. **TV:** Which US crime drama series was set in Baltimore and starred Dominic West as homicide detective Jimmy McNulty?

12. **Politics:** Who became the leader of the Liberal Democrats after the resignation of Tim Farron in 2017?
13. **Music:** Which Belgian singer had a UK No. 8 hit in 1978 with 'Ca Plane Pour Moi'?
14. **TV:** What was the name of the children's TV show featuring a five-foot robot which ran from 1980 to 1983, his favourite catchphrase being 'Boogie Boogie'?

HARD (3 Points)

15. **People:** What was the name of the leader of the 1981 hunger strike who died in the Maze Prison in Northern Ireland as a result of the strike?
16. **Films:** Which 2009 film starring Michelle Dockery as Ann, a patient in a sanatorium, and Dan Stevens as Dr Fisher, a psychiatrist, is based on a Henry James 1898 gothic horror novella?
17. **Music:** Which song was a No. 1 hit for Unit Four Plus Two in 1965?
18. **TV:** Peter Vaughan starred as which 'genial' hard man in the TV series *Porridge*?
19. **Films:** Which 1980 film starred Hazel O'Connor as a young singer and songwriter and featured the songs 'Eighth Day' and 'Will You' which both reached the UK Top 10?
20. **Music:** The song 'Amigo' was which group's biggest chart success when it reached No. 9 in 1980?

1. **Victoria Wood:** Her co-stars Julie Walters, Celia Imrie and Duncan Preston also starred in *Acorn Antiques*, a spoof soap opera sketch from her comedy series *Victoria Wood as Seen on TV*.
2. **Mortar Board:** It has been given that name due to its similarity to the mortar boards used by bricklayers for carrying mortar.
3. **Cassius Clay:** He was born Cassius Marcellus Clay in 1942, won Olympic gold in 1960 and won his first World title in 1964 when he beat Sonny Liston.
4. **Marble:** It was commissioned in 1632 by Shah Jahan to be built on the Yamuna River in Agra, India, as a mausoleum for his favourite wife Mumtaz Mahal.
5. **Jimmy Nail:** His real name is James Bradford, he starred as the title character in three series of *Spender* and had a UK No. 1 hit in 1992 with 'Ain't No Doubt'.
6. **The Doors:** Their lead singer Jim Morrison died in 1971 aged 27, two years to the day after Rolling Stones guitarist Brian Jones and around 9 months after the deaths of Jimi Hendrix and Janis Joplin – all were aged 27.

MEDIUM (2 Points)

7. **Terracotta Army:** A number of the figures were displayed at the British Museum in London in 2007 and then again in Liverpool in 2018.
8. **Cement Pond** (pronounced See-Ment Pond): The cast included Buddy Ebsen as Jed Clampett, Irene Ryan as Granny, Donna Douglas as Elly May and Max Baer Jr as Jethro.

9. **The Stone Roses:** The lead singer of the band is Ian Brown who also had a number of solo successes.
10. *Brick Lane*: Brick Lane is a street in Tower Hamlets in the East End of London, nicknamed 'Banglatown', being famous for its many curry houses.
11. *The Wire*: It ran for five series from 2002 to 2008 and each series featured law enforcement by a different institution of the city each time.
12. **Vince Cable:** He was also acting leader for two months in 2007 after the resignation of Menzies Campbell.
13. **Plastic Bertrand:** He also had a minor hit the same year with a cover of the Small Faces' 1966 hit 'Sha La La La Lee'.
14. *Metal Mickey*: The grandma was played by Irene Handl who starred in many films and TV shows including the 1970s sitcom *For the Love of Ada* with Wilfred Pickles.

HARD (3 Points)

15. **Bobby Sands:** The strike was called after the removal of Special Category Status for all prisoners incarcerated as a result of the Northern Ireland Troubles.
16. *The Turn of the Screw*: The following year Michelle Dockery and Dan Stevens first appeared in *Downton Abbey* as Lady Mary and Matthew Crawley.
17. **'Concrete and Clay':** Randy Edelman also had a No. 11 hit in 1976 with the song.
18. **Harry Grout:** Peter Vaughan's final TV role was as Maester Aemon in *Game of Thrones*.
19. *Breaking Glass*: The film was co-produced by Dodi Fayed and featured *Auf Wiedersehen, Pet* actor Gary Holton in a minor role as a guitarist.
20. **Black Slate:** Over the years, they backed a variety of reggae singers including Ken Boothe, Delroy Wilson and Bob Marley's favourite singer Dennis Brown.

1.   **Music:** Which group won the 1981 Eurovision Song Contest with 'Making Your Mind Up'?
2.   **Pot Luck:** Flat head, Phillips and Pozidriv are types of which common tool?
3.   **Music:** With which song did the Canadian singer Alannah Myles have a UK No. 2 hit in 1990?
4.   **History:** What nickname was given to Mary I of England, who ruled from 1553 to 1558, on account of the number of Protestants she had executed whilst trying to restore Roman Catholicism in England?
5.   **Music:** Which song did Australian duo Yolanda Be Cool and producer DCUP take to No. 1 in the UK in 2010?
6.   **Films:** Gene Hackman first played the detective Jimmy 'Popeye' Doyle in which 1971 film?

7.   **Pot Luck:** What is the name of the T-shaped tool with a screw tip for boring holes?
8.   **Music:** The Dutch group T-Spoon had a No. 2 hit in the UK in 1998 with which song?
9.   **Food & Drink:** What is the name of the traditional Neapolitan pizza with tomatoes, mozzarella and basil?
10.   **Music:** Which band had a 1964 UK No. 12 hit with 'She's Not There', written by keyboard player Rod Argent and with Colin Blunstone on vocals?
11.   **Places:** Which is the most densely populated of New York City's five boroughs?

12. **History:** What name was familiarly given to the opponents of the Bolshevik Red Army, largely from modern-day Belarus, in the Russian Civil War from 1917 to 1923?
13. **Music:** Which group had two UK Top 10 hits in 1985 with 'History' and 'Body and Soul'?
14. **Shopping & Fashion:** Which US magazine, a women's magazine since 1965, contains articles on fashion, health, beauty and celebrities and is often referred to by the first five letters of its name?

HARD (3 Points)

---

15. **TV:** In the 1970s TV show *On the Buses*, in what mode of transport does Olive travel when travelling with her husband Arthur?
16. **Art & Literature:** Which 1932 book by Ernest Hemingway revolves around the ceremony and traditions of Spanish bullfighting?
17. **Music:** Which Eagles song from their album *Desperado* has the 'middle eight' lyrics: 'Every night when the sun goes down, Just another lonely boy in town, And she's out runnin' 'round'?
18. **History:** What nickname was given to the group of largely English World War I veterans who went to Ireland to assist the Royal Irish Constabulary against the IRA during the Irish War of Independence?
19. **Food & Drink:** Which French steak dish, named after an Italian composer, consists of fillet steak served on a crouton and topped with foie gras, garnished with slices of black truffle and finished with a Madeira sauce?
20. **Music:** What was the subtitle of the 1980 Rupert Holmes song 'Escape'?

1. **Bucks Fizz:** The cocktail is two parts champagne to one part orange juice, similar to the Mimosa which is champagne and orange juice in equal parts.
2. **Screwdriver:** The cocktail is vodka and orange juice, although often orange soda is added.
3. **'Black Velvet':** The cocktail is stout (often Guinness) with white, sparkling wine, traditionally champagne.
4. **Bloody Mary:** The cocktail is vodka and tomato juice, typically mixed with spices and seasonings, being often Worcestershire sauce in the UK.
5. **'We No Speak Americano':** The Americano cocktail is Campari, sweet vermouth and club soda. It is a tribute to Primo Carnera, the first non-American to win boxing's world heavyweight title and was the first drink ordered by James Bond in the first novel, *Casino Royale*.
6. ***The French Connection:*** The cocktail is cognac and amaretto liqueur and is named after the film.

MEDIUM (2 Points)

7. **Gimlet:** The cocktail is now two parts gin, one part lime juice and soda, although the 1953 Raymond Chandler novel *The Long Goodbye* refers to the drink being 'half Plymouth Gin and half Rose's lime juice'.
8. **'Sex on the Beach':** The cocktail is vodka, peach schnapps, orange juice and cranberry juice and without the orange juice this becomes a Woo Woo.
9. **Margherita:** A margarita cocktail is tequila, orange liqueur (often Cointreau) and lime juice served with salt on the rim of the glass.

10. **The Zombies:** The Zombie cocktail is largely made up of three different rums along with various liqueurs and fruit juices, depending on the recipe used.
11. **Manhattan:** The cocktail is traditionally made with rye whiskey, sweet vermouth and Angostura bitters.
12. **White Russians:** The cocktail is vodka, coffee liqueur and cream or milk with ice.
13. **Mai Tai:** The cocktail is rum, Curaçao orange liqueur, orgeat (almond-flavoured) syrup and lime juice.
14. **Cosmopolitan:** The cocktail is vodka, triple sec, cranberry juice and lime juice and without the cranberry juice this becomes a Kamikaze.

HARD (3 Points)

15. **Sidecar:** In the TV series, Arthur has a motorbike and sidecar and the cocktail is cognac, triple sec and lemon juice.
16. ***Death in the Afternoon:*** The cocktail is absinthe and champagne, sometimes called Hemingway Champagne.
17. **'Tequila Sunrise':** The cocktail is tequila, orange juice and grenadine.
18. **Black and Tans:** A Black and Tan is a beer cocktail made with pale ale or lager topped with stout, often Guinness.
19. **Tournedos Rossini:** A Rossini cocktail is Prosecco with puréed strawberries, similar to a Bellini which is Prosecco and puréed peaches.
20. **'The Pina Colada Song':** The cocktail is rum, coconut cream and pineapple juice.

QUIZ No. 68: **CREEPY CRAWLIES**

1. **TV:** Which TV presenting duo started their careers as PJ and Duncan in the TV series *Byker Grove*?
2. **Music:** What was the name of Buddy Holly's backing group?
3. **Transport & Travel:** Which rear-engined Volkswagen model was manufactured from 1938 to 2003?
4. **Pot Luck:** The 'Swoosh' in the Nike logo resembles what check mark often used by teachers or on ballot papers, for example.
5. **Films:** Which 1968 comedy film starred Herbie, the Volkswagen Beetle with a mind of its own?
6. **Music:** Who became the lead singer with Ultravox after stints with Slik, Rich Kids, Visage and also a spell with Thin Lizzy, helping out on tour when Gary Moore left?

7. **Entertainment:** What is the alias of Peter Parker in the Marvel comics created by Stan Lee?
8. **Sport & Games:** What is the nickname of Watford Football Club?
9. **TV:** A spin-off of *The Great British Bake Off*, which sewing and dressmaking programme was presented by Claudia Winkleman from 2013 to 2016?
10. **Films:** Which 1986 film starred Jeff Goldblum as a scientist experimenting with a teleportation pod until an experiment goes wrong causing mutation with another creature?
11. **Entertainment:** What is the name given to the traditional fairground ride that goes round at speed, but when it reaches top speed the riders are covered with a canopy?

12. **Music:** Which song by Owl City reached No. 1 in the UK charts in 2009?

13. **TV:** Which Carla Lane sitcom starred Wendy Craig and Geoffrey Palmer as Ria and Ben Parkinson with Andrew Hall and Nicholas Lyndhurst as their children Russell and Adam?

14. **Sport & Games:** What is the nickname of the former Lancashire player and cricket commentator David Lloyd?

HARD (3 Points)

15. **Pot Luck:** What was the name of the boat in which Sir Francis Chichester completed his single-handed voyage around the world in 1967?

16. **Transport & Travel:** Which Second World War de Havilland twin-engined aeroplane was nicknamed 'The Wooden Wonder' as it was mainly constructed of wood?

17. **People:** What was the familiar name of Claudia Alta Johnson, wife of the 36th President of the United States Lyndon B Johnson?

18. **TV:** In the 1970s TV show *Kung Fu*, what name did Master Po give to his young student, played by David Carradine as a man, when he was training to be a Shaolin monk?

19. **Music:** Under what name does Michael Peter Balzary perform, the bassist and founder member of the Red Hot Chili Peppers?

20. **Sport & Games:** Which then London-based rugby union club moved to the Ricoh Arena in Coventry in 2014?

1. **Ant and Dec:** They also recorded several tracks as PJ and Duncan, the highest chart position being No. 9 in 1994 with 'Let's Get Ready to Rhumble'.

2. **The Crickets:** Buddy Holly was just 22 when he died in a plane crash in 1959 and it became known as 'The Day the Music Died' as referenced in Don McLean's 'American Pie'. Waylon Jennings gave up his seat to The Big Bopper and Ritchie Valens won a coin toss to be on board and they too also died.

3. **Beetle:** The Beetle is the longest-running and most-manufactured car of a single platform ever made.

4. **Tick:** The logo is said to represent the wing of Nike, the Greek goddess of victory.

5. *The Love Bug*: The car number 53 was chosen by the producer Bill Walsh who was a fan of the Los Angeles Dodgers baseball player Don Drysdale who wore number 53.

6. **Midge Ure:** He used the name 'Midge' as it is a phonetic reversal of the name 'Jim'; his real name is James Ure.

MEDIUM (2 Points)

7. **Spider-Man:** Various actors have played Spider-Man on screen including Nicholas Hammond, Tobey Maguire, Andrew Garfield and Tom Holland.

8. **The Hornets:** Elton John became club chairman in 1976 and appointed Graham Taylor as manager in 1977, whilst the team were in the old Fourth Division. After three promotions in five years, they were promoted to the old First Division at the end of the 1981–82 season.

9. *The Great British Sewing Bee*: Joe Lycett took over as the presenter when it was relaunched in 2019.

10. ***The Fly***: In the 1958 film, the scientist was played by David Hedison who starred in the '60s TV series *Voyage to the Bottom of the Sea* with Richard Baseheart.

11. **Caterpillar:** Caterpillars are the larval stage of the order *Lepidoptera*, including butterflies and moths.

12. **'Fireflies':** Owl City consists of US singer, songwriter and multi-instrumentalist Adam Young who teamed up with Carly Rae Jepsen on the 2012 UK No. 5 hit 'Good Time'.

13. ***Butterflies***: The theme tune 'Love is Like a Butterfly' was written and originally recorded by Dolly Parton.

14. **Bumble:** He was nicknamed Bumble after characters called the Bumblies in the children's TV show *Michael Bentine's Potty Time*. Lloyd also played 9 Tests for England, played football for Accrington Stanley and was a first-class umpire.

HARD (3 Points)

---

15. **Gipsy Moth IV:** Sir Francis Chichester was the first to sail around the world single-handedly eastwards via the clipper route, in 1969 Robin Knox-Johnston became the first to sail around the world nonstop and then in 1971 Chay Blyth became the first to do it westwards.

16. **Mosquito:** The Howard Hughes H-4 Hercules flying boat, nicknamed the 'Spruce Goose', was also made of wood, although mainly birch.

17. **Lady Bird (Johnson):** The B in the president's name stood for Baines.

18. **Grasshopper:** David Carradine's father John and his younger brother Robert both appeared in the series.

19. **Flea:** He is also an actor and appeared as Needles in *Back to the Future Part II* and *Part III*.

20. **Wasps:** They had previously been based at two other football clubs: QPR's Loftus Road from 1996–2002 and Wycombe Wanderers' Adams Park from 2002–14.

QUIZ No. 69: **IT'S ELEMENTARY**

1. **Films:** In the 1939 film *The Wizard of Oz*, Dorothy meets the Scarecrow who needs a brain and the Cowardly Lion who needs courage, but whom did she meet who wanted a heart?
2. **Music:** The last Top 10 hit in the UK for The Sweet was in 1978 called 'Love is Like...'?
3. **TV:** Which London theatre has hosted the most Royal Variety Performances?
4. **Mythology:** In Greek mythology, what was the name of the band of heroes who accompanied Jason in his quest to find the Golden Fleece?
5. **Places:** What name is given to the region in the San Francisco Bay area that is home to many technology companies, including Apple, Facebook and Google?
6. **Pot Luck:** Which wedding anniversary do you celebrate after 70 years of marriage?

MEDIUM (2 Points)

7. **Food & Drink:** What is the name of the pasta sauce made with bacon or ham, egg and cream?
8. **Music:** What is the name of Bob Seger's backing band?
9. **Science & Medicine:** What is the name of the diagnostic test which involves drinking a white liquid to detect abnormalities of the oesophagus, stomach and small bowel using X-ray imaging?
10. **Films:** In which 1964 James Bond film did Honor Blackman play Pussy Galore opposite Sean Connery?

11. **Music:** What is the name of the award given to the best album of the year by a British or Irish act?
12. **TV:** Which Granada TV show, involving both physical and mental tests, did Gordon Burns present from 1977 to 1995?
13. **Pot Luck:** What is the common name of a US five-cent piece?
14. **Food & Drink:** Although kitchen foil is often referred to as tin foil, what is it actually made of?

HARD (3 Points)
---

15. **Science & Medicine:** In the early 1500s, when virtually everyone believed that the Earth was the centre of the universe, which Polish scientist proposed that the planets instead revolved around the Sun?
16. **Films:** Which actor starred as Charles Ryder in the 1981 TV series *Brideshead Revisited* and appeared in the 1980s films *The French Lieutenant's Woman* and *The Mission*?
17. **Art & Literature:** Wilkins Micawber, Betsey Trotwood and Uriah Heep are characters from which Charles Dickens book?
18. **TV:** Which TV series starred Jack Dee as the struggling, cynical comedian Rick Spleen?
19. **Films:** Which 1944 dark comedy film starring Cary Grant revolves around two elderly spinsters poisoning old bachelors with elderberry wine laced with various poisons?
20. **Music:** Which 2011 UK No. 1 by David Guetta featured vocals by the Australian singer Sia?

1. **The Tin Man:** The original book was written by L Frank Baum. Tin (Sn) is no. 50 in the periodic table (PT).
2. **Oxygen:** The original band were Brian Connolly, Steve Priest, Mick Tucker and Andy Scott. Oxygen (O) is no. 8 in the PT.
3. **London Palladium:** In 2018, one year after he died, Bruce Forsyth's ashes were buried under the stage and a commemorative blue plaque was put there. Palladium (Pd) is no. 46 in the PT.
4. **Argonauts:** They got this name from their ship the *Argo*, named after its builder Argus (not the 100-eyed giant Argos). Argon (Ar) is no. 18 in the PT.
5. **Silicon Valley:** San Jose is the largest city in the Valley, the third most populous city in California after Los Angeles and San Diego, with San Francisco in fourth. Silicon (Si) is no. 14 in the PT.
6. **Platinum:** Silver (25), Pearl (30), Coral (35), Ruby (40), Sapphire (45), Golden (50), Emerald (55), Diamond (60) and Blue Sapphire (65) are the main ones before it. Platinum (Pt) is no. 78 in the PT.

7. **Carbonara:** The dish originated in Rome and often includes pancetta and black pepper. Carbon (C) is no. 6 in the PT.
8. **The Silver Bullet Band:** Their biggest UK hit was 1995's rerelease of 'We've Got Tonight', which was also a hit for Kenny Rogers and Sheena Easton in 1983. Silver (Ag) is no. 47 in the PT and is the most conductive metal.
9. **Barium (Swallow) Meal:** It is also useful to check the pharynx and larynx. Barium (Ba) in no. 56 in the PT.

10. ***Goldfinger***: The film also features Shirley Eaton as Jill Masterson (Masterton in the novels), the girl famously covered in gold paint. Gold (Au) is no. 79 in the PT.
11. **Mercury Prize:** P J Harvey is the only act to have won the award twice. Mercury (Hg) is no. 80 in the PT.
12. ***The Krypton Factor***: The show's title is a reference to Krypton, Superman's home planet. Krypton (Kr) is no. 36 in the PT.
13. **Nickel:** The coin is actually 75% copper and 25% nickel and features Thomas Jefferson. Nickel (Ni) is no. 28 in the PT.
14. **Aluminium:** It used to be made of tin but after World War II, aluminium proved to be much cheaper. Aluminium (Al) is no. 13 in the PT.

HARD (3 Points)

---

15. **(Nicolaus) Copernicus:** There is, however, some evidence that the Greek astronomer Aristachus of Samos put forward a similar theory some 1,800 years earlier. Copernicium (Cn) is no. 112 in the PT.
16. **Jeremy Irons:** He was also the voice of Scar in *The Lion King* and played Pope Alexander VI in the TV series *The Borgias*. Iron (Fe) is no. 26 in the PT.
17. ***David Copperfield***: David married Agnes Wickfield after his first wife, Dora Spenlow, died. Copper (Cu) is no. 29 in the PT.
18. ***Lead Balloon***: The series also stars Raquel Cassidy as Mel and Sean Power as his American co-writer Marty. Lead (Pb) is no. 82 in the PT.
19. ***Arsenic and Old Lace***: It was produced and directed by Frank Capra and is based on the 1939 play by Joseph Kesselring. Arsenic (As) is no. 33 in the PT.
20. **'Titanium':** Her full name is Sia Kate Isobelle Furler and David Guetta was actually born Pierre David Guetta. Titanium (Ti) is no. 22 in the PT.

1. **Pot Luck:** According to the nursery rhyme, where did Old Mother Hubbard go to?
2. **TV:** What was the name of the TV comedy programme hosted by Harry Hill between 2001 and 2012 which took a look at the previous week's TV programmes?
3. **History:** What name was given to the boundary dividing Europe into two separate areas, broadly from the end of World War II in 1945 until the end of the Cold War in 1991?
4. **Life & Lifestyle:** The cartoon *Andy Capp* has appeared in which daily newspaper since 1957?
5. **Transport & Travel:** After nationalisation of the railways in 1948, under what name did the railways operate after the amalgamation of the 'big four' railways until 1997?
6. **Politics:** What name is given to the collective decision-making body of Her Majesty's Government in the UK?

7. **Music:** Timbuk 3 had their only UK hit in 1987 with 'The Future's So Bright... ... ...'?
8. **Geography:** What is the name of the portion of a continent that is submerged under an area of relatively shallow water compared to the open ocean?
9. **Sport & Games:** Which Dutch defender signed for Manchester United in 2014 from Ajax but returned to Ajax in 2018, a club his father had also played for and managed?
10. **History:** Norwegian Roald Amundsen led the first expedition to reach where in 1911?

11. **TV:** On *The Graham Norton Show*, on what do certain audience members sit to try to tell a humorous story whilst Norton or a guest decide whether to pull a lever and tip the storyteller backwards?

12. **Entertainment:** What word is generally used for a small electronic device used for controlling video games?

13. **Science & Medicine:** What was the name of the safety lamp invented in 1815 by a Cornish chemist and inventor for use in coalmines where flammable gases were present?

14. **Music:** Which group's two biggest hits were 'This Is How It Feels' which got to no. 14 in 1990 and 'Dragging Me Down' which reached no. 12 in 1992?

HARD (3 Points)

15. **Sport & Games:** Chester Barnes and Desmond Douglas played which sport for England?

16. **Music:** The first UK chart entry for Genesis came in 1974 with 'I Know What I Like (.........)?

17. **History:** Which empire controlled much of south-east Europe, western Asia and North Africa from around 1300 until 1922 when it was abolished?

18. **TV:** Which Channel 4 TV series revolves around four bed and breakfast owners visiting each other's guest houses or hotels and marking them for cleanliness, breakfast etc. to decide which one was the best value for money?

19. **Sport & Games:** Which Fleetwood-born boxer was the first woman to be awarded a licence to fight professionally?

20. **Music:** Kid Creole & the Coconuts had three Top 10 hits in the UK in 1982. 'I'm a Wonderful Thing, Baby' and 'Annie I'm Not Your Daddy' were two of them but which song was the third?

1. **The Cupboard:** The first verse finishes ...to give the poor dog a bone; but when she got there, the cupboard was bare, and so the poor dog had none.
2. *TV Burp:* Hill's real name is Matthew Hall and he trained as a doctor. He took over presenting *You've Been Framed* in 2004 after Jeremy Beadle, Lisa Riley and Jonathan Wilkes.
3. **Iron Curtain:** The Iron Curtain is a term coined by Winston Churchill in a 1946 speech in Fulton, Missouri.
4. *Daily Mirror:* The cartoon was created by Reg Smythe who died in 1998 and a statue of Andy Capp was erected in 2007 in Smythe's home town of Hartlepool.
5. **British Rail:** The 'big four' railways were Great Western (GWR), London, Midland and Scottish (LMS), London and North Eastern (LNER) and Southern (SR).
6. **The Cabinet:** The current format was originated by David Lloyd George and including the prime minister it is usually around 22 members.

7. **'I Gotta Wear Shades':** The song received a lot of airplay but only reached no. 21 in the UK charts.
8. **Continental Shelf:** Along parts of the California coast, the shelf extends less than a mile but along the northern coast of Siberia, it extends about 800 miles.
9. **Daley Blind:** His father was Danny Blind who is one of only two Dutch players, along with Arnold Mühren, to have won all the European competitions.

10. **South Pole:** Amundsen reached the South Pole five weeks ahead of Robert Falcon Scott, but sadly the entire British party died on the return journey.
11. **Red Chair:** The concept was inspired by Ronnie Corbett's long-winded monologues in his armchair.
12. **Console:** Although a console table was originally a table top supported by ornamental brackets on a wall, the term is now generally used for a narrow table with a lower shelf to stand against a wall, usually in a hall.
13. **Davy Lamp:** Sir Humphry Davy also isolated the elements potassium, sodium, magnesium, calcium, strontium and barium as well as identifying nitrous oxide (laughing gas) as a potential anaesthetic.
14. **Inspiral Carpets:** The band were formed in Oldham in 1983 and were part of the early 1990s Madchester movement that also included the Happy Mondays, the Stone Roses, James and the Charlatans.

HARD (3 Points)

15. **Table Tennis:** When Barnes retired from table tennis, he became assistant to the racehorse trainer Martin Pipe.
16. **'In Your Wardrobe':** Mike Rutherford, Tony Banks and Phil Collins were the longest-serving members of the band. Steve Hackett left in 1977 and after Peter Gabriel left in 1975, Phil Collins took over as lead singer.
17. **Ottoman:** As leader of the Turkish National Movement, Mustafa Kemal (Atatürk) proclaimed the foundation of the Republic of Turkey after the abolition of the Ottoman Empire.
18. *Four in a Bed:* It started as *Three in a Bed* in 2010.
19. **Jane Couch:** She won five world titles before becoming a boxing promoter.
20. **'Stool Pigeon':** Kid Creole's real name is August Darnell (full name Thomas August Darnell Browder).

1. **Music:** Who had a 1978 No. 1 with 'Wuthering Heights'?
2. **Films:** Which film star's husbands included both Joe DiMaggio and Arthur Miller?
3. **Sport & Games:** The Redskins play American football in which US city?
4. **Politics:** Which Labour leader first became prime minister in 1964?
5. **Music:** Which violinist released a recording of Vivaldi's 'The Four Seasons' in 1989 and is a keen Aston Villa fan?
6. **TV:** Which TV show starred Jack Klugman as a Los Angeles medical examiner, ran from 1976 until 1983?
7. **Films:** Which actor played roles including Han Solo, Indiana Jones and Jack Ryan?
8. **Pot Luck:** What is the name of the comic strip created by American Jim Davis, first launched in 1978, about a lasagne-loving cat?
9. **Sport & Games:** Which darts player won a record 16 World Darts Championships?

10. **Films:** Which 1981 film starring Dudley Moore and Liza Minnelli had a theme tune sung by Christopher Cross?
11. **Music:** Who was the youngest of the Beatles?
12. **Places:** What was the name of the highest mountain in North America before it was changed to Denali in 2015?
13. **Sport & Games:** Which football club's nickname is The Imps?
14. **Music:** Which folk singer had a 1975 hit with 'The Rochdale Cowboy'?
15. **Entertainment:** What was Victoria Beckham's maiden name?

16. **TV:** Ricky Tomlinson played which character in *Brookside*?
17. **Music:** Which singer was married to Kris Kristofferson and had a UK hit with 'We're All Alone' in 1977?
18. **Films:** Which 1998 film features Jim Carrey unwittingly starring in a reality TV show surrounding his life?
19. **Places:** Which dam in the Black Canyon of the Colorado River is about 30 miles from Las Vegas?
20. **Music:** The group Starship dropped which word from their original group name?
21. **People:** In 1930, who became the first woman to fly solo from England to Australia?

HARD (3 Points)

22. **Sport & Games:** Which Canadian-born French tennis player won the Women's Australian Open in 1995 and the French Open in 2000?
23. **History:** Who led the Peasants' Revolt of 1381?
24. **TV:** Which magician was the first presenter of the British version of *Candid Camera* in 1960?
25. **Sport & Games:** Cincinnati Bengals are one of the two NFL teams based in Ohio, but which team is the other?
26. **Music:** Which DJ and record producer had his biggest UK hit in 2013 with 'This Is What It Feels Like'?
27. **Films:** Who directed the films in the *Lord of the Rings* trilogy and its prequel *The Hobbit*?
28. **Sport & Games:** Which Scottish lightweight boxer became Undisputed Lightweight World Champion in February 1971?
29. **TV:** The TV series *Mad Men* is named after which New York avenue, famously connected to the advertising industry?
30. **Sport & Games:** Who lost to Ronnie O'Sullivan in the World Snooker Championship finals in 2008 and 2012?

EASY (1 Point)

1. **Kate Bush:** George HW Bush and his son George W Bush both had Walker as a middle name.
2. **Marilyn Monroe:** Monrovia, the capital of Liberia, is named after James Monroe.
3. **Washington:** George Washington was the first president.
4. **Harold Wilson:** Woodrow Wilson was president during WWI and is the only one to be buried in Washington.
5. **Nigel Kennedy:** JF Kennedy was assassinated in Dallas by Lee Harvey Oswald, killed by Jack Ruby 2 days later.
6. *Quincy*: John Quincy Adams was the son of second president John Adams.
7. **Harrison Ford:** Gerald Ford became president after Nixon resigned and VP after Spiro Agnew resigned.
8. **Garfield:** James Garfield was shot and died 80 days later. He was the first president to speak on the phone.
9. **Phil Taylor:** Zachary Taylor died after only 16 months.

MEDIUM (2 Points)

10. *Arthur*: Chester A Arthur took over when Garfield was shot.
11. **George Harrison:** William Henry Harrison died after 32 days but his grandson Benjamin later became president.
12. **Mount McKinley:** William McKinley was the third to be shot and Lincoln's son Robert witnessed them all.
13. **Lincoln City:** Abraham Lincoln was shot by John Wilkes Booth watching *Our American Cousin* at Ford's Theatre.
14. **Mike Harding:** Warren Harding died in office and was the first to make a speech over the radio.
15. **Adams:** John Adams was the first vice-president and the first president to live in the White House.

16. **Bobby Grant:** Ulysses S Grant led the Union army to victory in the American Civil War.
17. **Rita Coolidge:** Calvin Coolidge was the only president born on the fourth of July.
18. ***The Truman Show:*** The 'S' in Harry S Truman doesn't stand for anything and a sign on his desk said, 'The buck stops here'.
19. **Hoover Dam:** Herbert Hoover was president during the Wall Street Crash of 1929 but is no relation to J Edgar Hoover, the first Director of the FBI.
20. **Jefferson:** Thomas Jefferson, main author of the Declaration of Independence in 1776, died exactly 50 years later on 4 July 1826, as did John Adams!
21. **Amy Johnson:** Andrew Johnson was the first to be impeached; Lyndon B Johnson followed John F Kennedy.

HARD (3 Points)

22. **Mary Pierce:** Franklin Pierce said his oath on a law book.
23. **Wat Tyler:** John Tyler had eight children from his first wife and seven from his second.
24. **David Nixon:** Richard Milhous Nixon is the only president to resign, doing so after the Watergate crisis.
25. **Cleveland Browns:** Grover Cleveland is the only president to serve two non-consecutive terms.
26. **Armin van Buuren:** Martin Van Buren was the first to be born a US citizen – all others were born British subjects.
27. **Peter Jackson:** The first attempt to assassinate a president was on Andrew Jackson but it failed.
28. **Ken Buchanan:** James Buchanan was the only president to be a lifelong bachelor.
29. **Madison Avenue:** James Madison was responsible for drafting the US Constitution and The Bill of Rights.
30. **Ali Carter:** Jimmy Carter was a peanut farmer from Georgia and he won the Nobel Peace Prize in 2002.

QUIZ No. 72: TUTTI FRUTTI

1. **Music:** Which was Fats Domino's only UK Top 10 hit?
2. **Religion:** In the Book of Genesis in the Bible, with what did Adam and Eve make loincloths to cover themselves?
3. **Pot Luck:** In the song 'Twelve Days of Christmas', what did my true love send to me on the first day of Christmas?
4. **TV:** Leigh Francis is the real name of which TV presenter?
5. **Places:** What is the most common nickname for New York?
6. **Music:** Who had a UK No. 2 hit in 1982 with 'Annie I'm Not Your Daddy'?
7. **Sport & Games:** Which suspect in the game Cluedo is represented by a purple playing piece?
8. **Pot Luck:** What name is often given to a third person in the company of two people, especially lovers?
9. **TV:** Which matchmaking show was hosted by Cilla Black from 1985 to 2003?

10. **Music:** Which song in 1968 was the only UK No. 1 hit for The Move?
11. **TV:** Which dance-based TV show was presented by Louie Spence in 2010?
12. **Films:** Which film and TV review website was founded in 1998 by three students at the University of California?
13. **Food & Drink:** Which dessert of peaches, raspberry sauce and vanilla ice cream was created by Auguste Escoffier?
14. **Music:** Which 1985 Prince song was about a hat, 'the kind you find in a second-hand store'?

15. **Sport & Games:** What is the nickname of the New Zealand rugby league team?
16. **Animals & Nature:** What is the main food source of the silkworm?
17. **TV:** Anna Karen played which character in the TV series *On the Buses*?
18. **Music:** Which Swedish singer's first UK hit was 'Buffalo Stance' in 1988?
19. **Places:** What is the name of Liverpool's main railway station?
20. **Pot Luck:** What is the most widely spoken language in the world?
21. **Music:** Dolores O'Riordan was the lead singer with which Irish band?

HARD (3 Points)

22. **Art & Literature:** In the Edward Lear poem *The Owl and the Pussycat*, they dined on mince and slices of what?
23. **Entertainment:** Which comic strip character is the alter ego of Eric Wimp who lives at 29 Acacia Road?
24. **Music:** Which female duo had a No. 5 hit in 1984 with 'Since Yesterday'?
25. **People:** What was the first name of Winston Churchill's wife?
26. **Pot Luck:** What is the Cockney rhyming slang name for the *Sun* newspaper?
27. **Music:** Which Donovan song, a UK No. 5 hit in 1968, was inspired by former model Jenny Boyd?
28. **TV:** What was the name of the pub in *Early Doors*?
29. **Art & Literature:** Which 1985 novel by Jeanette Winterson was about a lesbian girl growing up in an English Pentecostal community?
30. **Music:** Which German electronic band were founded in 1967 by Edgar Froese?

EASY (1 Point)

1. **'Blueberry Hill':** The song reached No. 6 in 1956.
2. **Fig Leaves:** Figs are part of the mulberry family.
3. **A Partridge in a Pear Tree:** Conference pears are the most widely grown in the UK.
4. **Keith Lemon:** He took over presenting *Through the Keyhole* in 2013, originally hosted by David Frost and Loyd Grossman.
5. **The Big Apple:** Kajagoogoo had a UK No. 8 hit in 1983 with a song called 'Big Apple'.
6. **Kid Creole and the Coconuts:** His stage name was adapted from the Elvis Presley film *King Creole*.
7. **Professor Plum:** The game is known as Clue in the USA and in a 1985 film of that name, Professor Plum was played by Christopher Lloyd.
8. **Gooseberry:** The kiwi fruit is also known as the Chinese gooseberry.
9. ***Blind Date***: Paul O'Grady became the new host when the show was relaunched in 2017 on Channel 5.

MEDIUM (2 Points)

10. **'Blackberry Way':** The Move's 'Flowers in the Rain' was the first song played on Radio 1 in 1967.
11. ***Pineapple Dance Studios***: Louie Spence was a dancer in the original West End musical *Miss Saigon* and went on to star in *Cats*.
12. **Rotten Tomatoes:** The idea developed from one of the students gathering reviews of Jackie Chan films.
13. **Peach Melba:** It was named after the Australian soprano Nellie Melba.
14. **'Raspberry Beret':** It reached No. 2 in the US but only No. 25 in the UK.

15. **The Kiwis:** The New Zealand rugby union team are the All Blacks.
16. **Mulberry Leaves:** Mulberry is also a UK fashion company founded in 1971 making leather goods.
17. **Olive:** She was Stan's sister (Reg Varney) and Arthur's wife (Michael Robbins).
18. **Neneh Cherry:** She is the half-sister of the singer Eagle-Eye Cherry.
19. **Lime Street:** The station opened in 1836.
20. **Mandarin Chinese:** It has been the official Chinese language since 1917.
21. **The Cranberries:** A.D.A.M. featuring Amy did a cover version of their song 'Zombie' in 1995.

22. **Quince:** The fruit is golden and shaped like a pear.
23. **Bananaman:** Eric turns into a superhero when he eats a banana and has appeared in the *Dandy* and the *Beano*.
24. **Strawberry Switchblade:** In 1985 they did a cover version of Dolly Parton's 'Jolene'.
25. **Clementine:** Winston Churchill proposed to her at his birthplace, Blenheim Palace.
26. **The Currant Bun:** It began as a broadsheet in 1964 as a successor to the *Daily Herald*.
27. **'Jennifer Juniper':** She was the sister of Pattie Boyd who was married to George Harrison.
28. **The Grapes:** It was written by Craig Cash and Phil Mealey who played Joe and Duffy and James McAvoy played Liam in the first series.
29. ***Oranges Are Not the Only Fruit:*** It was made into a 1990 TV programme with Charlotte Coleman and Geraldine McEwan.
30. **Tangerine Dream:** Arguably their most popular album was *Phaedra*, the first they released on the Virgin label.

QUIZ No. 73: **WHAT CAR?**

1. **Sport & Games:** Which football team won the Premier League in 1995?
2. **Places:** Which US city is the state capital of Texas?
3. **Politics:** Who became president of the USA in 1974 after the resignation of Richard Nixon?
4. **Shopping & Fashion:** The British fashion designer Mary Quant pioneered which article of clothing in 1964?
5. **Religion:** In the traditional Christian hymn, 'Jesus wants me for a......' what?
6. **Films:** Which US actor starred as Clark W Griswold in the *Vacation* series of films?
7. **People:** John Wilkes Booth assassinated whom in 1865?
8. **Food & Drink:** Which brand of rum did Seagram sell to Diageo in 2001?
9. **Places:** What is the English translation of the Paris monument dedicated to soldiers at the end of the Champs-Élysées?

10. **Music:** Natalie Cole had two Top 10 hits in the UK, 'Miss You Like Crazy' and which other?
11. **TV:** Who presented *Animal Magic* for over 20 years?
12. **Sport & Games:** Which British motor racing driver was World Champion in 2009 driving for Brawn?
13. **Food & Drink:** The name of which soft drink means 'be well' in the Maori language?
14. **Geography:** On which river do Hull and Grimsby stand?
15. **Sport & Games:** Which ex-Leicester Tigers player, 'The Leicester Lip', took part in *Strictly Come Dancing*?
16. **Animals & Nature:** Native to North and South America, which big cat is the third largest after the tiger and lion?

17. **Music:** Which T Rex hit starts with the lyrics 'You're so sweet, you're so fine, I want you all and everything just to be mine'?
18. **TV:** Brian Capron played which villainous character in *Coronation Street* from 2001 until his death in 2003, shortly after murdering Maxine Peacock?
19. **Films:** Which 1927 Al Jolson film was the first talking picture, later remade in 1980 starring Neil Diamond?
20. **Sport & Games:** Barry Sheene was the 1976 and 1977 500cc World Motorcycle Champion riding for which constructor?
21. **Music:** 'Green Onions' was a 1979 hit for which group?

HARD (3 Points)

22. **Animals & Nature:** Which flower is the national flower of both India and Vietnam?
23. **People:** Which man was hanged in 1953 for the murder of a policeman after he said, 'Let him have it'?
24. **Sport & Games:** What was the final name of the golf matchplay tournament, last played in 2014 and previously sponsored by Piccadilly, Suntory and Toyota?
25. **Music:** Which was the last recording made by Janis Joplin in 1970 before her death at the age of 27, a song asking the Lord to buy her a particular make of car?
26. **Places:** The headquarters of MI6 on Albert Embankment overlooks which bridge over the River Thames?
27. **TV:** The TV series *Gunsmoke*, which ran from 1955 to 1975, was set in which city in Kansas?
28. **Music:** Which US country singer had a hit in 1968 with 'Harper Valley PTA'?
29. **Sport & Games:** Which jockey won the 2018 Epsom Derby riding a horse called Masar?
30. **Places:** Which New York skyscraper was the world's tallest before the Empire State Building was completed?

1. **Blackburn Rovers:** Rover was bought by Leyland Motors in 1967 which became British Leyland in 1968.
2. **Austin:** Austin merged with Morris Motors in 1952 under the name BMC.
3. **Gerald Ford:** In 1908 Ford started production of the Model T, the first mass-produced car.
4. **Mini Skirt:** Alec Issigonis designed the Mini in 1959.
5. **Sunbeam:** Models included the Rapier and Alpine before Sunbeam became a model name for the Talbot Sunbeam.
6. **Chevy Chase:** Chevy is short for Chevrolet which is part of General Motors.
7. **Abraham Lincoln:** Lincoln is a luxury brand name of the Ford Motor Company in the US.
8. **Captain Morgan:** Morgan was founded by Henry Morgan, not the privateer of the same name after whom the rum is named.
9. **Arch of Triumph:** Popular models included the TR6, Spitfire, Herald, Stag, Toledo and Dolomite.

10. **'Pink Cadillac':** Cadillac is a luxury brand name of General Motors in the US.
11. **Johnny Morris:** The Morris Oxford and the Austin Cambridge were almost identical models.
12. **Jenson Button:** Jensen was based in West Bromwich and their most famous model was the Interceptor.
13. **Kia Ora:** Kia Motors was founded in Seoul, South Korea in 1944 but didn't start to make cars until 1974.
14. **Humber:** Models included the Super Snipe, Hawk and Sceptre.

15. **Austin Healey:** Austin-Healey was a joint venture between BMC's Austin and the Donald Healey Motor Company.
16. **Jaguar:** Ford acquired Jaguar in 1990 and Land Rover in 2000 before selling both to Tata Motors in 2008.
17. **'Jeepster':** Jeep is an American brand of cars which has been part of Chrysler since 1987.
18. **Richard Hillman:** Hillman was based near Coventry and models included the Minx, Imp, Hunter and Avenger.
19. *The Jazz Singer*: The two most famous Singer models were the Gazelle and the Vogue and the Jazz became a Honda model years later.
20. **Suzuki:** The company was founded in Japan in 1909 but didn't manufacture its first car until 1955.
21. **Booker T & The MG's:** The names Morris and Garages were chosen as a tribute to William Morris.

HARD (3 Points)

22. **Lotus Flower:** Jim Clark was the first driver to win the Formula 1 world title in a Lotus in both 1963 and 1965.
23. **Derek Bentley:** Bentley's headquarters are in Crewe and has been part of the Volkswagen Group since 1998.
24. **Volvo World Matchplay:** Simon Templar drove a Volvo P1800 in *The Saint* with the number plate ST1.
25. **'Mercedes-Benz':** The company was founded in 1926 as Daimler-Benz and has its headquarters in Stuttgart.
26. **Vauxhall Bridge:** Models have included the Victor, Viva, Chevette and Cavalier.
27. **Dodge City:** Dodge was sold to Chrysler in 1928 and became part of Fiat-Chrysler in 2014.
28. **Jeannie C Riley:** The last Riley car was produced in 1969.
29. **William Buick:** The first Buick was made in 1899.
30. **The Chrysler Building:** Chrysler merged with Daimler in 1998 but they split again in 2007.

1. **TV:** Ian Lavender played which character in *Dad's Army*?
2. **Pot Luck:** In the nursery rhyme, who could eat no fat?
3. **Sport & Games:** The boxers Robinson and Leonard shared which nickname?
4. **Food & Drink:** Which British slang word for tea can also mean a cleaning lady or to burn?
5. **Shopping & Fashion:** Which 1970s hairstyle is short at the front and sides but long at the back?
6. **Politics:** Who succeeded Alex Salmond as First Minister of Scotland in 2014?
7. **TV:** What is the name of the seafaring, pipe-smoking captain in Hergé's *Adventures of Tintin*?
8. **Words:** Which two words mean 'a clue or piece of information which can be misleading or distracting'?
9. **Sport & Games:** What is golfer Greg Norman's nickname?

10. **Music:** Who had a UK Top 10 hit in 1985 with 'St Elmo's Fire'?
11. **Places:** Which geographic cape extends into the Atlantic Ocean off the coast of Massachusetts?
12. **Animals & Nature:** What name is given to a sky dappled with rows of small, white fleecy clouds?
13. **TV:** Which actor and former wrestler played Brian 'Bomber' Busbridge in *Auf Wiedersehen, Pet*?
14. **Sport & Games:** What was the nickname of the African swimmer who swam the 100 metres freestyle in the slowest ever time at the 2000 Olympics?
15. **Pot Luck:** Which imperial unit of measurement, also called a pole or a rod, is equal to five and a half yards?

16. **Music:** Whose only UK No. 1 hit was 'Dizzy' in 1969?
17. **Art & Literature:** Which American artist was nicknamed Jack the Dripper?
18. **Sport & Games:** Kickflip and heelflip are terms used in which sport and recreational activity?
19. **TV:** Troy Tempest, Phones and Marina were characters in which 1960s TV puppet series?
20. **Politics:** Who was Home Secretary from July 2016 to April 2018?
21. **Words:** Which British slang word is often used to mean fingerprints?

HARD (3 Points)

22. **Music:** Which English classical guitarist was born in 1933 in Battersea and studied at the Royal College of Music aged 12?
23. **History:** King Henry I of England is reported to have died in 1135 after eating a surfeit of what?
24. **Places:** What is the name of the sea strait that separates Tasmania from the Australian mainland?
25. **Films:** Which 2001 film, starring Hugh Jackman, John Travolta and Halle Berry, is about hacking into a computer to steal money from an illegal slush fund?
26. **Sport & Games:** Which Scottish RU prop won 44 caps, 25 as captain, and was the captain when Scotland beat England to win their third Grand Slam in 1990?
27. **Finance:** Barclays bought which credit card company in 2008, once owned by Lloyds TSB and Morgan Stanley?
28. **Music:** What is the popular name of Franz Schubert's Piano Quintet in A Major?
29. **Politics:** Who was appointed the Secretary of State for Transport in July 2016?
30. **Films:** What was the name of the 2016 sequel to the 2003 animated film *Finding Nemo*?

1. **(Private Frank) Pike:** *Dad's Army* was written by Jimmy Perry and David Croft and set in Walmington-on-Sea.
2. **Jack Sprat:** It goes on to say, 'his wife could eat no lean'.
3. **Sugar Ray:** Robinson was born Walker Smith Jr and Leonard was born Ray Charles Leonard.
4. **Char:** The word comes from the Chinese *ch'a*.
5. **Mullet:** Paul McCartney, Rod Stewart and David Bowie all sported the look in the 1970s but the Beastie Boys are credited with first calling it by that name.
6. **Nicola Sturgeon:** Donald Dewar was the first Scottish First Minister but died in office in 2000.
7. **Captain Haddock:** Tintin's dog Snowy, Professor Calculus and the 'twin' detectives Thomson and Thompson also feature.
8. **Red Herring:** The origin of the phrase comes from using the fish to set a false trail when hunting.
9. **Great White Shark:** Norman won the Open twice but finished second seven times in Majors, including losing four playoffs.

10. **John Parr:** The song was the soundtrack to the 1985 film starring Emilio Estevez, Rob Lowe and Demi Moore.
11. **Cape Cod:** The islands Martha's Vineyard and Nantucket are just south of Cape Cod.
12. **Mackerel Sky:** The clouds are typically cirrocumulus or altocumulus clouds.
13. **Pat Roach:** He made his acting debut as a bouncer in the 1971 film *A Clockwork Orange*.
14. **Eric the Eel:** His name was Eric Moussambani and he was from Equatorial Guinea.

15. **Perch:** There are 4 rods in a chain, 10 chains in a furlong and 8 furlongs in a mile.
16. **Tommy Roe:** Vic Reeves and the Wonder Stuff also took the song to No. 1 in 1991.
17. **Jackson Pollock:** He was killed in a car accident in 1956 aged 44 and was played by Ed Harris in the 2000 biopic.
18. **Skateboarding:** The sport will make its debut at the Olympics in Tokyo 2020.
19. *Stingray*: They work for W.A.S.P. (World Aquanaut Security Patrol) and there were only 39 episodes made.
20. **Amber Rudd:** She took up the position of Secretary of State for Work and Pensions in November 2018.
21. **Dabs:** No fingerprints are the same, even with identical twins who share their DNA.

HARD (3 Points)

22. **Julian Bream:** He was influenced by Django Reinhardt amongst others and later called his dog Django.
23. **Lampreys:** Henry I was known as Henry Beauclerc and he succeeded his brother William II, or William Rufus.
24. **Bass Strait:** It separates Tasmania, capital Hobart, from the state of Victoria, capital Melbourne.
25. *Swordfish*: Vinnie Jones was in the film, and was also in *Lock, Stock and Two Smoking Barrels* and *Snatch*.
26. **David Sole:** His total of 25 matches as captain was a record until it was surpassed by Greig Laidlaw.
27. **Goldfish:** Goldfish actually have good memories and will turn white if kept in the dark.
28. **'The Trout Quintet':** Schubert died in 1828 in Vienna aged 31, without completing his 'Unfinished Symphony'.
29. **Chris Grayling:** He was previously Leader of the House of Commons from May 2015 to July 2016.
30. *Finding Dory*: Dory is a regal blue tang voiced by Ellen DeGeneres.

1. **Music:** Which song was Alice Cooper's only UK No. 1?
2. **Sport & Games:** What is the name of the home ground of Fulham FC?
3. **Films:** Which 2006 film stars Ben Stiller taking over as nightwatchman from Dick Van Dyke and his colleagues?
4. **Food & Drink:** Which coffee consists of an espresso with microfoam, like a latte but with less milk and foam?
5. **TV:** Which US TV series starred Hugh Laurie leading a medical team at a teaching hospital in New Jersey?
6. **Pot Luck:** What is known by the nickname 'The Old Lady of Threadneedle Street'?
7. **Music:** Which Welsh singer had a UK No. 2 hit in 2005 with 'Crazy Chick'?
8. **Sport & Games:** What is the nickname of Manchester United's Old Trafford football ground?
9. **Entertainment:** Which all-round entertainer presented the TV series *Record Breakers* for over 20 years before his death in 1994 at the age of just 62?

10. **Religion:** Which is the largest Roman Catholic place of worship in England and Wales?
11. **Music:** The 1985 UK No. 14 hit 'Some Like It Hot' was the highest chart entry for which group?
12. **Films:** Which 1980 film is set at an exclusive golf club and stars Chevy Chase, Rodney Dangerfield and Bill Murray?
13. **Animals & Nature:** Which is the world's most common owl?
14. **TV:** Which series starred Wentworth Miller as Michael Scofield trying to get his half-brother out of jail?

15. **Sport & Games:** Which club did Chelsea beat in the 2000 FA Cup final, the last at the old Wembley?
16. **Music:** Which group's first UK hit was 'Lifted' in 1996?
17. **Food & Drink:** Which American restaurant chain specialising in Italian-American cuisine was founded in 1958 by brothers Dan and Frank Carney?
18. **History:** Rudolf Hess was the last person to be held prisoner in which London building?
19. **Films:** Which child actress sang the song 'On the Good Ship Lollipop' in the 1934 film *Bright Eyes*?
20. **Music:** Which band had a UK No. 7 hit in 1988 with 'The King of Rock 'n' Roll'?
21. **Sport & Games:** Which club lost to Manchester United in the 1990 FA Cup final after a replay?

HARD (3 Points)

22. **Places:** Scotland's Great Glen runs from Inverness on the Moray Firth in the east to which town in the west?
23. **Art & Literature:** What was the name of Andy Warhol's famous New York studio?
24. **Sport & Games:** In Monopoly, which is the third pink property with Whitehall and Northumberland Avenue?
25. **Films:** Which song by Noel Harrison featured in the 1968 film *The Thomas Crown Affair*?
26. **Music:** Which group had a UK No. 8 hit in 1996 with 'Going For Gold'?
27. **Sport & Games:** Which horse ridden by Geoff Lewis won the 1971 Derby?
28. **Food & Drink:** What is the French term for coffee with hot milk added?
29. **Films:** Which 2004 film starring Don Cheadle centred on the 1994 civil war between the Hutu and Tutsi peoples?
30. **Music:** Which rock band from Bangor, Northern Ireland had minor hits with 'Sleep Alone' and 'Sun' in 2012?

1. **'School's Out':** His real name is Vincent Furnier.
2. **Craven Cottage:** England captain Johnny Haynes was the first £100 a week player and only played for Fulham.
3. *Night at the Museum*: Robin Williams, Steve Coogan and Ricky Gervais play exhibits coming to life.
4. **Flat White:** A double espresso is a doppio and an Americano is an espresso with hot water.
5. *House*: Hugh Laurie starred with Stephen Fry in *A Bit of Fry & Laurie*, *Blackadder* and *Jeeves and Wooster*.
6. **Bank of England:** It was established in 1694 and the name first appeared in a 1797 James Gillray cartoon.
7. **Charlotte Church:** Born Charlotte Reed, her first performance on TV was aged 11 on a phone-in on *This Morning* in 1997.
8. **The Theatre of Dreams:** Bobby Charlton gave it that name; the club were originally known as Newton Heath.
9. **Roy Castle:** He was a dancer, trumpet player and appeared in the film *Carry on up the Khyber*.

10. **Westminster Cathedral:** Basil Hume was Archbishop of Westminster for 23 years until his death in 1999.
11. **Power Station:** The band fronted by Robert Palmer included Andy Taylor and John Taylor from Duran Duran, with the other members forming Arcadia.
12. *Caddyshack*: Bill Murray was a groundskeeper and a caddie in his youth and ad-libbed a lot of his scenes.
13. **Barn Owl:** It is one of the most widespread of all birds, being found on every continent except Antarctica.
14. *Prison Break*: His half-brother Lincoln Burrows was played by Dominic Purcell.

15. **Aston Villa:** Aston Villa beat Man United 2-1 in the 1957 FA Cup final, a team including most of the Busby Babes.
16. **Lighthouse Family:** This song and 'High' in 1998 both reached No. 4, their highest chart position.
17. **Pizza Hut:** Their first restaurant was at Wichita State University in Kansas catering for students.
18. **Tower of London:** The last person to be executed there was the German spy Josef Jakobs in 1941.
19. **Shirley Temple:** In later life she served as the US ambassador to Ghana and then Czechoslovakia.
20. **Prefab Sprout:** The lead singer was called Paddy McAloon and his brother Martin also played bass guitar.
21. **Crystal Palace:** They also lost the 2016 final to Manchester United after extra time.

HARD (3 Points)

22. **Fort William:** The town sits on the shores of Loch Linnhe which is the only sea loch in the Great Glen.
23. **The Factory:** The 2006 film *Factory Girl* is about the life of Edie Sedgwick and her association with Andy Warhol.
24. **Pall Mall:** All three roads lead off Trafalgar Square.
25. **'Windmills of Your Mind':** The film starred Steve McQueen and Faye Dunaway; the singer was the son of Rex Harrison.
26. **Shed Seven:** The York band's lead singer is Rick Witter.
27. **Mill Reef:** He was trained by Ian Balding but was beaten in the 2000 Guineas by Brigadier Gerard.
28. **Café au Lait:** It is similar to an Italian latte but in France it is often served in a bowl rather than a cup.
29. *Hotel Rwanda***:** The film also starred Nick Nolte and Joaquin Phoenix.
30. **Two Door Cinema Club:** The lead singer is called Alex Trimble.

1. **Music:** Which singer had hits with 'Runaway' and 'Hats Off To Larry' in 1961?
2. **TV:** Adam West and Burt Ward starred as which superheroes in a 1960s TV series?
3. **Sport & Games:** What is the nickname of Bolton Wanderers?
4. **Pot Luck:** Which ornamental branched light fitting is usually suspended from the ceiling?
5. **Films:** Who won the Best Actor Oscar for his role as an LAPD narcotics officer in the 2001 film *Training Day*?
6. **People:** Which future leader was imprisoned on Robben Island for 27 years before being released in 1990?
7. **Music:** The Village People had a 1978 UK No. 1 with 'Y.M.C.A.' but what was their follow-up hit in 1979?
8. **TV:** Don Johnson and Philip Michael Thomas starred in which 1980s US crime drama series?
9. **Pot Luck:** What is the motto of the Special Air Service (SAS)?

10. **Music:** Clive Dunn took which song to No. 1 in the UK in 1970?
11. **TV:** In *The Likely Lads*, Terry Collier was played by James Bolam, but who played Bob Ferris?
12. **Films:** What was the nickname of actor John Wayne?
13. **Sport & Games:** Which football club play at The Valley?
14. **Transport & Travel:** Which car manufacturer based in Tamworth produced mainly three-wheeled cars?
15. **Entertainment:** Which Welsh comedian of the 1970s told stories about coal mining and Welsh rugby and was often accompanied by a giant leek or daffodil?

16. **TV:** In *The Roy Rogers Show* from the 1950s, what was the name of Roy Rogers' horse?

17. **Films:** What was the name of the 1978 sequel to the 1976 film *The Omen*?

18. **Music:** Gilbert and Sullivan were the librettist William (Schwenk) Gilbert and which composer?

19. **Pot Luck:** Which word is used in the NATO phonetic alphabet for the letter 'M'?

20. **TV:** Formerly UK Gold and other similar names, to what man's name did UKTV change the channel in 2007?

21. **Music:** Toni Basil took which song to No. 2 in the UK charts in 1982?

HARD (3 Points)

22. **Food & Drink:** What name is given to shortbread topped with caramel with a layer of chocolate on top?

23. **Films:** Which US actress first came to prominence in the 1966 film *One Million Years BC*?

24. **Music:** Which 1971 US No. 1 by Paul and Linda McCartney was a song in two parts, the second being 'Admiral Halsey', but what was the first part written about his uncle?

25. **Mythology:** Which daughter of King Priam and Hecuba of Troy was cursed to utter prophecies that no one believed?

26. **Places:** In which Indiana town were the Jacksons born?

27. **Music:** The first No. 1 for Tom Jones was 'It's Not Unusual' in 1965 but what was his second in 1966?

28. **TV:** Which 1950s collection of children's programmes included *Andy Pandy* and *Flower Pot Men*?

29. **Films:** Which German actress, born in 1901, joined her forenames Marie Magdalene to make her stage name?

30. **Music:** Which 1971 song achieved the highest UK chart position of No. 5 for C.C.S.?

ANSWERS QUIZ No. 76: **MEET THE TROTTERS**

1. **Del Shannon:** Derek Trotter played by David Jason was usually called Del (Boy).
2. **Batman and Robin:** Del and Rodney dress as Batman and Robin in the 1996 episode 'Heroes and Villains'.
3. **The Trotters:** Trotters Independent Trading Co. was based in New York, Paris and Peckham!
4. **Chandelier:** The Trotters broke a priceless chandelier in the 1982 episode 'A Touch of Glass'.
5. **Denzel Washington:** Paul Barber played Denzil (Tulser).
6. **Nelson Mandela:** They lived in Nelson Mandela House in Peckham but the actual location was in Acton before it moved to Bristol.
7. **'In the Navy':** Uncle Albert was in the Royal Navy 'during the war' and in the Merchant Navy after the war.
8. *Miami Vice*: 'Miami Twice' was the 1991 Christmas special.
9. **Who Dares Wins:** One of Del's favourite sayings was 'He who dares, wins'.

10. **'Grandad':** The character was played by Lennard Pearce from the show's first episode in 1981 until his death in 1984.
11. **Rodney Bewes:** Nicholas Lyndhurst played Rodney, named after the actor Rod Taylor.
12. **Duke:** 'Sleeping Dogs Lie' was a 1985 episode where Del and Rodney babysit Boycie and Marlene's Great Dane 'Duke'.
13. **Charlton Athletic:** Rodney's middle name was Charlton, after Charlton Athletic, his mother's favourite team.
14. **Reliant:** The Trotters drove a Reliant Regal not a Robin.

15. **Max Boyce:** John Challis played Boycie.
16. **Trigger:** Colin Ball (Trigger) was played by Roger Lloyd-Pack, who also played Owen Newitt in *The Vicar of Dibley*.
17. *Damien: Omen II*: Damien was Del and Raquel's son, indirectly named after Damien Thorn in the horror film.
18. **Arthur (Seymour) Sullivan:** John Sullivan wrote the series as well as *Citizen Smith*, *Just Good Friends* and several others.
19. **Mike:** The landlord at the Nag's Head pub Mike Fisher was played by Kenneth MacDonald.
20. **Dave:** Trigger always called Rodney 'Dave' in error.
21. **'Mickey':** Mickey Pearce was played by Patrick Murray.

HARD (3 Points)

22. **Millionaire's Shortbread:** Del often said, 'This time next year, we'll be millionaires.'
23. **Raquel Welch:** Tessa Peake-Jones played Raquel Turner.
24. **'Uncle Albert':** Uncle Albert (Gladstone) Trotter was played by Buster Merryfield.
25. **Cassandra:** Cassandra Trotter (née Parry) was played by Gwyneth Strong.
26. **Gary:** Nabil Elouahabi played Gary, an illegal immigrant in 'Strangers of the Shore' in 2002.
27. **'Green Green Grass of Home':** *The Green Green Grass* was a spin-off series and sequel about Boycie and Marlene.
28. *Watch With Mother*: They eventually became millionaires in 1996 after finding an antique pocket watch.
29. **Marlene Dietrich:** Sue Holderness played Marlene.
30. **'Tap Turns on the Water':** In the 1992 episode 'Mother Nature's Son', Del tries to sell tap water as 'Peckham Spring'.

QUIZ No. 77: **IN A STATE**

1. **Sport & Games:** At which ground did Manchester City play their home matches before the Etihad Stadium?
2. **Entertainment:** In which musical are the songs 'Oh What a Beautiful Morning' and 'The Surrey With The Fringe On Top'?
3. **Food & Drink:** Which dessert consists of ice cream and cake topped with browned meringue?
4. **Music:** Sharleen Spiteri is lead singer with which group?
5. **Films:** Which character was played by Harrison Ford for the first time in the 1981 film *Raiders of the Lost Ark*?
6. **People:** Who was the first president of the USA?
7. **Places:** Tbilisi is the capital of which European country?
8. **TV:** Miley Cyrus played the lead in which TV series about a girl's double life as a schoolgirl and a famous pop star?
9. **Sport & Games:** Which tennis player won the Wimbledon Women's Singles in 1977?

10. **Music:** Which song was the first UK No. 1 for the Bee Gees in 1967?
11. **Animals & Nature:** Which US breed of chicken was a result of cross-breeding with birds from the Far East?
12. **Places:** Which mountain range in Spain means 'mountain range covered in snow' in Spanish?
13. **Films:** Which 1987 Coen Brothers film, starring Nicolas Cage and Holly Hunter, involves the kidnap of a baby?
14. **Art & Literature:** Who wrote *Cat on a Hot Tin Roof*?
15. **TV:** Which TV police show starred Jack Lord as Steve McGarrett and James MacArthur as 'Danno'?
16. **Music:** Which classic album by the Eagles featured 'New Kid in Town' and 'Life in the Fast Lane'?

17. **Food & Drink:** Which chicken dish, cooked in a creamy gravy, is often served with corn and baked bananas?
18. **Sport & Games:** The Belmont Stakes, The Preakness Stakes and which other race form the US Triple Crown?
19. **Places:** Which is the only one of the five Great Lakes of North America to be located entirely within the USA?
20. **Films:** Jackie Gleason played the character of which pool player in the 1961 film *The Hustler*?
21. **Music:** Which US band had a minor UK hit in 1978 with 'Carry on Wayward Son'?

HARD (3 Points)

---

22. **History:** On which US battleship did the Japanese sign the instrument of surrender to end World War II?
23. **TV:** In which vehicle in the cartoon *Wacky Races* would you find the hillbilly Lazy Luke and Blubber Bear?
24. **Animals & Nature:** Which beetle, also known as the ten-striped spearman, is a major pest of potato crops?
25. **Places:** What is the actual address of the White House in Washington DC?
26. **Pot Luck:** Which US newspaper is nicknamed 'The Gray Lady'?
27. **Sport & Games:** Which horse ridden by Adrian Maguire and trained by Willie Mullins won the 2001 King George VI Chase at Kempton, beating Best Mate?
28. **Music:** Which group had a UK No. 5 hit in 1968 with 'Yummy Yummy Yummy'?
29. **Films:** Which 1988 film starred Gene Hackman and Willem Dafoe as FBI agents coming up against the Ku Klux Klan?
30. **History:** Which US wagon route went through Missouri, Kansas, Nebraska, Wyoming and Idaho before landing in a west coast state?

EASY (1 Point)

1. **Maine Road:** Its capital is Augusta (US Masters one is in Georgia); its biggest and most populous city is Portland.
2. *Oklahoma*: Its capital and biggest city is Oklahoma City, its name coming from words in the Choctaw language.
3. **Baked Alaska:** Its capital is Juneau and its biggest city is Anchorage.
4. **Texas:** Its capital is Austin and its biggest city is Houston.
5. **Indiana Jones:** Its capital and biggest city is Indianapolis, home to the Indy 500 and Elvis Presley's final concert.
6. **George Washington:** Its capital is Olympia and its biggest city is Seattle.
7. **Georgia:** Its capital and biggest city is Atlanta, the venue for the 1996 Olympic Games.
8. *Hannah Montana*: Its capital is Helena and its biggest city is Billings.
9. **Virginia Wade:** Its capital is Richmond and its biggest city is Virginia Beach.

MEDIUM (2 Points)

10. **'Massachusetts':** Its capital and biggest city is Boston, home to the oldest marathon and the setting for the TV show *Cheers*.
11. **Rhode Island Red:** Its capital and biggest city is Providence; Brown University is in the smallest state.
12. **Sierra Nevada:** Its capital is Carson City and its biggest city is Las Vegas.
13. *Raising Arizona*: Its capital and biggest city is Phoenix, the sunniest major US city with 85% sunshine.
14. **Tennessee Williams:** Its capital and biggest city is Nashville, known as 'Music City', home to the weekly Grand Ole Opry.

15. *Hawaii Five-0*: Its capital and biggest city is Honolulu, the birthplace of Barack Obama.
16. *Hotel California*: Its capital is Sacramento and its biggest city is Los Angeles.
17. **Chicken Maryland:** Its capital is Annapolis and its biggest city is Baltimore.
18. **Kentucky Derby:** Its capital is Frankfort and its biggest city is Louisville, the birthplace of Muhammad Ali.
19. **Lake Michigan:** Its capital is Lansing and its biggest city is Detroit.
20. **Minnesota Fats:** Its capital is St Paul and its biggest city is Minneapolis.
21. **Kansas:** Its capital is Topeka and its biggest city is Wichita.

HARD (3 Points)

---

22. **USS *Missouri*:** Its capital is Jefferson City and its biggest city is Kansas City.
23. **Arkansas Chugabug:** Its capital and biggest city is Little Rock; the airport is named after ex-governor Bill Clinton.
24. **Colorado Beetle:** Its capital and biggest city is Denver, the 'Mile High City', exactly one mile above sea level.
25. **1600 Pennsylvania Avenue:** Its capital is Harrisburg and its biggest city is Philadelphia.
26. ***New York Times***: Its capital is Albany and its biggest city is New York City.
27. **Florida Pearl:** Its capital is Tallahassee and its biggest city is Jacksonville.
28. **Ohio Express:** Its capital and biggest city is Columbus, followed by Cleveland and Cincinnati.
29. ***Mississippi Burning***: Its capital and biggest city is Jackson, named after Andrew Jackson.
30. **Oregon Trail:** Its capital is Salem and its biggest city is Portland.

1. **Music:** Who is the lead singer with M People?
2. **TV:** Lynne Perrie played which character in *Coronation Street* from 1971 to 1994?
3. **Food & Drink:** Which brand, famous for its evaporated and condensed milk, was sold to Nestlé in 1985?
4. **Sport & Games:** Which grey horse trained by David Elsworth won the King George VI Chase at Kempton four times between 1986 and 1990?
5. **TV:** What did Dame Edna Everage often throw into the audience during her TV shows?
6. **Music:** Which singer had UK No. 1 hits with 'Smile' in 2006 and 'The Fear' in 2008?
7. **Art & Literature:** In the William Wordsworth poem *I Wandered Lonely as a Cloud*, what did he see a host of?
8. **TV:** Which actor played Private Pike in *Dad's Army*?
9. **Music:** Which group had a UK No. 1 in 1993 with 'Young at Heart'?
10. **Pot Luck:** In the UK, which cream colour is considered to be the standard colour of household paint?
11. **History:** On which ship did the Pilgrim Fathers travel to the USA from Plymouth in 1620?
12. **Food & Drink:** Which TV chef, the daughter of a former Chancellor of the Exchequer, was married to businessman Charles Saatchi from 2003 to 2013?

13. **TV:** Patricia Routledge plays which character in *Keeping Up Appearances*?
14. **Music:** Which 1968 song from the Foundations includes the lyrics 'I need you (I need you) more than anyone, darlin', you know that I have from the start'?

15. **Films:** Which 2011 comedy-drama film featured a group of British pensioners moving to a retirement hotel in Jaipur in India?
16. **Art & Literature:** Which author wrote the 1978 novel *The Sea, The Sea*?
17. **Music:** Which 1982 song gave Patrice Rushen her only UK Top 10 hit?
18. **TV:** Which actress played Ena Sharples in *Coronation Street* for 20 years from 1960 to 1980?
19. **Sport & Games:** Which English golfer won his first major, the US Open, in 2013?
20. **Music:** Elkie Brooks' first two hits were 'Pearl's a Singer' and 'Sunshine after the Rain' followed by which song, a Top 20 hit in 1978?
21. **Art & Literature:** What was the name of the two series of paintings by Vincent van Gogh, the first showing flowers on the ground and the other showing flowers in vases?
22. **TV:** On which street in the fictional Fairview, Eagle State was the TV show *Desperate Housewives* set?
23. **Films:** Which 1989 film stars Morgan Freeman as a chauffeur driving an elderly lady around and Dan Aykroyd as her son Boolie?
24. **Entertainment:** What was the name of the character in the *Beano*, also known as the Strongman's Daughter?
25. **Music:** Which instrument is very similar to a violin but is slightly larger and has a lower, deeper sound?
26. **TV:** Which original member of the *Eggheads* quiz team retired in 2014, being replaced by the returning CJ de Mooi?
27. **Mythology:** In Greek mythology, what was the name of the hunter who fell in love with his own reflection?
28. **Music:** With which song did Vince Hill have a UK No. 2 hit in 1967?

29. **Entertainment:** In the comic strip Bananaman, Eric Wimp lived at no. 29 on which road?

30. **TV:** Which actress played driver Samantha 'Sam' Stewart in *Foyle's War* from 2002 to 2015?

31. **Music:** Which song became the signature song for the US singer and ukulele player Tiny Tim?

32. **Sport & Games:** Jim Clark won the Formula 1 world title in 1963 and 1965 driving for which team?

33. **Food & Drink:** From which plant does the spice saffron come?

34. **Places:** Which hill at the northern end of Regent's Park is over 200 feet high and has clear views of Central London?

35. **People:** What is the name of the daughter of Paula Yates and Michael Hutchence, adopted by Bob Geldof after her mother's death?

36. **Entertainment:** What is the name of the baby left on Popeye's doorstep whom he raises as his son?

37. **TV:** Which Australian-American actress played FBI agent Samantha Spade in *Without a Trace* and Detective Carrie Wells in *Unforgettable*?

38. **Religion:** In the Gospel of St Matthew, what is the alternative name for the Christmas Star which includes the place of Jesus' birth?

39. **Sport & Games:** Which filly, trained in France by Maurice Zilber, won the King George VI and Queen Elizabeth Stakes twice, in 1973 and 1974?

40. **Art & Literature:** Which series of over 250 oil paintings did Claude Monet paint of his flower garden?

1. **Heather Small:** The band name was taken from the first letter of Mike Pickering's name who formed the band.
2. **Ivy Tilsley / Brennan:** She was first married to Bert Tilsley (Peter Dudley) and then Don Brennan (Geoffrey Hinsliff).
3. **Carnation:** The brand was originally created in 1899 and a town in Washington state is named after the company.
4. **Desert Orchid:** He also famously won the 1989 Cheltenham Gold Cup and the 1990 Irish Grand National.
5. **Gladioli:** She was played by Barry Humphries, who also had the alter ego Sir Les Patterson, and her assistant was Madge Allsop, played by Emily Perry.
6. **Lily Allen:** She had a further No. 1 in 2013 with a cover of Keane's 'Somewhere Only We Know' which featured in the John Lewis Christmas advert.
7. **Golden Daffodils:** He published a collection of poems, *Lyrical Ballads*, with Samuel Taylor Coleridge which is considered to have started the Romantic movement.
8. **Ian Lavender:** He has also featured as Derek Harkinson in *EastEnders*.
9. **The Bluebells:** It originally reached the Top 10 in 1984 but got to No. 1 nine years later after being featured in a Volkswagen commercial.
10. **Magnolia:** There was a 1999 film of that name with Tom Cruise, Philip Seymour Hoffman, William H Macy and Julianne Moore. It was the last film of Jason Robards.
11. *The Mayflower:* They landed at what is now called Plymouth in Massachusetts.
12. **Nigella Lawson:** *Nigella damascena* is also called love-in-a-mist.

13. **Hyacinth Bucket:** It was written by Roy Clarke who also wrote *Last of the Summer Wine* and *Open All Hours*.
14. **'Build Me Up Buttercup':** It reached No. 2 but their debut hit 'Baby Now That I've Found You' got to No. 1.
15. ***The Best Exotic Marigold Hotel*:** It starred Judi Dench, Bill Nighy, Maggie Smith and Tom Wilkinson.
16. **Iris Murdoch:** She was later portrayed by Kate Winslet and Judi Dench in a 2001 film?
17. **'Forget Me Nots':** The song was sampled on George Michael's 1996 No. 1 'Fastlove' and Will Smith's 1997 No. 1 'Men in Black'.
18. **Violet Carson:** She appeared in the first episode of *Coronation Street* in 1960 and also regularly appeared on the TV show *Stars on Sunday*.
19. **Justin Rose:** He was born in Johannesburg and also won the gold medal at the 2016 Olympics in Rio de Janeiro.
20. **'Lilac Wine':** She started out in a group called Vinegar Joe with Robert Palmer.
21. ***Sunflowers*:** The 1956 film *Lust For Life* starred Kirk Douglas as Van Gogh and Anthony Quinn as his friend Paul Gauguin.
22. **Wisteria Lane:** The series starred Teri Hatcher, Eva Longoria, Felicity Huffman and Marcia Cross.
23. ***Driving Miss Daisy*:** Jessica Tandy played the elderly lady and won the Best Actress Oscar.
24. **Pansy Potter:** She also appeared in the *Sparky* comic which, along with *Buzz*, merged with the *Topper* and then eventually the *Beezer*.
25. **Viola:** A string quartet usually consists of two violins, a viola and a cello.
26. **Daphne (Fowler):** The original *Eggheads* were Kevin Ashman, Daphne Fowler, Chris Hughes, Judith Keppel and CJ de Mooi.

27. **Narcissus:** Echo fell in love with Narcissus but was unable to tell him after being cursed by Hera.
28. **'Edelweiss':** It was originally from the musical *Sound of Music*, sung by Christopher Plummer in the 1965 film.

HARD (3 Points)

29. **Acacia Road:** The strip first appeared in the comic *Nutty* before it merged with the *Dandy* in 1985.
30. **Honeysuckle Weeks:** The series was written by Anthony Horowitz who was also chosen to write James Bond books by the Ian Fleming estate.
31. **'Tiptoe Through the Tulips':** His real name was Herbert Buckingham Khaury.
32. **Lotus:** Other title winners driving for Lotus were Graham Hill (1968), Jochen Rindt (1970), Emerson Fittipaldi (1972) and Mario Andretti (1978).
33. **Crocus (sativus):** Iran produces well over 90% of the world's saffron.
34. **Primrose Hill:** London Zoo, which opened in 1828, is also in Regent's Park.
35. **Tiger Lily:** Her full name is Heavenly Hiraani Tiger Lily Hutchence.
36. **Swee'pea:** Other regular characters were Olive Oyl, Bluto and Wimpy.
37. **Poppy Montgomery:** Her sisters were also called after flowers; Montgomery was her mother's maiden name.
38. **Star of Bethlehem:** Bethlehem is a Palestinian city in the West Bank, about six miles south of Jerusalem.
39. **Dahlia:** She was the only horse to have achieved the feat until Swain did the same in 1997 and 1998.
40. *Water Lilies:* His painting *Impression, Sunrise*, of his home town of Le Havre, is thought to have inspired the name Impressionism.

1. **Music:** Which music genre, sometimes called rap music, developed in the Bronx in New York City in the 1970s?
2. **TV:** Which actor, whose real name is James Bradford, played Leonard 'Oz' Osborne in *Auf Wiedersehen, Pet*?
3. **Sport & Games:** Which is the slowest of the four official styles in competitive swimming?
4. **Films:** Which 1985 film starred Michael J Fox as Marty McFly and Christopher Lloyd as Dr Emmett 'Doc' Brown travelling back to 1955 in a time-travelling DeLorean?
5. **Places:** What is the name of the observation wheel on the South Bank of the River Thames which opened in 2000?
6. **Pot Luck:** What is the oldest military award still presented to Americans wounded or killed in action, originally called the Badge of Military Merit?
7. **Music:** Whose debut hit in 1970 was 'Come and Get It' which reached No. 4 in the UK charts?
8. **Art & Literature:** What is the name for the part of a book's cover that encloses the inner edges of the pages and typically bears the title and the author's name?
9. **Animals & Nature:** Which flatfish's common variety is often named after Dover due to the port landing the most fish of this type back in the 19th century?
10. **Sport & Games:** What nickname has been given to the 'handball' goal scored by Diego Maradona in the 1986 World Cup quarter-final v England?
11. **Music:** Guy Garvey is the singer and lyricist with which rock band?
12. **Films:** Which 1975 Steven Spielberg film was about a giant great white shark attacking beachgoers on Amity Island?

13. **TV:** What was the name of the last all-girl dance troupe to appear on *Top of the Pops*, appearing from 1976–81?

14. **People:** Which politician, Labour leader from 1980–83, lost the 1983 general election to Margaret Thatcher?

15. **Music:** With which Rolling Stones song did Wayne Gibson have a UK Top 20 hit in 1974?

16. **Art & Literature:** What is the section at the end of a book that gives additional information on the contents of the text?

17. **Maths & Numbers:** What is the name of a straight line from the centre of a circle to any point on its circumference?

18. **Music:** Which song achieved the highest chart position in the UK for XTC, reaching No. 10 in 1982?

19. **Theatre:** Which Willy Russell musical is about two fraternal twins called Mickey and Eddie who were separated at birth?

20. **TV:** Which TV comedy series, set in Liverpool and written by Carla Lane and Myra Taylor, starred Nerys Hughes as Sandra and Polly James as Beryl?

21. **Music:** Which singer had a UK No. 12 hit in 1984 with 'One Night in Bangkok'?

22. **Films:** Which 1997 science fiction action film stars John Travolta and Nicolas Cage as an FBI agent and a terrorist who assume each other's appearance?

23. **Animals & Nature:** What is the name of the young of an elephant?

24. **Art & Literature:** Which Irish author's best-known work is the Booker Prize-winning *The Sea, The Sea*?

25. **Music:** Which 1995 song by Mike + the Mechanics starts with the lyrics 'Looking back...', followed by the title?

26. **Sport & Games:** In horse racing, what is the shortest distance that a horse can win a race by?

27. **Films:** Which 1983 comedy film starred Steve Martin as pioneering neurosurgeon Dr Michael Hfuhruhurr and Kathleen Turner as his scheming wife?

28. **TV:** What was the nickname of Loretta Swit's character Major Margaret Houlihan in the TV series *M*A*S*H*?

HARD (3 Points)

---

29. **Music:** What is the name of the lead vocalist and guitarist with the British rock band Skunk Anansie?

30. **Art & Literature:** Which 1929 Ernest Hemingway novel is about an American driving an ambulance in the Italian army during World War I?

31. **History:** In December 1890, which creek in South Dakota was the site of a massacre of over 200 Native Americans from the Lakota Sioux tribe?

32. **Sport & Games:** Which outbreak was responsible for the cancellation of the Cheltenham Festival in 2001?

33. **Music:** Fifth Dimension's 1969 hit 'Aquarius/Let the Sunshine In' came from which rock musical?

34. **Religion:** What is the name of the Christian moveable feast day that falls on the Sunday before Easter?

35. **Art & Literature:** In the pirates' song in *Treasure Island* by Robert Louis Stevenson, what is the first line of the song which precedes 'Yo-ho-ho and a bottle of rum'?

36. **Films:** Which 1999 film stars Denzel Washington as a forensics expert confined to bed after being paralysed?

37. **Music:** Which American rock band have had minor hits with 'Phantom Limb', and 'Simple Song' in the 2000s?

38. **History:** What name is given to the conflict between Britain and Spain from 1739–48, the name deriving from the severed ear of the captain of a British ship?

39. **Art & Literature:** Which novel by Zadie Smith features Archie Jones and his Muslim friend Samad Iqbal?

40. **Music:** Toploader had two Top 10 hits in 2000, 'Dancing in the Moonlight' was one but what was the other?

EASY (1 Point)

1. **Hip-hop:** The 1979 hit 'Rapper's Delight' by the Sugarhill Gang was the first mainstream rap record.
2. **Jimmy Nail:** He also played the title role in *Spender* and had a 1992 UK No. 1 hit with 'Ain't No Doubt'?
3. **Breaststroke:** Olympic gold medal winners include Anita Lonsborough (1960), David Wilkie (1976), Duncan Goodhew (1980), Adrian Moorhouse (1988) and Adam Peaty (2016).
4. *Back To The Future***:** It was directed by Robert Zemeckis whose other films included *Romancing the Stone* (1984), *Who Framed Roger Rabbit* (1988) and *Forrest Gump* (1994).
5. **London Eye:** There are 32 capsules but numbered up to 33 as there is no number 13.
6. **Purple Heart:** John F Kennedy was the only president to receive one for saving a man's life during World War II.
7. **Badfinger:** They had 2 other hits, 'No Matter What' and 'Day After Day', and Pete Ham and Tom Evans wrote 'Without You', a No. 1 for Nilsson and Mariah Carey.
8. **Spine:** The spine consists of 33 vertebrae, 24 bones making up the cervical, thoracic and lumbar sections and 9 fused bones making up the sacrum and coccyx.
9. **Sole:** Dover sole are found in the Atlantic and Mediterranean but a Pacific Dover sole is a flounder.
10. **Hand of God:** Argentina went on to beat Belgium 2-0 in the semi-finals and West Germany 3-2 in the final.
11. **Elbow:** The band are from Bury and their two best-selling singles are 'Grounds for Divorce' and 'One Day Like This'.
12. *Jaws***:** The film starred Roy Scheider, Richard Dreyfuss and Robert Shaw and was based on the book by Peter Benchley.

13. **Legs & Co:** They were the fourth dance troupe after the Go-Jos, Pan's People and Ruby Flipper, and were followed by Zoo.
14. **Michael Foot:** He followed former prime minister James Callaghan and was succeeded by Neil Kinnock.
15. **'Under My Thumb':** It wasn't released as a single by the Rolling Stones but was a minor hit for the Who.
16. **Appendix:** The plural is appendices and a bibliography of references would also appear at the end of a book.
17. **Radius:** The area of a circle = πr^2 and the circumference of a circle = $2\pi r$ where r = the radius and π = 3.142.
18. **'Senses Working Overtime':** The band were from Swindon and the main songwriter was Andy Partridge.
19. **_Blood Brothers_:** Willy Russell also wrote the plays _Educating Rita_ and _Shirley Valentine_ and both became very successful films in 1983 and 1989 respectively.
20. **_The Liver Birds_:** Pauline Collins featured in the pilot with Nerys Hughes.
21. **Murray Head:** The song is from _Chess_, written by Tim Rice, Benny Andersson and Björn Ulvaeus.
22. **_Face/Off_:** Cage's first two wives were Patricia Arquette and Lisa Marie Presley and he is Francis Ford Coppola's nephew.
23. **Calf:** The calf is also the young of camels, giraffes, rhinos, hippos, dolphins, whales and walruses.
24. **Iris Murdoch:** Judi Dench and Kate Winslet played her in the 2001 film _Iris_ about her life, with Jim Broadbent and Hugh Bonneville playing her husband John Bayley.
25. **'Over My Shoulder':** The group is fronted by Mike Rutherford (ex-Genesis) and has included Paul Carrack (ex-Squeeze) and Paul Young (ex-Sad Café).
26. **A Nose:** The winning distances then increase to short head, head, short neck (France), neck and half a length.

27. **The Man with Two Brains**: Steve Martin's films include *Planes, Trains and Automobiles* (1987), *Dirty Rotten Scoundrels* (1988) and *Parenthood* (1989).
28. **Hot Lips**: She appeared in all 11 seasons from 1972–83, as did Alan Alda (Hawkeye Pierce), Jamie Farr (Corporal Klinger) and William Christopher (Father Mulcahy).

HARD (3 Points)

29. **Skin:** Her real name is Deborah Dyer.
30. *A Farewell To Arms*: The 1996 film *In Love and War* depicts Hemingway's own life driving an Italian ambulance during the war.
31. **Wounded Knee:** Their chief, Spotted Elk, was killed in the battle; he was the half-brother of Sitting Bull.
32. **Foot and Mouth Disease:** Only 2,000 cases were reported but over 6 million animals were killed.
33. *Hair*: The US singer Oliver also had a UK No. 6 hit in 1969 with 'Good Morning Starshine' from the musical.
34. **Palm Sunday:** It celebrates the entry of Jesus into Jerusalem.
35. **'Fifteen Men on the Dead Man's Chest':** An island in the British Virgin Islands is called Dead Chest Island.
36. *The Bone Collector*: The film co-stars Angelina Jolie as officer Amelia Donaghy and Queen Latifah as his carer.
37. **The Shins:** The band are from Albuquerque.
38. **The War of Jenkins' Ear:** Its name was coined by Thomas Carlyle in 1858.
39. *White Teeth*: Channel 4 screened a 4-part TV adaptation in 2002 starring Phil Davis and Om Puri.
40. **'Achilles Heel':** Toploader were the last British band to play at the old Wembley when supporting Bon Jovi.

1. **Pot Luck:** In the popular saying, if something you say or do does not go down very well, you say, 'It went down like a...'?

2. **Music:** Tom Jones' first No. 1 in the UK in 1965 was 'It's Not Unusual' but his second in 1966 was called the '... ... ... of Home'?

3. **Proverbs:** Complete the traditional proverb: ... ... flock together?

4. **Entertainment:** In 'bingo lingo', what does the caller normally shout to tell the players that he is about to start?

5. **Sport & Games:** In cricket, what name is given to any run not scored from the bat e.g. no-balls, byes and wides, also called sundries in Australia?

6. **Transport & Travel:** What name is given to goods sold which are exempt from tax, often sold at airports, which are taken out of the country?

7. **House & Home:** What name is given to the moisture that has entered the walls having moved upwards from the ground by capillary action?

8. **Religion:** In the Church of England marriage vows, what five words follow '...to love and to cherish... ... ...?

9. **Pot Luck:** Complete the traditional saying, '... ..., three's a crowd'?

10. **Music:** In the ABBA song lyrics, what three words complete the opening chorus line '... ... ... a man after midnight'?

11. **Sport & Games:** In professional darts, what does the scorer call to the players and the audience to tell them that the match has now officially started?

12. **Food & Drink:** What is the English translation of *Santé!* (French), *Salute!* (Italian) and *Prost!* (German)?

13. **Films:** Which 1961 film starred Cliff Richard as Nicky and Robert Morley as his father trying to close down their youth club, the film giving Cliff Richard and the Shadows a UK No. 1 hit in 1962?

14. **Proverbs:** Meaning that your offensive words or actions are likely to rebound on you at some point, finish the expression, 'Chickens always come … … …'.

15. **Animals & Nature:** Gatekeeper, cabbage white and meadow brown are types of which insects?

16. **Religion:** In Church of England wedding vows, what five words follow 'for better for worse, for richer for poorer, … … … … …?

17. **Music:** Elvis Costello's first UK chart entry was in 1977 with the song 'Watching … … '?

18. **Pot Luck:** Which three-word phrase is sometimes used about the Women's Institute, describing their making of preserves and the singing of their anthem?

19. **Food & Drink:** A spurtle is a wooden Scottish kitchen tool for traditionally stirring what?

20. **Music:** David Gates was lead singer and chief songwriter with which American group?

21. **Films:** Complete the 1976 film title in which Robert De Niro played Travis Bickle: '… *Driver*'.

22. **History:** Dating back to the 15th century, what name is given to a sequence of pictures viewed through a lens or hole in a box, formerly offered as public entertainment?

23. **Places:** Which Spanish holiday resort on the Costa Blanca was a fishing village until the 1960s but now has over 300 skyscrapers?

24. **Music:** Which Irish group's first and last UK No. 1 hits were 'C'est La Vie' and 'Blame it on the Weatherman'?

25. **TV:** The TV show *Noel's House Party* was set in the fictional village of Crinkley… what?

26. **Food & Drink:** In the brewing of beer, what name is given to the mixture of powdered malt and hot water?
27. **Religion:** The Quakers are alternatively known as the Religious Society of ...?
28. **Music:** Which US group had a UK No. 2 hit in 1992 with 'People Everyday'?

HARD (3 Points)

29. **TV:** In the TV show *South Park*, what was the nickname of Jerome McElroy, voiced by Isaac Hayes?
30. **Art & Literature:** What is the name of the 1928 René Magritte painting which shows a man and a woman attempting to kiss but covered by grey hoods?
31. **Music:** Which 1963 hit for Tony Bennett was originally a French song called 'La Belle Vie' by Sacha Distel?
32. **Science & Medicine:** Which type of star is the most common in the Milky Way, an example being Proxima Centauri, the closest star to the Sun?
33. **Pot Luck:** Which three letters or numbers form the first three digits of London PO box numbers?
34. **Religion:** In the Gospels of Matthew and Mark, Jesus says: 'Love the Lord thy God' is the most important commandment and the second is to '... ... ...' as thyself.
35. **Theatre:** 'The Lambeth Walk' is from which musical?
36. **TV:** What was the cross-eyed lion in *Daktari* called?
37. **Films:** In the film *Casablanca*, which song does Ingrid Bergman ask Sam, played by Dooley Wilson, to play?
38. **Pot Luck:** When two people are completely different, unsuitable for each other or are unable to agree, the phrase often used is '... ... ... shall meet'.
39. **Sport & Games:** Which horse won the 1976 Grand National?
40. **Music:** Which song was a 1980 double-A side with 'Simon Templar' for Splodgenessabounds?

1. **Lead Balloon:** *Lead Balloon* (2006–11) starred Jack Dee as comedian Rick Spleen with Raquel Cassidy (Mel), Sean Power (Marty) and Anna Crilly (Magda).
2. **Green Green Grass:** *The Green Green Grass* (2005–09) was a spin-off of *Only Fools and Horses* with Boycie and Marlene.
3. **Birds of a Feather:** *Birds of a Feather* (1989–98) starred Pauline Quirke (Sharon), Linda Robson (Tracey) and Lesley Joseph (Dorien).
4. **Eyes Down:** *Eyes Down* (2003–04) starred Paul O'Grady as Ray Temple, a bingo caller in Liverpool.
5. **Extras:** *Extras* (2005–07) starred Ricky Gervais, Stephen Merchant and Ashley Jensen.
6. **Duty Free:** *Duty Free* (1984–86) starred Keith Barron and Gwen Taylor as David and Amy Pearce.
7. **Rising Damp:** *Rising Damp* (1974–78) starred Leonard Rossiter as Rigsby with Richard Beckinsale (Alan), Don Warrington (Philip) and Frances de la Tour (Ruth).
8. **Till Death Us Do Part:** *Till Death Us Do Part* (1965–75) starred Warren Mitchell as Alf Garnett with Dandy Nichols (Else), Una Stubbs (Rita) and Tony Booth (Mike).
9. **Two's Company:** *Two's Company* (1975–79) starred Elaine Strich and Donald Sinden.
10. **Gimme Gimme Gimme:** *Gimme Gimme Gimme* (1999–2001) starred Kathy Burke and James Dreyfus.
11. **Game On:** *Game On* (1995–98) starred Samantha Janus, Ben Chaplin, Matthew Cottle and Neil Stuke.
12. **Cheers:** *Cheers* (1982–93) starred Ted Danson, Shelley Long, George Wendt, John Ratzenberger, Kelsey Grammer, Woody Harrelson, Kirstie Alley and Rhea Perlman.

13. **The Young Ones**: *The Young Ones* (1982–84) starred Rik Mayall (Rick), Adrian Edmondson (Vyvyan), Nigel Planer (Neil) and Christopher Ryan (Mike).
14. **Home to Roost:** *Home to Roost* (1985–90) starred John Thaw as Henry Willows and Reece Dinsdale as his son Matthew.
15. **Butterflies:** *Butterflies* (1978–83) starred Wendy Craig as Ria Parkinson with Geoffrey Palmer (Ben), Nicholas Lyndhurst (Adam) and Andrew Hall (Russell).
16. **In Sickness and in Health:** *In Sickness and in Health* (1985–92) was a follow-up to *Till Death Us Do Part* with the same main characters apart from Tony Booth.
17. **The Detectives:** *The Detectives* (1993–97) starred Jasper Carrott as Bob Louis and Robert Powell as Dave Briggs.
18. **Jam and Jerusalem:** *Jam and Jerusalem* (2006–09) starred Jennifer Saunders, Dawn French and Joanna Lumley.
19. **Porridge:** *Porridge* (1974–77) starred Ronnie Barker as Fletcher and Richard Beckinsale as Godber.
20. **Bread:** *Bread* (1986–91) was about the Boswell family led by matriarch Nellie played by Jean Boht.
21. **Taxi:** *Taxi* (1978–83) starred Danny DeVito (Louie), Judd Hirsch (Alex) and Marilu Henner (Elaine).
22. **Peep Show:** *Peep Show* (2003–15) starred David Mitchell as Mark and Robert Webb as Jeremy ('Jez').
23. **Benidorm:** In *Benidorm* (2007–18), the only characters in all ten series were Mateo and Jacqueline.
24. **B*witched:** *Bewitched* (1964–72) starred Elizabeth Montgomery as the witch Samantha.
25. **Bottom:** *Bottom* (1991–95) starred Adrian Edmondson (Eddie Hitler) and Rik Mayall (Richie Richard).
26. **Mash:** *M*A*S*H* (1972–83) starred Alan Alda (Hawkeye), Mike Farrell (BJ), Gary Burghoff (Radar) and Harry Morgan (Col. Potter) amongst others.

27. **Friends:** *Friends* (1994–2004) starred Jennifer Aniston, Courteney Cox, Lisa Kudrow, Matt LeBlanc, Matthew Perry and David Schwimmer.
28. **Arrested Development:** *Arrested Development* (2003–06 and 2013–) is produced / narrated by Ron Howard.

HARD (3 Points)

29. **Chef:** *Chef!* (1993–96) starred Lenny Henry as the chef.
30. ***The Lovers*:** *The Lovers* (1970–71) starred Richard Beckinsale as Geoffrey and Paula Wilcox as Beryl.
31. **'The Good Life':** *The Good Life* (1975–78) starred Richard Briers and Felicity Kendal as Tom and Barbara Good and Paul Eddington and Penelope Keith as Jerry and Margo Leadbetter.
32. **Red Dwarf:** *Red Dwarf* (1988–99, 2009, 2012–17) starred Craig Charles (Lister) and Chris Barrie (Rimmer).
33. **W1A:** *W1A* (2014–17) starred Hugh Bonneville and Jessica Hynes in the roles they played in *Twenty Twelve*.
34. **Love Thy Neighbour:** *Love Thy Neighbour* (1972–76) starred Jack Smethurst as Eddie and Rudolph Walker as Bill.
35. ***Me and My Girl*:** *Me and My Girl* (1984–88) starred Richard O'Sullivan as Simon Harrap.
36. **Clarence:** *Clarence* (1988) starred Ronnie Barker as Clarence.
37. **'As Time Goes By':** *As Time Goes By* (1992–2005) starred Judi Dench and Geoffrey Palmer.
38. **Never the Twain:** *Never the Twain* (1981–91) starred Windsor Davies and Donald Sinden as antique dealers.
39. **Rag Trade:** *The Rag Trade* (1961–63) starred Reg Varney, Sheila Hancock and Barbara Windsor.
40. **'Two Pints of Lager and a Packet of Crisps':** *Two Pints of Lager and a Packet of Crisps* (2001–11) starred Will Mellor, Natalie Casey, Ralf Little and Sheridan Smith.

1. **Sport & Games:** Which English team won the European Cup in 1979 and 1980?
2. **Music:** Whose first UK hit was 'Heaven is a Place on Earth' which reached No. 1 in 1987?
3. **Pot Luck:** Which Midlands building did Sir Basil Spence design when it was rebuilt after World War II?
4. **TV:** Who appeared with Karl Pilkington in *An Idiot Abroad 3* and has presented the game show *Tenable*?
5. **Places:** What is the capital of Western Australia?
6. **Sport & Games:** Which British driver was never world champion but finished second four times in the 1950s?
7. **History:** St Augustine was first to hold which position?
8. **TV:** The opening titles for *Sale of the Century* were, 'And now, from ......(where?), it's the quiz of the week!'?
9. **Films:** Which 1986 film starred Paul Hogan as a bushman in Walkabout Creek and Linda Kozlowski as a journalist?
10. **Sport & Games:** Which famous race is run at Epsom in June over a mile and a half for 3-year-old colts?
11. **Food & Drink:** Which bottled beer, launched in 1927 in the NE of England, is sometimes called 'Brown Dog'?
12. **Music:** Which was the only UK No. 1 for Simple Minds?
13. **Pot Luck:** In the children's nursery rhyme, Doctor Foster went to where?
14. **Sport & Games:** Which horse race run at Doncaster is the key race on the first Saturday of the Flat season?
15. **People:** Who became Rod Stewart's third wife when they married in 2007?

16. **Places:** Which is the most populous city in Alabama?

17. **History:** From which English port did the RMS *Titanic* begin her ill-fated voyage to New York in 1912?
18. **Art & Literature:** Which US novelist wrote the novels *Call of the Wild* and *White Fang*?
19. **Music:** Which US singer had a UK No. 3 hit in 1974 with 'Hang on in There Baby'?
20. **TV:** David Ogden Stiers played which character in *M*A*S*H*?
21. **Sport & Games:** Which rugby union team's home ground is Welford Road?
22. **History:** Which was the last battle of the English Civil War in 1651, won by Cromwell's New Model Army?
23. **Transport & Travel:** What was the equivalent car made by Austin to the Morris Oxford?
24. **Sport & Games:** What was the home ground of Huddersfield Town before the Kirklees Stadium?
25. **Art & Literature:** Which Leeds-born author's first novel, *A Woman of Substance*, was first published in 1979?
26. **Food & Drink:** Which hard, dry cracker was invented by physician William Oliver around 1750?
27. **People:** Which yachtsman sailed around the world in *Gipsy Moth IV* in 1967?
28. **Sport & Games:** Who scored the goal in the 1976 FA Cup final for Southampton to beat Manchester United?
29. **Religion:** St Mungo is patron saint of which British city?
30. **Places:** The Ashmolean Museum can be found in which establishment?
31. **Sport & Games:** Who became the first non-English club to win the FA Cup when they lifted the trophy in 1927?
32. **TV:** The series *Our Zoo* starred Lee Ingleby as George Mottershead, the founder of which establishment?
33. **Music:** Which song was the debut hit for Roger Whittaker, reaching No. 12 in the UK in 1969?
34. **Sport & Games:** Which Scottish sprinter won the Olympic 100 metres gold medal in 1980 in Moscow?

35. **Words:** Which word can mean the main body of a ship and also the outer covering of a fruit or seed?

HARD (3 Points)

---

36. **History:** The last prime minister of Queen Victoria's reign served under which title?
37. **Music:** Fiddler's Dram had a 1979 hit with which song?
38. **Animals & Nature:** Which Scottish breed of cattle is usually black, but sometimes red, and has no horns?
39. **Food & Drink:** Which shortcrust custard and fruit tart is topped with raspberry jam, coconut and a cherry?
40. **Films:** Which actor played Logan 5 in the 1976 film *Logan's Run* and Basil Exposition in all of the *Austin Powers* films?
41. **Music:** With which US singer did Syreeta duet on the 1979 UK No. 2 hit 'With You I'm Born Again'?
42. **Sport & Games:** What is the name of the domestic first-class cricket competition in Australia, played by six of the states?
43. **Places:** What name did the Pilgrim Fathers give to the colony in Massachusetts where they landed in 1620?
44. **History:** The Cato Street Conspiracy of 1820 was an attempt to kill which prime minister and his cabinet?
45. **Music:** What is the title of the song known as 'Danny Boy'?
46. **TV:** What was the name of the TV series set in Roman Britain starring Rory McGrath and Jimmy Mulville?
47. **Sport & Games:** Which player scored the winning goal in the last minute of the 1979 FA Cup final for Arsenal?
48. **Places:** Which seaside resort forms part of the Merseyside town of Wallasey on the Wirral peninsula?
49. **People:** Eaton Hall in Eccleston, Cheshire is the family country seat of which English duke?
50. **Music:** Which song was Mike Oldfield's highest UK chart hit, a sea song arrangement which got to No. 3 in 1976?

1. **Nottingham Forest:** In 1979 they beat Malmo 1-0 in Munich and in 1980 they beat Hamburg 1-0 in Madrid.
2. **Belinda Carlisle:** She originally came to fame as the lead singer of the American new wave band the Go-Gos.
3. **Coventry Cathedral:** Its full name is the Cathedral Church of St Michael.
4. **Warwick Davis:** He played Wicket in *Return of the Jedi*, originally due to be played by Kenny Baker (R2-D2).
5. **Perth:** It sits at the mouth of the Swan River with Fremantle Harbour serving as the port of Perth.
6. **Stirling Moss:** He lost the 1958 title to Mike Hawthorn by just one point.
7. **Archbishop of Canterbury:** His official residence is Lambeth Palace.
8. **Norwich:** The show ran from 1971–83 and was hosted by Nicholas Parsons, with the voice of John Benson.
9. *Crocodile Dundee*: They were married from 1990–2014.
10. **The Derby:** The race is also open to fillies but most fillies run in the Oaks the day before over the same distance.
11. **Newcastle Brown Ale:** It is Clint Eastwood's favourite beer.
12. **'Belfast Child':** Jim Kerr was married to Chrissie Hynde from 1984–90 and Patsy Kensit from 1992–96.
13. **Gloucester:** King Edward II is buried in Gloucester Cathedral, having been allegedly murdered in Berkeley Castle in 1327.
14. **The Lincoln:** It is so called as it used to be run at the course in Lincoln before its closure in 1964.
15. **Penny Lancaster:** His first two wives were Alana Hamilton (previously married to George Hamilton) and Rachel Hunter.

16. **Birmingham:** Alabama is known as the Yellowhammer State and its capital is Montgomery.
17. **Southampton:** The liner then docked at Cherbourg in France and Cobh (then Queenstown) in Ireland.
18. **Jack London:** Both novels were set during the Klondike Gold Rush and he was just 40 years old when he died.
19. **Johnny Bristol:** He also wrote the song 'Love Me for a Reason', the only UK No. 1 for the Osmonds in 1974.
20. **(Major) Charles (Emerson) Winchester (III):** He replaced the departed Frank Burns played by Larry Linville.
21. **Leicester Tigers:** Famous players include Dusty Hare, Rory Underwood, Martin Johnson and Austin Healey.
22. **Battle of Worcester:** Charles II hid in an oak tree in Boscobel Wood before fleeing to France.
23. **(Austin) Cambridge:** Nuffield (Morris, MG, Riley and Wolseley) merged with Austin in 1952 to form BMC.
24. **Leeds Road:** The new stadium has been sponsored by McAlpine, Galpharm and John Smith's.
25. **Barbara Taylor Bradford:** She was in the same primary school class as writer Alan Bennett.
26. **Bath Oliver:** Bath was the home of Jane Austen and also William Herschel when he discovered Uranus in 1781.
27. **Sir Francis Chichester:** He was the first person to sail single-handedly from west to east via the great capes.
28. **Bobby Stokes:** Stokes died at the age of just 44 in 1995 on the same day as Southampton legend Ted Drake.
29. **Glasgow:** They hosted the 2014 Commonwealth Games.
30. **Oxford University:** It is the second-oldest university but the oldest is the University of Bologna, founded in 1088.
31. **Cardiff City:** They have also been runners-up twice, in 1925 to Sheffield United and 2008 to Portsmouth.
32. **Chester Zoo:** The zoo first opened in 1931.
33. **'Durham Town':** He was born in Kenya and his biggest UK hit was 'The Last Farewell', No. 2 in 1975.

34. **Allan Wells:** He dead-heated with Mike McFarlane in the 1982 Commonwealth Games 200m in Brisbane.
35. **Hull:** Poet and novelist Philip Larkin was the librarian at the University of Hull for over 30 years.

36. **Lord (3rd Marquess of) Salisbury:** His name was Robert Gascoyne-Cecil and he was prime minister three times.
37. **'Day Trip to Bangor':** Bangor is on the River Dee and is the only British racecourse without a grandstand.
38. **Aberdeen Angus:** Bulls can weigh up to 850kg.
39. **Manchester Tart:** A variation of the dish includes bananas.
40. **Michael York:** He was in the 1973 film *The Three Musketeers* with Oliver Reed, Frank Finlay and Richard Chamberlain.
41. **Billy Preston:** He was credited on the Beatles' 'Get Back', one of only two non-Beatles credited on a track.
42. **Sheffield Shield:** No team represents Northern Territory due to the size of the population and the rainy season.
43. **Plymouth (Rock):** They had set sail from Plymouth, England.
44. **Lord Liverpool:** Born Robert Jenkinson, he took over in 1812 after the assassination of Spencer Perceval.
45. **'Londonderry Air':** It is played as the sporting anthem of Northern Ireland at the Commonwealth Games.
46. *Chelmsford 123*: McGrath and Mulville met at Cambridge and co-founded Hat Trick Productions.
47. **Alan Sunderland:** He began his career at Wolves before moving to Arsenal and then to Ipswich Town.
48. **New Brighton:** It has the UK's longest promenade.
49. **Duke of Westminster:** Gerald Grosvenor, the 6th Duke of Westminster, died of a heart attack aged 64 in 2016.
50. **'Portsmouth':** He had two No. 4 hits with 'Il Dulce Jubilo' in 1975 and 'Moonlight Shadow' in 1983.

EASY (1 Point)

1. **TV:** Which BBC drama series has starred Jenny Agutter as Sister Julienne and Pam Ferris as Sister Evangelina?
2. **Music:** Which duo had hits called 'Yesterday Once More' and 'Only Yesterday' in the 1970s?
3. **Sport & Games:** Which large-headed golf club, also called the 1 wood, is able to strike the ball the furthest from the tee?
4. **TV:** Robson Green and Jerome Flynn starred in which 1990s drama series as members of the King's Fusiliers?
5. **Entertainment:** Which magician was born in Caerphilly in 1921 before moving to Exeter at the age of three?
6. **Pot Luck:** What was the nickname of a pre-decimal sixpence?
7. **TV:** In the game show *Deal or No Deal*, whom did Noel Edmonds ring to get an offer for the contestants?
8. **History:** Napoleon once supposedly called England a nation of...what?
9. **Sport & Games:** Which character is represented by the purple playing piece in Cluedo?
10. **TV:** What was the name of Ronnie Barker's character in *Porridge*?
11. **Art & Literature:** Which writer's first published book was *The Tale of Peter Rabbit* in 1902?
12. **TV:** What was the maiden name of Jessie Wallace's character in *EastEnders*?
13. **Pot Luck:** What was the name of the armed citizen militia supporting the Army during World War II?
14. **Music:** Which song was the debut hit for Gerry Rafferty, reaching No. 3 in the UK in 1978?
15. **TV:** Which children's TV character was voiced by Neil Morrissey?

16. **Films:** Which 1976 Martin Scorsese film stars Robert De Niro as Travis Bickle, a Vietnam War veteran?
17. **Sport & Games:** Which horse won the Cheltenham Gold Cup in five consecutive years from 1932 to 1936?
18. **TV:** Barry Evans and Robin Nedwell starred in which sitcom, the first in a series about junior doctors?
19. **Food & Drink:** Highland Cream is a brand of whisky distilled by which company?
20. **People:** Who was the first American astronaut to travel into space in 1961?
21. **TV:** Which TV show starred Lenny Henry as Gareth Blackstock running a gourmet restaurant?
22. **Music:** Which group's only No. 1 was 'January' in 1975?
23. **Theatre:** Which Harold Pinter play, which premiered in 1960, is about a tramp being taken in by two brothers?
24. **TV:** Which TV show revolved around the players at Earls Park FC and their partners?
25. **Music:** Which 1966 Beatles No. 1 was the only song for which they appeared live in the *Top of the Pops* studio?
26. **Sport & Games:** Which British athlete won a gold medal in the women's 800m at the 1964 Tokyo Olympics?
27. **TV:** Which show, which looks to turn round the fortunes of a hotel, has been hosted by Alex Polizzi since 2008?
28. **Places:** What is the name of the stretch of water that separates the North and South Islands of New Zealand?
29. **Films:** Which 2002 film starred Jennifer Lopez as a New York hotel worker and Ralph Fiennes as a politician?
30. **TV:** Which children's TV show is about a firefighter and his colleagues in the Welsh town of Pontypandy?
31. **Sport & Games:** Which Indian wicketkeeper played 46 Tests and played for Lancashire from 1968 to 1976?
32. **TV:** In which legal drama did Martin Shaw star in the title role as a High Court judge?
33. **Music:** Who had a hit in 1982 with 'Mama Used To Say'?

34. **Sport & Games:** Which ex-Ipswich Town player played in a bloodied England shirt in Sweden in 1989?
35. **Films:** Which 1967 Mel Brooks satirical comedy film featured the song 'Springtime for Hitler'?

HARD (3 Points)
---

36. **TV:** Tom Hiddleston starred as the titular character in which 2016 series based on a book by John le Carré?
37. **Sport & Games:** Which darts player is 'The Artist'?
38. **Theatre:** Which 1949 play by Arthur Miller revolves around the life of the main character Willy Loman?
39. **TV:** Which actor appeared as Liam Connor in *Coronation Street* and Thomas Barrow in *Downton Abbey*?
40. **Art & Literature:** What does the W.B. stand for in the name of the Irish poet W.B. Yeats?
41. **Music:** Which American new wave band had a minor hit in 1982 with 'Christmas Wrapping'?
42. **Sport & Games:** What was jockey Harry Wragg's nickname?
43. **Films:** Which 2016 film stars Ben Affleck as a financial expert looking into criminal organisations' books?
44. **Art & Literature:** Which Irish author wrote the 1766 novel *The Vicar of Wakefield*?
45. **TV:** Which sitcom from 1969–70 starred Bryan Pringle (Cheese & Egg) and Trevor Bannister (Heavy Breathing)?
46. **Films:** Which black-and-white silent film won the 2011 Best Picture Oscar?
47. **Music:** Which song was a 1984 hit for Smiley Culture?
48. **Sport & Games:** Which British cyclist won 4 track cycling World Championship gold medals from 1968 to 1973?
49. **TV:** Who played Makepeace in *Dempsey and Makepeace*?
50. **Films:** Which 1981 film starred Jack Nicholson and Jessica Lange plotting to murder her husband?

1. *Call the Midwife*: The series is based on the memoirs of Sister Jennifer Worth (née Lee) played by Jessica Raine.
2. **The Carpenters:** Karen died in 1983 aged just 32.
3. **Driver:** Players may play with a maximum of 14 clubs.
4. *Soldier, Soldier*: As Robson & Jerome they had 3 UK No. 1 hits starting with 'Unchained Melody' which featured in the show.
5. **Tommy Cooper:** He collapsed from a heart attack on live TV on stage at Her Majesty's Theatre in London in 1984 and later died, aged 63.
6. **Tanner:** It was worth 2½ new pence and there were 240 old pence in a pound.
7. **The Banker:** The show ran from 2005 to 2016.
8. **Shopkeepers:** He was born in Corsica, exiled on Elba in 1814 but escaped and then exiled again after Waterloo on St Helena where he died.
9. **Professor Plum:** Mrs White was replaced by Dr Orchid (pink) in 2016.
10. **Norman Stanley Fletcher:** His wife was called Isobel and his children were Ingrid, Raymond and Marion.
11. **Beatrix Potter:** *The Tale of Squirrel Nutkin* followed in 1903.
12. **Kat Slater:** She married Alfie Moon played by Shane Richie in the 2003 Christmas special.
13. **The Home Guard:** The characters in *Dad's Army* were famously in the Home Guard.
14. **'Baker Street':** The saxophone solo was the subject of an urban myth that it was played by *Blockbusters*' Bob Holness.
15. **Bob the Builder:** He had the Christmas No. 1 song in the UK in 2000 with 'Can We Fix It?'.

16. ***Taxi Driver***: The film won Best Picture Oscar and De Niro and Jodie Foster won Best Actor and Best Supporting Actress.
17. **Golden Miller**: He is also the only horse to win the Gold Cup and the Grand National in the same year (1934).
18. ***Doctor in the House***: It was set in St Swithin's Hospital and followed by *Doctor at Large* and *Doctor in Charge*.
19. **Teacher's**: The whisky is still produced in Glasgow but is now owned by Beam Suntory.
20. **Alan Shepard**: John Glenn was the first to orbit the Earth and Shepard also played golf on the Moon.
21. ***Chef!***: The series ran from 1993 to 1996.
22. **Pilot**: Founding members David Paton and Billy Lyall were previously with the Bay City Rollers.
23. ***The Caretaker***: It was made into a 1963 film starring Alan Bates, Donald Pleasence and Robert Shaw.
24. ***Footballers' Wives***: The show ran from 2002 to 2006.
25. **'Paperback Writer'**: The BBC wiped the videotape but 11 seconds of footage was found in 2019 by a collector.
26. **Ann Packer**: She also won a silver medal in the 400m.
27. ***The Hotel Inspector***: She has also hosted *Alex Polizzi: The Fixer* since 2012 which deals with family businesses.
28. **Cook Strait**: It is named after James Cook who was the first European commander to sail through it.
29. ***Maid in Manhattan***: Natasha Richardson also stars in the film, daughter of Vanessa Redgrave and wife of Liam Neeson until her death in 2009.
30. ***Fireman Sam***: Pontypandy is a portmanteau of Pontypridd and Tonypandy.
31. **Farokh Engineer**: He played against Derbyshire in June 1975 when the match was stopped due to snow!
32. ***Judge John Deed***: It ran for six series from 2001 to 2007.
33. **Junior**: Born Norman Giscombe, he had been in the group Linx from 1980 to 1982.

258

34. **Terry Butcher:** He was born in Singapore in 1958.
35. ***The Producers:*** It was the first film directed by Mel Brooks and was later turned into a musical.

HARD (3 Points)

36. ***The Night Manager:*** The series also starred Hugh Laurie, Olivia Colman and Tom Hollander.
37. **Kevin Painter:** He lost 7-6 in the 2004 PDC final to Phil Taylor, the first PDC final to go to a sudden death leg.
38. ***Death of a Salesman:*** Miller was the third husband of Marilyn Monroe, after Jim Dougherty and Joe DiMaggio.
39. **Rob James-Collier:** He was actually born Robert Collier but had to change his name to comply with Equity rules.
40. **William Butler:** Yeats was the first Irish winner of the Nobel Prize for Literature in 1923, followed two years later by George Bernard Shaw.
41. **The Waitresses:** Lead singer Patty Donahue had previously been a waitress.
42. **The Head Waiter:** He was called that due to his 'come from behind' style.
43. ***The Accountant:*** Affleck was married to Jennifer Garner from 2005 to 2018; they met on the set of *Pearl Harbor*.
44. **Oliver Goldsmith:** He also wrote the play *She Stoops to Conquer* and the poem *The Deserted Village*.
45. ***The Dustbinmen:*** It also starred Graham Haberfield who more famously played Jerry Booth in *Coronation Street*.
46. ***The Artist:*** Jean Dujardin also won the Best Actor Oscar.
47. **'Police Officer':** His real name is David Emmanuel.
48. **Hugh Porter:** He married Olympic gold medal-winning swimmer Anita Lonsbrough in 1965.
49. **Glynis Barber:** She married Michael Brandon who played James Dempsey in 1989.
50. ***The Postman Always Rings Twice:*** It was based on a 1934 novel by James M Cain.

EASY (1 Point)

1. **Sport & Games:** Where is the home of Surrey CCC?
2. **Art & Literature:** Michael Bond is best known for his series of children's stories about which bear?
3. **History:** Sir Christopher Wren designed the rebuild of which cathedral after the Great Fire of London in 1666?
4. **Sport & Games:** Arsenal played at which ground before their move to the Emirates Stadium in 2006?
5. **Art & Literature:** On which London street did Sherlock Holmes live?
6. **Pot Luck:** What is nicknamed 'The Old Lady of Threadneedle Street'?
7. **History:** What was the name of the eldest child of Queen Victoria, born in 1840?
8. **Sport & Games:** Which England player missed the decisive penalty in the Euro '96 semi-final defeat to Germany?
9. **Films:** Which actress first sang the song 'On the Good Ship Lollipop' in the 1934 film *Bright Eyes*?
10. **Art & Literature:** Antony Gormley's 20-metre tall steel sculpture near Gateshead is called ..... *of the North*?
11. **Sport & Games:** The rules of boxing established in 1867 were named after the Marquess of where?
12. **TV:** Which children's drama series set in a secondary school, written by Phil Redmond, first aired in 1978?
13. **History:** Which 1815 battle was fought between Napoleon's army and the British and Prussian armies?
14. **Sport & Games:** Although officially called the Boleyn Ground, what was the familiar name of West Ham United's home ground until 2016?
15. **Transport & Travel:** What is the British equivalent of the German car brand Opel?

16. **Pot Luck:** Which bridge, formerly spanning the Thames, was sold to a US entrepreneur and rebuilt in Arizona?

17. **Sport & Games:** Which team were called 'The Invincibles' when they won the Premier League in the 2003–04 season?

18. **Entertainment:** What was the name of the West London venue, now the Apollo, from 1962 to 1992?

19. **Sport & Games:** Which park next to Buckingham Palace has a similar name to two football grounds?

20. **Places:** Which palace is home to the Duke and Duchess of Cambridge and other members of the Royal family?

21. **Transport & Travel:** The Eurostar terminus in London moved from Waterloo in 2007 to which other station?

22. **Sport & Games:** In Monopoly, the green group properties are Regent Street, Oxford Street and......?

23. **Places:** Hampton Court Palace is in which borough?

24. **Sport & Games:** Which team lost the 1984 FA Cup final to Everton?

25. **History:** The murderer Jack the Ripper committed his crimes in which area of London?

26. **Films:** The 1949 Ealing comedy with Stanley Holloway and Margaret Rutherford was *Passport to ....*?

27. **Sport & Games:** In cricket, for what does the letter M stand in the MCC's name?

28. **Places:** In which London park is London Zoo?

29. **Animals & Nature:** The Royal Botanic Gardens are based in which south-west London location?

30. **Sport & Games:** In which greyhound stadium was the Uruguay v France match played in the 1966 World Cup?

31. **Places:** The Houses of Parliament is known as the Palace of ....?

32. **Sport & Games:** Which team beat Liverpool in the 1988 FA Cup final?

33. **TV:** Which actor played DI Charlie Barlow in *Z Cars*?

34. **Transport & Travel:** The West Coast Main Line starts in Glasgow and arrives at which London station?
35. **Sport & Games:** What was the name of the home ground of Reading FC until 1998?

HARD (3 Points)

---

36. **Places:** One Canada Square is in which area of London?
37. **People:** Karl Marx is buried in which London cemetery?
38. **Sport & Games:** Which Scottish football club play their home games at Hampden Park?
39. **Music:** Which venue is home to the London Symphony Orchestra and the BBC Symphony Orchestra?
40. **Transport & Travel:** At which venue was the British Motor Show held between 1937 and 1976?
41. **Sport & Games:** On a Monopoly board, which station is between Whitechapel Road and The Angel, Islington?
42. **History:** Which pub name is derived from Charles II hiding in a tree after the Battle of Worcester in 1651?
43. **Sport & Games:** What is the name of the race for two-year-olds over seven furlongs at Royal Ascot?
44. **Places:** Lord's cricket ground is in which district of the City of Westminster?
45. **Entertainment:** Which game on Radio 4's *I'm Sorry I Haven't a Clue* involves listing a series of locations?
46. **Sport & Games:** The Oval, the home ground of Surrey CCC, is located in which area of London?
47. **Places:** What is the residence of the Lord Mayor of London?
48. **Religion:** Which Dominican Order's name is derived from their dark cloaks and the French for brothers?
49. **Sport & Games:** What was the location of the Football Association from 1929 to 2000?
50. **Places:** What is the name of the series of chalk cliffs on the south coast between Seaford and Eastbourne?

1. **The Oval:** It also hosted the first FA Cup final in 1872.
2. **Paddington:** He comes from Peru and likes marmalade sandwiches.
3. **St Paul's:** It sits on Ludgate Hill, the highest point in the city, and is the seat of the Bishop of London.
4. **Highbury:** Arsenal's all-time record goalscorer Thierry Henry scored a hat-trick in the last game at the ground.
5. **Baker Street:** He lived at 221B Baker Street with Dr John Watson and his landlady was Mrs Hudson.
6. **Bank of England:** It was established in 1694 and was nationalised in 1946.
7. **Victoria:** She married German Emperor and King of Prussia Frederick III, but he died 99 days into his reign.
8. **Gareth Southgate:** Shearer, Platt, Pearce, Gascoigne and Sheringham all scored their penalties before sudden death.
9. **Shirley Temple:** As an adult she was US Ambassador to Ghana and later to Czechoslovakia.
10. *Angel*: Completed in 1998, it has a wingspan of 54 metres.
11. **Queensberry:** Not to be confused with Queensbury, a London area which didn't exist before the Tube station.
12. *Grange Hill*: Phil Redmond has also written the Channel 4 soaps *Brookside* and *Hollyoaks*.
13. **Waterloo:** It was the last battle of the Napoleonic Wars, Louis XVIII was restored to the throne and Napoleon was exiled to St Helena.
14. **Upton Park:** They moved to the London Stadium in 2016, originally constructed for the 2012 Olympics.
15. **Vauxhall:** Famous models include the Victor, Viva, Cavalier, Carlton and Astra.

16. **London Bridge:** It was rebuilt in Lake Havasu City, Arizona.

17. **Arsenal:** Preston NE were first given that nickname after going unbeaten in 1888–89, the first to win the Double.

18. **Hammersmith Odeon:** In 1958, Buddy Holly performed two shows at the venue, his last in the UK.

19. **St James's Park:** Newcastle United play at St James' Park but Exeter City play at St James Park.

20. **Kensington Palace:** Others include Princess Eugenie and the Duke and Duchess of Kent.

21. **St Pancras:** The first Eurostar left Waterloo in 1994.

22. **Bond Street:** It is home to Sotheby's auction house.

23. **Richmond:** The palace was originally built for Cardinal Wolsey and then given to Henry VIII.

24. **Watford:** Their chairman at the time was Elton John who oversaw their three promotions in seven years.

25. **Whitechapel:** Home to Royal London Hospital and many of the best Bangladeshi restaurants on Brick Lane.

26. *Pimlico*: Other Ealing comedies released that year were *Whisky Galore!* and *Kind Hearts and Coronets*.

27. **Marylebone:** The club was founded in 1787 and is based at Lord's, the home of Middlesex CCC.

28. **Regent's Park:** It opened in 1828 and in 1831 all animals from the Tower of London were transferred there.

29. **Kew Gardens:** It has its own police force called the Kew Constabulary.

30. **White City:** It was built for the 1908 Olympics and hosted the Greyhound Derby until 1985.

31. **Westminster:** Big Ben is the name of the bell housed in the Elizabeth Tower.

32. **Wimbledon:** Lawrie Sanchez scored; Dave Beasant was the first goalkeeper to save a penalty in the final.

33. **Stratford Johns:** The cast included Frank Windsor, James Ellis, Colin Welland and Brian Blessed.

34. **Euston:** It was named after Euston Hall in Suffolk.
35. **Elm Park:** They moved to the Madejski Stadium, named after the chairman, along with RU club London Irish.

HARD (3 Points)

---

36. **Canary Wharf:** It was the tallest building in the UK before the Shard was built.
37. **Highgate:** Other famous people buried there are Michael Faraday, Henry Moore and George Eliot.
38. **Queen's Park:** They are Scotland's oldest club and the only amateur club playing league football.
39. **Barbican Centre:** The Royal Shakespeare Company moved back there in 2013, having left in 2001.
40. **Earl's Court:** From 1978 it moved to the NEC, Birmingham until 2004.
41. **King's Cross:** The other stations are Marylebone, Fenchurch Street and Liverpool Street.
42. **Royal Oak:** It is the third most common name in the UK after the Red Lion and the Crown.
43. **Chesham Stakes:** The race was 6 furlongs until 1996.
44. **St John's Wood:** It is also the home of Abbey Road Studios where the Beatles recorded most of their hits.
45. **Mornington Crescent:** The Tube station is on the Northern line and is in Camden Town.
46. **Kennington:** Not to be confused with the Kensington Oval which is in Bridgetown, Barbados.
47. **Mansion House:** The position is different to the Mayor of London, a position held by Sadiq Khan since 2016.
48. **Black Friars:** Franciscans wear grey; Carmelites white.
49. **Lancaster Gate:** In 2000 the FA moved to Soho Square before relocating to Wembley Stadium in 2009.
50. **Seven Sisters:** They form part of the South Downs and are used for filming in place of the White Cliffs of Dover.

1. **Films:** Which Batman villain did Danny DeVito play in the 1992 film *Batman Returns*?

2. **TV:** What is the name of the character played by Steve Coogan who is a TV and radio presenter from Norwich?

3. **Pot Luck:** In the game of Cluedo, which character is represented by the blue playing piece?

4. **Places:** Which group of Spanish islands in the Atlantic Ocean are located just off the west coast of Morocco?

5. **Sport & Games:** What is the nickname of Sheffield Wednesday football club?

6. **Music:** Who is the lead singer with Jamiroquai?

7. **Films:** Which 2000 animated film revolves around escaping from a farm when the farmer decides to sell pies not eggs?

8. **Transport & Travel:** InterCity was a brand name introduced by which organisation in 1966?

9. **Entertainment:** Who was Rod Hull's co-star in most of his television appearances during the 1970s and 1980s?

10. **History:** What is the name of the wizard who commonly features in Arthurian legend?

11. **Films:** What was the wrestling ring name of actor Dwayne Johnson?

12. **Food & Drink:** Which chef presented BBC's *Saturday Kitchen* from 2006 to 2016?

13. **Sport & Games:** What is the nickname of the New Zealand men's rugby league team?

14. **Places:** Ankara is the capital of which country, part of which is in Europe and part in Asia?

15. **Films:** Johnny Depp played which character in the *Pirates of the Caribbean* series of films?

16. **Music:** Which instrumental hit released in 1968 gave Fleetwood Mac their only UK No. 1?

17. **Pot Luck:** Which type of festive decoration is typically in the form of strings of colourful triangular flags?
18. **TV:** Burt Ward played which superhero in a 1960s TV series?

MEDIUM (2 Points)

---

19. **Films:** Which 1975 film stars Jack Nicholson as Randle McMurphy, a patient in a mental institution?
20. **Sport & Games:** Which rugby union team was formed in 2003 by the merger of the Neath and Swansea clubs?
21. **Art & Literature:** Which author wrote *Gulliver's Travels*?
22. **Music:** Which singer had a UK No. 8 hit in 1975 with 'Right Back Where We Started From'?
23. **TV:** What was the full name of the character played by Kelsey Grammer in the sitcom *Cheers*?
24. **Films:** Which actor starred with Woody Harrelson in the 1992 film *White Men Can't Jump* and with Sylvester Stallone in the 1993 film *Demolition Man*?
25. **Music:** Which US singer had a UK No. 6 hit in 1974 with 'I Can Help'?
26. **Sport & Games:** What is the name of the NFL American football team based in Baltimore?
27. **TV:** Which US soap featured the feuding Gioberti and Channing families in the Californian wine industry?
28. **Films:** Jodie Foster won the Best Actress Award for playing which character in the 1991 film *Silence of the Lambs*?
29. **Music:** Manfred Mann had three No. 1 hits: 'Do Wah Diddy Diddy' in 1964, 'Mighty Quinn' in 1968 and which other hit in 1966?
30. **Sport & Games:** Which chess piece is informally called the castle?
31. **Transport & Travel:** In which hydroplane did Donald Campbell set 7 water speed records from 1955–1964?

32. **Films:** Which 1995 James Bond film was the first to star Pierce Brosnan and the first to feature Judi Dench as M and Samantha Bond as Miss Moneypenny?

33. **Music:** Snowy White had a UK No. 6 hit in 1983 with which song?

34. **Sport & Games:** In boxing, which weight (excluding superweights) comes between flyweight and featherweight?

35. **Art & Literature:** Which 1930 novel by Arthur Ransome tells about the adventures of the children of the Walker and Blackett families in the Lake District?

36. **TV:** Which children's TV show, which ran from 1968 to 1980, featured presenters including Tony Bastable, Susan Stranks, Mick Robertson and Jenny Hanley?

37. **Places:** The Bedfordshire town between Dunstable and Milton Keynes is called Leighton ....?

38. **Pot Luck:** What was the common name for women who served in the Women's Royal Naval Service?

39. **Music:** Canadian singer Anne Murray was best known for which song which reached No. 23 in the UK in 1970?

40. **Films:** Which actor played Superman in the first four *Superman* films?

41. **TV:** In the 1960s TV series *The Man from U.N.C.L.E.*, which organisation were the primary adversary of U.N.C.L.E.?

42. **Art & Literature:** Which 1975 book by Jack Higgins told the story of a German plot to kidnap Winston Churchill?

HARD (3 Points)

---

43. **Music:** Which group had a UK No. 10 hit in 1982 with 'Wishing (If I Had a Photograph of You)'?

44. **TV:** Which BBC costume drama, which ran from 2008 to 2011, starred Julia Sawalha as Dorcas Lane, a postmistress at the local post office?

45. **Sport & Games:** Which American football team won the Super Bowl for the first time in the 2013 season?
46. **Films:** Which 1933 Marx Brothers film, the last starring Zeppo, was also the title of a Laurel and Hardy film?
47. **People:** Which leader of the RMT trade union died in March 2014?
48. **Music:** Which band from Leeds had UK Top 20 hits in 2007 with 'I'm Not Sorry' and 'Take Her Back'?
49. **Art & Literature:** What is the name of the lawyer in the 1960 Harper Lee novel *To Kill a Mockingbird* who defends a black man accused of rape?
50. **TV:** In the comedy panel show *Shooting Stars*, which game would start with Vic Reeves and Bob Mortimer encouraging the guests to summon down a large bird?
51. **Music:** Which group had a 1973 hit with 'Nice One Cyril', about Cyril Knowles, the Tottenham Hotspur left back?
52. **Sport & Games:** Which US golfer won his only Major when he won the 1992 US Open at Pebble Beach?
53. **Places:** What is the name of the uninhabited island east of Anglesey, named after a bird of the auk family?
54. **Music:** Who had a No. 4 hit in 1972 with 'Loop Di Love'?
55. **History:** What was the original name of Sir Francis Drake's ship *Golden Hind*?
56. **TV:** Which actress played Carla Tortelli through all 11 series of the US sitcom *Cheers*?
57. **Music:** Which group had their biggest hit with the 1966 hit 'Guantanamera' which reached No. 7 in the UK?
58. **Entertainment:** What was the nickname of the comedian Freddie Davies who wore a bowler hat?
59. **Films:** In the 1986 film *Top Gun*, Tom Cruise played Maverick, Val Kilmer played Iceman but which character did Anthony Edwards play?
60. **Sport & Games:** In golf, a birdie is one under par, an eagle two under par and an albatross three under par but what term is used for four under par?

EASY (1 Point)

1. **The Penguin:** Played by Burgess Meredith in the '60s TV series, his real name is Oswald Chesterfield Cobblepot.
2. **Alan Partridge:** The character was created by Coogan and Armando Iannucci.
3. **Mrs Peacock:** The object of the game is to discover who murdered Dr Black.
4. **Canary Islands:** The islands include Tenerife, Lanzarote, Gran Canaria and Fuerteventura.
5. **The Owls:** The club started as an offshoot of the Wednesday Cricket Club, so called after their day off.
6. **Jay Kay:** His real name is Jason Luis Cheetham and took his name from his mother, Karen Kay.
7. *Chicken Run*: It features the voices of Mel Gibson, Julia Sawalha, Timothy Spall and Miranda Richardson.
8. **British Rail:** The InterCity 125 high speed diesel train is widely credited with saving British Rail.
9. **Emu:** Hull died in 1999 when he fell from his roof whilst trying to adjust his TV aerial.
10. **Merlin:** King Arthur's father is reputed to be Uther Pendragon.
11. **The Rock:** His first leading role was in the 2002 fantasy film *The Scorpion King*.
12. **James Martin:** In 2017 he began presenting *Saturday Morning with James Martin* on ITV at the same time.
13. **The Kiwis:** The All Blacks play rugby union, the All Whites football, the Black Caps cricket, the Tall Blacks basketball.
14. **Turkey:** Other countries straddling Europe and Asia are Russia, Georgia, Kazakhstan and Azerbaijan.
15. **Jack Sparrow:** Depp claims that the character is partly based on the Rolling Stones' Keith Richards, who appears as his father in the third and fourth films.

16. **'Albatross'**: They twice reached No. 2 with 'Man of the World' and 'Oh Well' and again with 'Albatross' in 1973.
17. **Bunting**: The origin of the word is uncertain but *bunt* means colourful in German.
18. **Robin**: His real name in the series is Dick Grayson and Batman's is Bruce Wayne.

MEDIUM (2 Points)

19. ***One Flew Over The Cuckoo's Nest***: It was based on the 1962 novel written by Ken Kesey.
20. **Ospreys**: Since 2005 they have played home games at the Liberty Stadium, sharing it with Swansea City FC.
21. **Jonathan Swift**: Gulliver's first name was Lemuel and Swift was the first to use the phrase 'sweetness and light'.
22. **Maxine Nightingale**: Her only other UK hit was 'Love Hit Me' which reached No. 11 in 1977.
23. **Frasier Crane**: He subsequently starred in 11 series of *Frasier* which ran from 1993 to 2004.
24. **Wesley Snipes**: He also starred as Michael Jackson's nemesis in the music video of his 1987 hit 'Bad'.
25. **Billy Swan**: Swan wrote the song on a keyboard given by Kris Kristofferson and Rita Coolidge as a wedding gift.
26. **Ravens**: They won the Super Bowl of the 2000 and 2012 seasons.
27. ***Falcon Crest***: Jane Wyman, the first wife of future president Ronald Reagan, played Angela Channing.
28. **Clarice Starling**: Foster decided not to play the character in the 2001 sequel *Hannibal*, the part going to Julianne Moore.
29. **'Pretty Flamingo'**: Cream's Jack Bruce played on the track and soon after singer Paul Jones was replaced by Mike d'Abo.
30. **Rook**: The rook and king can 'castle' where the king moves two squares and the rook 'jumps' the king.

31. **Bluebird (K7):** He was the son of Malcolm Campbell but died in 1967, aged 45, on Coniston Water during another attempt.
32. *GoldenEye*: During World War II, author Ian Fleming was involved in 'Operation Goldeneye' and subsequently named his estate in Jamaica Goldeneye.
33. **'Bird of Paradise':** Real name Terence White, he has been a guitarist with both Thin Lizzy and Pink Floyd.
34. **Bantamweight:** The next three categories are lightweight, welterweight and middleweight.
35. *Swallows and Amazons*: He wrote a further 11 books in the series, all about the adventures of various children.
36. *Magpie*: Jenny Hanley's mother was Dinah Sheridan, who starred in *Genevieve* and *The Railway Children*.
37. **Buzzard:** It is often bracketed with nearby Linslade and the area referred to as Leighton-Linslade.
38. **Wrens:** It was fully integrated into the Royal Navy in 1993.
39. **'Snowbird':** The song was recorded by Elvis Presley and Bing Crosby amongst others.
40. **Christopher Reeve:** He was left quadriplegic after a riding accident in 1995 and died aged just 52 in 2004.
41. **THRUSH:** U.N.C.L.E. stood for United Network Command for Law and Enforcement but the TV series did not disclose the meaning of THRUSH.
42. *The Eagle Has Landed*: The 1976 film starred Michael Caine, Donald Sutherland and Robert Duvall.

HARD (3 Points)

43. **A Flock of Seagulls:** Lead singer Mike Score had a distinctive haircut which was referenced in *Pulp Fiction* by Samuel L Jackson when referring to Roger.
44. *Lark Rise to Candleford*: The series was based on Flora Thompson's trilogy of semi-autobiographical novels.

45. **Seattle Seahawks:** Pete Carroll coached them to a 43-8 win over the Denver Broncos.

46. *Duck Soup*: The film stars Groucho as Rufus T Firefly, who becomes the leader of the country of Freedonia.

47. **Bob Crow:** The full title of the union is the Rail, Maritime and Transport Workers Union.

48. **The Pigeon Detectives:** The band supported the Kaiser Chiefs, also from Leeds, on three dates in 2007.

49. **Atticus Finch:** He is played by Gregory Peck in the 1962 film of the same name.

50. **The Dove From Above:** The original team captains were Ulrika Jonsson and Mark Lamarr.

51. **Cockerel Chorus:** It was released before the 1973 League Cup final in which Spurs beat Norwich City; Knowles died in 1991 at the age of just 47.

52. **Tom Kite:** He tied for second in the 1978 Open when Jack Nicklaus won his third and final Open and was also a Ryder Cup captain in 1997 along with Seve Ballesteros.

53. **Puffin Island:** It is now better known for its great cormorant colony.

54. **Shag:** Shag was a pseudonym of Jonathan King, as was Sakkarin; he was also involved with St Cecilia and the Piglets.

55. *Pelican*: It was renamed by Drake in 1578 in honour of his patron whose crest was a golden hind.

56. **Rhea Perlman:** She married Danny DeVito in 1982 and they played the parents of Matilda in the 1996 film.

57. **The Sandpipers:** It is a Cuban song about a woman from Guantanamo.

58. **Parrot-Face:** He came to fame on *Opportunity Knocks* as his alter ego called Samuel Tweet.

59. **Goose:** He also played Dr Mark Greene in *ER* for which he won the 1997 Golden Globe Award for Best Actor.

60. **Condor:** Mike Crean holed his 517-yard drive on the par 5 ninth hole in Denver in 2002.

1. **Films:** In the 1967 film, whom did Doctor Dolittle want to talk to?

2. **Sport & Games:** What surname is shared by former Republic of Ireland footballers Roy and Robbie?

3. **Religion:** In the Bible, what is the first book of the Old Testament?

4. **Transport & Travel:** What misnomer is sometimes given to an aircraft's flight recorder since it is orange to aid recovery?

5. **Food & Drink:** Which fruit preserve is made from the juice and peel of citrus fruits?

6. **TV:** What was the name of the prison in the sitcom *Porridge*?

7. **Films:** What was the shared surname of actresses Audrey and Katharine, although they weren't related?

8. **Music:** The title of Maria Muldaur's only chart entry was 'Midnight at the .....'?

9. **Pot Luck:** What telephone number do you need to dial in the USA for the emergency services?

10. **Places:** Austin is the capital of which US state?

11. **TV:** The comedy panel show hosted first by Mark Lamarr and then by Simon Amstell was called *Never Mind the.........*?

12. **Films:** Steve Guttenberg played Carey Mahoney in the 1984 film *...... Academy*, as well as three sequels?

13. **Science & Medicine:** Which brand of adhesive bandages made by Johnson & Johnson has become a generic name for bandages in the US and Australia?

14. **TV:** What colour is Thomas the Tank Engine?

15. **Animals & Nature:** What name is given to the dominant bee in a beehive, usually the mother of most of the bees in the hive?

16. **Pot Luck:** According to the proverb, what gather no moss?

17. **Words:** Which word can mean a sweet preserve, congestion or a difficult situation?

18. **Food & Drink:** A Mimosa cocktail is champagne and orange juice in equal parts but which similar cocktail has two parts champagne and one part orange juice?

MEDIUM (2 Points)

---

19. **Places:** Which area of London's West End is well known for its entertainment, nightlife and boutiques?

20. **Theatre:** Which musical features the characters Roxie Hart, Velma Kelly and Billy Flynn?

21. **Animals & Nature:** The word aquiline refers to which birds?

22. **Transport & Travel:** Which is the longest numbered road in the UK, connecting London to Edinburgh?

23. **Sport & Games:** In poker, a pair of bullets is a pair of which playing card?

24. **Places:** The Brandenburg Gate can be found in which European city?

25. **Religion:** Although Jesus was born in Bethlehem, in which city in Israel did he spend most of his life?

26. **Animals & Nature:** What is the abbreviated name for the dinosaur whose name comes from the Greek for 'tyrant lizard' and the Latin for 'king'?

27. **TV:** The sequel to the sitcom ...And Mother Makes Three starring Wendy Craig was ...And Mother Makes ....?

28. **Food & Drink:** The chocolate-based dessert, usually with a crunchy biscuit-type base and a gooey chocolate sauce is called a Mississippi ...... pie?

29. **Pot Luck:** What was the shortened reference number of the Unemployment Benefit Form 40?

30. **Words:** Which two-word Latin phrase means 'the existing state of things'?

31. **Music:** Which 1962 novelty song by Bernard Cribbins involves three men struggling to move an item of furniture and having numerous tea breaks?

32. **Places:** Holy Island is an alternative name for which island off the Northumberland coast?

33. **Animals & Nature:** Which predatory fish with sharp teeth and strong jaws are indigenous to South America?

34. **Religion:** In Buddhism, what is the name of the highest state that someone can attain?

35. **TV:** What was the name of the 1950s TV show that featured Bill, Ben and Little Weed?

36. **Films:** What is the name of Dorothy's dog in the 1939 film *The Wizard of Oz*?

37. **Music:** Which group named themselves after the postcode of Walthamstow where they were from?

38. **Animals & Nature:** What is the second largest species of penguin after the emperor penguin?

39. **Shopping & Fashion:** The menswear company who specialise in formal wear, founded in 1851 by Moses Moss, was renamed after his sons to Moss ....?

40. **Food & Drink:** Which sweet dessert is commonly made with milk or cream and sugar, sometimes flavoured and is thickened with gelatin?

41. **TV:** The sitcom *Cheers* was set in which US city?

42. **Pot Luck:** What shortened name is used for a postgraduate doctoral degree, short for a Doctor of Philosophy?

HARD (3 Points)

43. **Sport & Games:** Which collective name is given to the 11th, 12th and 13th holes at Augusta National in Georgia, home to the US Masters?

44. **Religion:** Which Christian feast day is celebrated on 1 November?

45. **History:** In the wake of France's defeat in the Franco-Prussian War, what name was given to the supporters of the short-lived 1871 Paris Commune?
46. **TV:** Which series of monologues written by Alan Bennett included Thora Hird in 'A Cream Cracker under the Settee'?
47. **Shopping & Fashion:** Which group owned by Philip Green includes Topshop, Burton and Dorothy Perkins?
48. **Animals & Nature:** Harebells is another name for which woodland plants, producing tubular violet-blue flowers?
49. **TV:** Which 1976 documentary series showed life on board the aircraft carrier HMS *Ark Royal*?
50. **Films:** Which 2013 film centres on the motor racing rivalry between James Hunt and Niki Lauda?
51. **History:** John Lilburne, Richard Overton and William Walwyn were three members of which movement, popular at the end of the First English Civil War?
52. **Pot Luck:** What name is given to the group of eight top US universities, including Harvard, Yale and Princeton?
53. **Places:** The Trinita dei Monti church in Rome is reached by climbing the Spanish ......?
54. **Films:** The 1968 film *Barbarella* starred Jane Fonda as a space traveller sent to find which scientist?
55. **Sport & Games:** Which horse ridden by Olivier Peslier and trained by Geoff Huffer won the English and Irish 2000 Guineas in 2007?
56. **History:** Which agricultural pioneer invented the seed drill in 1701?
57. **Films:** In the 1976 film *Taxi Driver*, Robert De Niro plays ...... Bickle?
58. **Sport & Games:** Lucas Radebe moved to Leeds United in 1994 from which South African club?
59. **Pot Luck:** What is the currency in Hong Kong and Singapore?
60. **History:** Which medieval torture device was a cabinet big enough for a person with spikes on the inside?

1. **The Animals:** Lead singer was Eric Burdon; Alan Price went on to record with Georgie Fame; Chas Chandler became the manager of Jimi Hendrix and Slade.
2. **Keane:** Their lead singer is Tom Chaplin and they are from Battle in East Sussex.
3. **Genesis:** Members have included Tony Banks, Mike Rutherford, Peter Gabriel, Phil Collins, Steve Hackett.
4. **Black Box:** The Italian band had a 1989 UK No. 1 with 'Ride on Time'.
5. **Marmalade:** They had a UK No. 1 in 1968 with the Beatles' 'Ob-La-Di Ob-La-Da'.
6. **Slade:** The members were Noddy Holder, Dave Hill, Jim Lea and Don Powell.
7. **Hepburn:** Their biggest hit was 'I Quit' in 1999.
8. **Oasis:** The early band members were Liam and Noel Gallagher, Paul 'Bonehead' Arthurs, Paul McGuigan and Tony McCarroll (replaced by Alan White in 1995).
9. **911:** They were in the 2013 TV series *The Big Reunion* with Five, Atomic Kitten, B*Witched, Blue, Honeyz and Liberty X.
10. **Texas:** Formed in 1986 with singer Sharleen Spiteri and Johnny McElhone, ex-Altered Images and Hipsway.
11. *Buzzcocks:* The band was formed in 1976 by Pete Shelley and Howard Devoto, but Devoto left in 1977 to form Magazine.
12. *Police:* The three members were Sting (Gordon Sumner), Stewart Copeland and Andy Summers.
13. **Band Aid:** In the song 'Do They Know It's Christmas?', the order of the main singers was Paul Young, Boy George, George Michael, Simon Le Bon, Sting and Bono.
14. **Blue:** The band members are Simon Webbe, Lee Ryan, Antony Costa and Duncan James.

15. **Queen:** Since Freddie Mercury died in 1991, both Paul Rodgers and Adam Lambert have performed with Brian May and Roger Taylor, but John Deacon retired in 1997.
16. **Rolling Stones:** The main band members since 1975 have been Mick Jagger, Keith Richards, Charlie Watts and Ronnie Wood, Bill Wyman having left in 1993.
17. **Jam:** Paul Weller, Bruce Foxton and Rick Buckler first charted with 'In the City' in 1977.
18. **Buck's Fizz:** Mike Nolan, Cheryl Baker, Bobby G and Jay Aston won the 1981 Eurovision Song Contest with 'Making Your Mind Up'.

MEDIUM (2 Points)

19. **Soho:** They had a 1991 UK No. 8 hit with 'Hippy Chick'.
20. *Chicago*: Singer Terry Kath accidentally shot himself in 1978 aged 31 and Peter Cetera became lead singer.
21. **Eagles:** Members have included Glenn Frey, Don Henley and Joe Walsh.
22. **A1:** The band included three Brits and a Norwegian, their first No. 1 being a cover of Norwegian band A-Ha's 'Take on Me'?
23. **Ace:** Paul Carrack was the singer on their 1974 hit 'How Long' before he joined Mike + the Mechanics.
24. **Berlin:** They had a UK No. 1 in 1986 with 'Take My Breath Away' from the film *Top Gun*.
25. **Nazareth:** Dan McCafferty was the lead singer of the Scottish rock band.
26. **T Rex:** Lead singer Marc Bolan died in a car crash in Barnes, London aged just 29 in 1977.
27. *Five*: The original members of 5ive were Sean Conlon, Ritchie Neville, Scott Robinson, Abz Love and Jason 'J' Brown.
28. **Mud:** Most songs were written by Nicky Chinn and Mike Chapman; lead singer was Les Gray who died in 2004.

29. **UB40:** Band members over the years have included the three brothers Ali, Robin and Duncan Campbell.
30. **Status Quo:** The original line-up was Francis Rossi, Rick Parfitt, Alan Lancaster and John Coghlan.
31. **'Right Said Fred':** Brothers Richard and Fred Fairbrass had their only UK No. 1 hit with 'Deeply Dippy' in 1992.
32. **Lindisfarne:** The Newcastle upon Tyne folk rock band were formed in 1968 and Ray Jackson played the mandolin on Rod Stewart's 'Maggie May'.
33. **Piranhas:** Their biggest UK hit was 'Tom Hark' in 1980.
34. **Nirvana:** Singer Kurt Cobain committed suicide in 1994; drummer Dave Grohl later founded the Foo Fighters.
35. *Flower Pot Men*: The Flowerpot Men had their only UK hit in 1967 with 'Let's Go to San Francisco'.
36. **Toto:** Their best year in the UK was 1983 with 'Africa' which reached No. 3 and 'Rosanna' which got to No. 12.
37. **East 17:** Brian Harvey was lead singer and their only UK No. 1 was the 1994 Christmas No. 1 'Stay Another Day'.
38. **King:** Named after the lead singer Paul King, who went on to be a VJ on MTV and VH1, their biggest UK hit was 'Love and Pride' which reached No. 2 in 1985.
39. **Bros:** The band originally consisted of twins Matt and Luke Goss and their school friend Craig Logan.
40. **Blancmange:** Their lead singer is Neil Arthur and their biggest UK hit was 'Living on the Ceiling' which got to No. 7 in 1982.
41. **Boston:** They are best known for their 1977 hit 'More Than a Feeling'.
42. **PhD:** Their only UK hit was 1982's 'I Won't Let You Down' and their lead singer was Jim Diamond.

HARD (3 Points)

43. **Amen Corner:** The lead singer was Andy Fairweather-Low and they had a 1969 UK No. 1 with '(If Paradise Is) Half as Nice'.

44. **All Saints (Day):** The group consisted of Nicole and Natalie Appleton, Melanie Blatt and Shaznay Lewis.

45. **Communards:** The duo were Jimmy Somerville, who had left Bronski Beat, and the (now Reverend) Richard Coles.

46. *Talking Heads***:** David Byrne led the group and their biggest UK hit was 'Road to Nowhere' which reached No. 6 in 1985.

47. **Arcadia:** The group included Simon Le Bon, Nick Rhodes and Roger Taylor of Duran Duran.

48. **Bluebells:** Their big hit was 'Young at Heart' which reached No. 1 in 1993 after featuring in a VW advert.

49. *Sailor***:** They had two UK Top 10 hits with 'A Glass of Champagne' in 1975 and 'Girls Girls Girls' in 1976.

50. *Rush***:** The band were Geddy Lee, Alex Lifeson and Neil Peart.

51. **Levellers:** The Brighton band are best known for their 1997 hit 'What a Beautiful Day'.

52. **Ivy League:** They had two Top 10 hits in 1965 with 'Funny How Love Can Be' and 'Tossing and Turning'.

53. **Steps:** The members were Claire, Lee, Lisa, Faye and 'H'.

54. **Duran(d) Duran(d):** Their first UK chart entry was 'Planet Earth' in 1981.

55. **Cockney Rebel:** Led by Steve Harley, they had a 1975 UK No. 1 hit with 'Make Me Smile (Come Up and See Me)'.

56. **Jethro Tull:** Ian Anderson is their frontman and they are best known for their 1969 hit 'Living in the Past'.

57. **Travis:** Fran Healy is lead singer with the Glasgow band.

58. **Kaizer Chiefs:** Kaiser Chiefs were formed in Leeds and are led by singer Ricky Wilson.

59. **Dollar:** The duo were David Van Day and Thereza Bazar.

60. **Iron Maiden:** Their lead singer is Bruce Dickinson who is also an airline pilot.

Pair
No.

Answer both questions and take one name from each answer to find the name of a (one-time) *Coronation Street* character.

1. **Films:** Which actor starred as James Braddock in the three *Missing in Action* films?
   TV: Who played Arthur Daley in *Minder*?

2. **TV:** Which game show was hosted by Bruce Forsyth, then Matthew Kelly and finally Darren Day?
   Music: Which singer had a 1962 hit with 'Up on the Roof' and featured on the cover of *Band on the Run*?

3. **Art & Literature:** What was Kingsley Amis's first novel?
   History: Who was the first Labour prime minister?

4. **Music:** Whose first hit was 'I'm Too Sexy' in 1991?
   Entertainment: Who was Les Dennis's comedy partner who died in 1986?

5. **Music:** What was Pink Floyd's first UK Top 10 single?
   Sport & Games: Which chess piece only moves diagonally?

6. **Pot Luck:** Which doll is the male equivalent of Barbie?
   Music: Whose first solo UK No. 1 was 'Forever Love'?

7. **Films:** Which 1982 film tells the story of an orphan taken in by 'Daddy' Warbucks?
   TV: Who was the first presenter of *Catchphrase*?

8. **Music:** Which Kosovo-born singer came to prominence on the 2012 DJ Fresh No. 1 single 'Hot Right Now'?
   TV: Who wrote the sitcoms *Only Fools and Horses*, *Citizen Smith* and *Just Good Friends*?

9. **Music:** What was singer Alison Moyet's nickname?
   Politics: What was Margaret Thatcher's maiden name?

10. **TV:** Una Stubbs played which character in *Worzel Gummidge*?
    TV: Which actor played Ray Daley in *Minder*?

11. **Religion:** In the Bible, who was the wife of Abraham and the mother of Isaac?
    Sport & Games: Which player scored the winner when England beat Belgium 1-0 in the 1990 World Cup?

12. **Music:** The first UK No. 1 for Dexy's Midnight Runners was 'Geno' but what was their second?
    Entertainment: Which DJ took over the Radio 1 breakfast show from Chris Moyles in 2012?

13. **TV:** Rhea Perlman played which character in *Cheers*?
    TV: Which former *Carry On* actor played Monsieur Alphonse in *'Allo 'Allo*?

14. **Religion:** Which word do Scots use for 'church'?
    Art & Literature: Who painted the 1954 portrait of Winston Churchill, later destroyed by Lady Churchill?

15. **Pot Luck:** What word is used to represent the letter 'M' in the phonetic alphabet?
    History: Which British prime minister was succeeded by Neville Chamberlain in 1937?

16. **TV:** Who took over as presenter of *Countdown* after the death of Richard Whiteley in 2005?
    Sport & Games: Which footballer rapped on the 1990 World Cup song 'World in Motion'?

17. **TV:** Brenda Blethyn stars as DCI Stanhope in which crime drama series, first aired in 2011?
    Sport & Games: What method is used in cricket to adjust target scores in rain-affected matches?

18. **Shopping & Fashion:** Which Welsh fashion designer became famous for her traditional floral designs?
    Sport & Games: Who is represented by the blue playing piece in Cluedo?

19. **Films:** In *The Imitation Game*, Benedict Cumberbatch plays which man who helped crack the Enigma code during World War II?
    Sport & Games: Which cyclist became the first British winner of the Tour de France in 2012?

20.	**TV:** David Jason played whom in *Only Fools and Horses*? **TV:** Who played Isobel Crawley in *Downton Abbey*?
21.	**TV:** Who played Herman Munster in *The Munsters*? **Films:** What is the name of the boy who befriends E.T. in the 1982 film?
22.	**TV:** January Jones plays which character in *Mad Men*? **History:** Which highwayman was hanged in York in 1739?
23.	**TV:** Which actor played McCloud in the 1970s police drama series of the same name? **Pot Luck:** An old sixpence had what nickname?
24.	**Music:** Which group won the 1981 Eurovision Song Contest with 'Making Your Mind Up'? **Politics:** Who was British PM from 2007 to 2010?
25.	**Places:** Aberdeen and Doncaster lie on which rivers? **Sport & Games:** Which jockey rode Imperial Commander to win the 2010 Cheltenham Gold Cup?
26.	**Music:** Which singer had a UK Top 5 hit in 1966 and 1987 with 'When a Man Loves a Woman'? **TV:** Who played Mrs Slocombe in *Are You Being Served?*?
27.	**Music:** Who had a 1985 UK No. 1 with 'Move Closer'? **Sport & Games:** Which former England left back was nicknamed 'Psycho'?
28.	**TV:** Who presented the first show on Channel 4? **Transport & Travel:** Which British make of car included models called Imp, Minx, Hunter and Avenger?
29.	**Films:** Vivien Leigh played which character in the 1951 film *A Streetcar Named Desire*? **Sport & Games:** Which British racing driver won the 1976 Drivers' World Championship?
30.	**Entertainment:** Which Liverpool-born comedian said, 'The Germans bombed our chippy'? **TV:** Who played Charles Winchester in *M*A*S*H*?

1. Chuck Norris & George Cole
Norris Cole: He has been played by Malcolm Hebden since 1994.

2. *You Bet!* & Kenny Lynch
Bet Lynch: Played by Julie Goodyear, she was a barmaid then landlady of the Rovers Return from 1970 and married Alec Gilroy in 1987.

3. *Lucky Jim* & Ramsay MacDonald
Jim McDonald: Played by Charles Lawson, his first appearance was in 1989.

4. Right Said Fred & Dustin Gee
Fred Gee: He was played by Fred Feast from 1975 to 1984.

5. 'See Emily Play' & Bishop
Emily Bishop: Played by Eileen Derbyshire, Emily Nugent married Ernest Bishop (Stephen Hancock) in 1972.

6. Ken & Gary Barlow
Ken Barlow: Played by William Roache, he was in the very first episode on 9 December 1960.

7. *Annie* & Roy Walker
Annie Walker: Played by Doris Speed, she was landlady of the Rovers Return with her husband Jack (Arthur Leslie).

8. Rita Ora and John Sullivan
Rita Sullivan: Played by Barbara Knox, she was born Rita Littlewood, married Len Fairclough in 1977, then Ted Sullivan in 1992, before her brief marriage to Dennis Tanner in 2012.

9. Alf and (Margaret) Roberts
Alf Roberts: Alf died of a heart attack on New Year's Eve 1998 and the actor Bryan Mosley who played him died just five weeks later, of a heart attack.

10. Aunt Sally and Gary Webster
Sally Webster: She has been played by Sally Dynevor (née Whittaker) since 1986.

11. Sarah and David Platt
Sarah Platt: Originally Tilsley and later Grimshaw, Sarah has been played by Tina O'Brien since 1999.

12. 'Come On Eileen' and Nick Grimshaw
Eileen Grimshaw: Played by Sue Cleaver since 2000, she is the mother of Jason (Ryan Thomas) and Todd (Bruno Langley).

13. Carla (Tortelli) and Kenneth Connor
Carla Connor: She made her first appearance in 2006 and is played by Alison King.

14. Kirk & Graham Sutherland
Kirk Sutherland: Played by Andrew Whyment since 2000, after he had played Darren in *The Royle Family*.

15. Mike & Stanley Baldwin
Mike Baldwin: He appeared from 1976 until he died of a heart attack in 2006 and was played by Johnny Briggs.

16. Des Lynam & John Barnes
Des Barnes: He appeared from 1990 to 1998 when he died and was played by Philip Middlemiss.

17. *Vera* & Duckworth-Lewis Method
Vera Duckworth: She appeared from 1974 until her death in 2008 and the actress Liz Dawn died in 2017.

18. Laura Ashley & Mrs Peacock
Ashley Peacock: Played by Steven Arnold from 1995 to 2010, he married Maxine (Tracy Shaw) in 1999 and Claire (Julia Haworth) in 2004.

19. Alan Turing & Bradley Wiggins
Alan Bradley: Played by Mark Eden from 1986, he was famously killed by a Blackpool tram in 1989.

20. Derek Trotter & Penelope Wilton
Derek Wilton: The character, played by Peter Baldwin, died in 1997 and Baldwin subsequently died in 2015, aged 82.

21. Fred Gwynne & Elliott
    Fred Elliott: John Savident played the bald-headed butcher, prone to repeating himself, from 1994 to 2006.

22. Betty Draper & Dick Turpin
    Betty Turpin: Later Betty Williams, she was played by Betty Driver for 42 years until the actress herself died in 2011.

23. Dennis Weaver & Tanner
    Dennis Tanner: Played by Philip Lowrie, he was in the first episode in 1960 but left in 1968 before returning in 2011.

24. Bucks Fizz & Gordon Brown
    Fiz Brown: Played by Jennie McAlpine, she first appeared in 2001.

25. Don & Paddy Brennan
    Don Brennan: Played by Geoffrey Hinsliff, he married Ivy Tilsley in 1988 but was killed in a car crash in 1997.

26. Percy Sledge & Mollie Sugden
    Percy Sugden: Bill Waddington, a brother-in-law to the Chuckle Brothers, played the part from 1983 to 1997.

27. Phyllis Nelson & Stuart Pearce
    Phyllis Pearce: She was played by Jill Summers from 1982 until 1996, but Summers died just eight months later.

28. Richard Whiteley & Hillman
    Richard Hillman: Brian Capron played the villain from 2001 until his death in 2003 while attempting to kill his family.

29. Blanche DuBois & James Hunt
    Blanche Hunt: Maggie Jones played Blanche from 1974 until the actress's own death in 2009.

30. Stan Boardman & David Ogden Stiers
    Stan Ogden: Bernard Youens played Stan from 1964 until his death in 1984.

Answer both questions and take both surnames to find the name of a recording artist(s).

1. **TV:** Whose TV show in the 1980s used to feature clips from the Japanese show *Endurance*?
   Politics: Who became British prime minister in 2007?

2. **Sport & Games:** Which darts player from the '70s and '80s is well known for wearing lots of jewellery?
   Sport & Games: Which British boxer won super-heavyweight Olympic gold in Sydney in 2000?

3. **Films:** Which actor starred in the films *Rebel Without a Cause* and *East of Eden*?
   Food & Drink: Which chef presented *Saturday Kitchen* from 2006 to 2016?

4. **Music:** Who duetted with Aretha Franklin on the 1987 No. 1 hit 'I Knew You Were Waiting (For Me)?
   TV: Who played the butler Angus Hudson in the 1970s TV series *Upstairs Downstairs*?

5. **Sport & Games:** Which boxer fought in both the 'Rumble in the Jungle' and the 'Thriller in Manila'?
   Politics: Who was the Labour Party 'spin doctor' under Tony Blair from 1997 to 2003?

6. **Music:** Who had hits with '7 Days' and 'Walking Away'?
   People: Which American business magnate formed Microsoft with Paul Allen in 1975?

7. **TV:** Which Welsh comedian became the permanent host of *Never Mind the Buzzcocks* in 2014?
   TV: Who played Robin Tripp in *Man About The House*?

8. **Sport & Games:** Which golfer was nicknamed 'The Great White Shark'?
   Politics: Which Labour MP, Foreign Secretary from 1997 to 2001, died of a heart attack out walking in 2005?

9.   **Music:** Which singer had a 1973 hit with 'Me and Mrs Jones'?

Music: Whose biggest hit was 'You're So Vain' in 1972?

10. **Sport & Games:** Which writer is the ex-jockey who rode Devon Loch when it fell in the 1956 Grand National?

Sport & Games: Which Italian striker won the Golden Boot in the 1982 World Cup?

11. **Art & Literature:** Who wrote *To Kill a Mocking Bird*?

Films: Which actress starred in the films *Sleepless in Seattle* and *You've Got Mail*?

12. **Films:** Which composer arranged the James Bond theme and wrote many of the film scores?

Sport & Games: Which snooker player nicknamed 'The Whirlwind' has lost in six World finals?

13. **Music:** Which singer had a 1969 hit with 'Wonderful World, Beautiful People'?

TV: Who played Miss Brahms in *Are You Being Served?*?

14. **Politics:** Who was the British prime minister from 1964 to 1970 and 1974 to 1976?

Films: Which actor is famous for his catchphrase 'I say, Ding Dong' from a *Carry On* film?

15. **TV:** Which actor played the lead alongside Diane Keen in the sitcom *Rings on Their Fingers*?

Music: Whose cover of the Beatles' 'With a Little Help From My Friends' reached No. 1 in 1968?

16. **Sport & Games:** Which former England rugby union fly-half was a director of Newcastle Falcons until 2006?

People: Which lingerie businessman became co-chairman of West Ham United in 2010?

17. **TV:** Which actor played the lead alongside June Whitfield in the sitcom *Terry and June*?

Sport & Games: Who was the lead F1 commentator for the BBC and then ITV from 1978 to 2001?

18. **Music:** Which actress had a 1963 hit with 'All I Want For Christmas is a Beatle'?

History: Who was the second president of the USA?

19. **People:** Who was Australian prime minister from 1996 to 2007?
    TV: Which Welsh presenter replaced Christine Bleakley on *The One Show* in 2010?

20. **TV:** Who co-writes and plays the title character Mr Khan in the TV sitcom *Citizen Khan*?
    Sport & Games: Which Welsh striker known as 'The Gentle Giant' went from Leeds Utd to Juventus in 1957?

ANSWERS QUIZ No. 87: **POP MUSIC PAIRS**

1. Clive James & Gordon Brown
    James Brown: His biggest hit in the UK was 'Living in America' which reached No. 5 in 1986.

2. Bobby George & Audley Harrison
    George Harrison: He was the youngest Beatle and the first to have a solo No. 1.

3. James Dean & James Martin
    Dean Martin: Real name Dino Paul Crocetti, he was part of a comedy act with Jerry Lewis.

4. George Michael & Gordon Jackson
    Michael Jackson: The extended version of his 'Thriller' video is nearly 14 minutes long.

5. Muhammad Ali & Alastair Campbell
    Ali Campbell: He was lead singer with UB40 and his brother Robin was also in the group.

6. Craig David & Bill Gates
    David Gates: The songwriter and lead singer with Bread.

7. Rhod Gilbert & Richard O'Sullivan
    Gilbert O'Sullivan: He had two successive No. 1 hits in the '70s with 'Clair' and 'Get Down'.

8. Greg Norman & Robin Cook
    Norman Cook: He was a member of The Housemartins, Beats International and Freak Power.

9. Billy Paul & Carly Simon
Paul Simon: His video of 'You Can Call Me Al' featured Chevy Chase lip-syncing the lyrics.

10. Dick Francis & Paolo Rossi
Francis Rossi: He is lead singer and guitarist with Status Quo.

11. Harper Lee & Meg Ryan
Lee Ryan: A member of the boy band Blue with Simon Webbe, Duncan James & Antony Costa.

12. John Barry & Jimmy White
Barry White: 'The Walrus of Love' died in 2003 aged 58.

13. Jimmy Cliff & Wendy Richard
Cliff Richard: His first chart hit was 'Move It' (1958) and his first No. 1 was 'Livin' Doll' (1959).

14. Harold Wilson & Leslie Phillips
Wilson Phillips: All were children of members of the Beach Boys and Mamas and the Papas.

15. Martin Jarvis & Joe Cocker
Jarvis Cocker: Born in Sheffield, lead singer with Pulp.

16. Rob Andrew & David Gold
Andrew Gold: He formed Wax with Graham Gouldman of 10cc but died in 2011 at just 59.

17. Terry Scott & Murray Walker
Scott Walker: He was born Noel Scott Engel and was one of the Walker Brothers.

18. Dora Bryan & John Adams
Bryan Adams: His '(Everything I Do) I Do It For You' spent 16 weeks at No. 1 in 1991.

19. John Howard & Alex Jones
Howard Jones: He first broke into the charts when his 'New Song' reached No. 3 in 1983.

20. Adil Ray & John Charles
Ray Charles: Born Raymond Charles Robinson, he was blind from the age of seven.

1. **Music:** Which song was a 1987 hit for Freddie Mercury and Montserrat Caballé?
2. **Places:** What was the name of New York before 1664?
3. **History:** The Aztecs were the dominant people in which country before the arrival of Europeans in the 1500s?
4. **TV:** Which theatre has hosted the *Royal Variety Performance* on the most occasions?
5. **Science & Medicine:** Which condition causes hostages to develop feelings of trust or affection towards their captors?
6. **Music:** From which 1982 Duran Duran album did the singles 'Hungry Like the Wolf' and 'Save a Prayer' come?
7. **Sport & Games:** Which US city do the American football team the Falcons come from?
8. **Transport & Travel:** What was the name of Charles Lindbergh's plane on the first solo transatlantic flight?
9. **Places:** Which city lies on the Scheldt River and is the most populous in Belgium?
10. **Music:** Which US composer's songs include 'There's No Business Like Show Business' and 'White Christmas'?
11. **Sport & Games:** For which NBA basketball team did Kobe Bryant and Magic Johnson play all their careers?
12. **Films:** Which 2005 film was about revenge carried out for the murder of 11 Israeli athletes in 1972?
13. **History:** Who was Queen Victoria's first prime minister?
14. **Places:** Which is the most populous city in the Canadian province of Quebec?
15. **Music:** Who had a hit in 1989 with 'If Only I Could'?
16. **Mythology:** In Greek mythology who was the son of King Priam and Queen Hecuba of Troy?
17. **Politics:** Which 1957 treaty brought about the creation of the European Economic Community (EEC)?
18. **History:** What name was given during WWII to female English-speaking broadcasters of Japanese propaganda?

19. **Places:** Piraeus is the port of which European capital?
20. **Music:** Which 1961 song was the biggest hit for Kenny Ball and his Jazzmen?

ANSWERS QUIZ No. 88: **OLYMPICS HOST CITIES**

1. **'Barcelona':** Host city in 1992.
2. **New Amsterdam:** Host city in 1928.
3. **Mexico:** Host city in 1968.
4. **London Palladium:** Host city in 1908, 1948 (would have been held in 1944 but for World War II) and 2012.
5. **Stockholm Syndrome:** Host city in 1912 and hosted the 1956 equestrian events due to quarantine restrictions.
6. *Rio*: Host city in 2016.
7. **Atlanta:** Host city in 1996.
8. **Spirit of St Louis:** Host city in 1904.
9. **Antwerp:** Host city in 1920.
10. **Irving Berlin:** Host city in 1936 and would have been the host city in 1916 but for World War I.
11. **Los Angeles Lakers:** Host city in 1932 and 1984.
12. *Munich*: Host city in 1972.
13. **Lord Melbourne:** Host city in 1956.
14. **Montreal:** Host city in 1976.
15. **Sydney Youngblood:** Host city in 2000.
16. **Paris:** Host city in 1900 and 1924.
17. **Treaty of Rome:** Host city in 1960.
18. **Tokyo Rose:** Host city in 1964 (would have been the hosts in 1940 but for World War II) and is hosting the 2020 Olympics.
19. **Athens:** Hosted the first Olympics in 1896 and again in 2004.
20. **'Midnight in Moscow':** Host city in 1980.

Other cities: **Helsinki** (1952), **Seoul** (1988) and **Beijing** (2008).

EASY (1 Point)

1. **TV:** Which Bolton-born comedian starred as Brian Potter in *Phoenix Nights*?
2. **Music:** Who was the original lead singer with Genesis?
3. **TV:** Who was Dudley Moore's partner for many years, including in 'Derek and Clive'?
4. **Films:** Which actor played Inspector Clouseau in the *Pink Panther* films?
5. **TV:** Who is the only 'Dragon' to have appeared in every series of *Dragons' Den*?
6. **Music:** Which singer had a UK No. 1 hit in 2004 with 'Mysterious Girl'?
7. **TV:** Chris Gascoyne has played which *Coronation Street* character since 2000?
8. **Entertainment:** Which boy, created by J M Barrie, lives on Neverland and is the leader of The Lost Boys?
9. **TV:** Which actor played Cleggy in *Last of the Summer Wine* and voiced Wallace in the *Wallace and Gromit* films?
10. **Films:** Which actor played Hercule Poirot in six films between 1978 and 1988 starting with *Death on the Nile*?
11. **TV:** Who is the main character in the American animated sitcom *Family Guy*?
12. **Music:** Which former Radio 1 DJ was married to Anthea Turner from 1990 to 1998?
13. **TV:** Who starred as Tristan Farnon in *All Creatures Great and Small* and was the fifth Doctor Who from 1982–84?
14. **Art & Literature:** The first book published by Beatrix Potter was *The Tale of ....* in 1902?
15. **TV:** Who co-presented *Blue Peter* with John Noakes, Valerie Singleton and later Lesley Judd from 1967 to 1978?

16. **TV:** Which actor starred in *Only When I Laugh*, *The Bounder* and *To the Manor Born*?

17. **Music:** Which original member of the group Chicago had a UK No. 3 hit in 1986 with 'Glory of Love'?

18. **Films:** Which British actor famously played T E Lawrence in the 1962 film *Lawrence of Arabia*?

19. **TV:** Which US actor played Lieutenant Columbo in the TV series which ran from 1968 to 2003?

20. **Music:** Who was lead singer with Herman's Hermits?

21. **TV:** In the 1968 animated TV series *Wacky Races*, which driver was in the No. 9 car, the Turbo Terrific?

22. **Entertainment:** Which Sheffield-born nightclub owner died in 2018, aged 77?

23. **TV:** Which actor played Pete Beale in *EastEnders* from 1985 to 1993?

24. **Music:** Which singer had a UK No. 10 hit in 1976 with 'Show Me the Way'?

25. **Films:** Which New Zealand-born film director directed the *Lord of the Rings* trilogy and *The Hobbit* trilogy?

26. **TV:** Who played Harry Pearce in the TV series *Spooks*?

27. **Sport:** Which flamboyant Chelsea and Southampton centre-forward was nicknamed 'Ossie'?

28. **TV:** Which actor played Len Fairclough in *Coronation Street* from 1961 to 1983?

29. **Music:** Who is the lead singer with the group Go West?

30. **Entertainment:** What is the alter ego of Spider-Man who works for the *Daily Bugle*?

31. **TV:** Which actor played Joey Boswell in the first four series of *Bread* from 1986 to 1988?

32. **Films:** Which actor was in many Hammer horror films, including as Baron Frankenstein and Dr Van Helsing?

33. **TV:** Which Scottish actor starred as Malcolm Tucker in *The Thick of It* and *Doctor Who* from 2013–17?

34. **Music:** Which singer had a 1969 UK No. 1 with 'Where Do You Go To (My Lovely)'?

35. **TV:** Which 1980s *Blue Peter* presenter was Chief Scout from 2004 to 2009?

HARD (3 Points)

---

36. **Music:** Which singer had Top 10 hits in the 1970s with 'Gee Baby' and 'Love Me Love My Dog'?

37. **TV:** Which actor played Harry Grout in *Porridge* and Maester Aemon in *Game of Thrones*?

38. **Music:** Which composition by Sergei Prokofiev is based on a children's fairy tale?

39. **Films:** Which *Carry On* actor was married to the actress and impressionist Janet Brown?

40. **Music:** Who was the first lead singer with Fleetwood Mac?

41. **Films:** Who was the fifth 'Rat Pack' member with Frank Sinatra, Dean Martin, Sammy Davis Jr. and Joey Bishop?

42. **Music:** Which 1986 Art of Noise hit featured Duane Eddy who had previously had a hit with it in 1959?

43. **TV:** Which actor played Derek Wilton in *Coronation Street* until 1997; he made his first appearance in 1976?

44. **Films:** Dennis Hopper played one of the bikers in the 1969 film *Easy Rider*, but who played the other?

45. **Music:** The 1960s group the Monkees comprised Davy Jones, Mike Nesmith, Micky Dolenz and which other?

46. **Sport:** Which darts player, nicknamed Snakebite, is known for his multicoloured Mohawk hairstyle?

47. **TV:** Who played Tyrion Lannister in *Game of Thrones*?

48. **Music:** Which opera by Benjamin Britten is based on a poem in George Crabbe's book *The Borough*?

49. **TV:** Which actor played Eric Duffy in *Please Sir!*?

50. **Music:** Which bass player co-founded Joy Division and then New Order after the death of Ian Curtis?

EASY (1 Point)

1.   **Peter Kay:** His first TV series was Channel 4's *That Peter Kay Thing* in 2000.
2.   **Peter Gabriel:** He was replaced by Phil Collins in 1975.
3.   **Peter Cook:** They wrote the comedy stage revue *Beyond the Fringe* with Alan Bennett and Jonathan Miller.
4.   **Peter Sellers:** He starred in *The Goon Show* with Spike Milligan, Harry Secombe and briefly Michael Bentine.
5.   **Peter Jones:** *Dragons' Den* is presented by Evan Davis who also presented *Newsnight* from 2014 to 2018.
6.   **Peter Andre:** He married Katie Price in 2005 at Highclere Castle where Downton Abbey was filmed.
7.   **Peter Barlow:** He was born in 1965 with his twin sister Susan to parents Ken and Valerie Barlow.
8.   **Peter Pan:** Wendy Darling accompanies Peter to Neverland; Tinker Bell is a fairy, is Peter's best friend.
9.   **Peter Sallis:** He also voiced Rat in the 1980s TV series *Wind in the Willows*.
10. **Peter Ustinov:** He won two Best Supporting Actor Oscars for *Spartacus* (1960) and *Topkapi* (1964).
11. **Peter Griffin:** He has a dog named Brian and is voiced by the series' creator Seth MacFarlane.
12. **Peter Powell:** Pete Tong made his first Radio 1 appearance in 1981 with a slot on Peter Powell's show.
13. **Peter Davison:** In 1978 he married Sandra Dickinson; their daughter Georgia Moffett married David Tennant in 2011.
14. ***Peter Rabbit*:** She then published *The Tale of Squirrel Nutkin* and *The Tailor of Gloucester* in 1903.
15. **Peter Purves:** After *Blue Peter* he presented the motorcycle trials show *Kick Start* and the darts coverage for the BBC.

16. **Peter Bowles:** He turned down *The Good Life* and has played the Duke of Wellington in the ITV drama *Victoria*.

17. **Peter Cetera:** The song was the signature tune from the film *The Karate Kid Part II*.

18. **Peter O'Toole:** He holds the record of eight Best Actor nominations without winning an Oscar.

19. **Peter Falk:** Only 69 episodes of *Columbo* were made.

20. **Peter Noone:** His only solo hit was the Bowie song 'Oh You Pretty Things' on which Bowie played piano.

21. **Peter Perfect:** Only 17 episodes of *Wacky Races* were made.

22. **Peter Stringfellow:** His first job was selling ties.

23. **Peter Dean:** He was encouraged to act by Prunella Scales who saw him ad-libbing some Shakespeare.

24. **Peter Frampton:** He was in The Herd before joining with Steve Marriott of the Small Faces to form Humble Pie.

25. **Peter Jackson:** He won the Best Director Oscar for the 2003 film *The Lord of the Rings: The Return of the King*.

26. **Peter Firth:** He came to prominence in the 1977 film *Equus* in which he starred with Richard Burton.

27. **Peter Osgood:** The 'King of Stamford Bridge' died of a heart attack in 2006 at just 59 whilst at a family funeral.

28. **Peter Adamson:** Len married Rita in 1977 and in 1982 they fostered Sharon Gaskell played by Tracie Bennett.

29. **Peter Cox:** Richard Drummie was Go West's other member.

30. **Peter Parker:** Not to be confused with Clark Kent (Superman) who worked at the *Daily Planet*.

31. **Peter Howitt:** He has since written and directed films including *Sliding Doors* and *Johnny English*.

32. **Peter Cushing:** Cushing appeared in many horror films with Christopher Lee and occasionally Vincent Price.

33. **Peter Capaldi:** His second cousin once removed is the singer-songwriter Lewis Capaldi.

34. **Peter Sarstedt:** His brothers were Eden Kane ('Well I Ask You') and Robin Sarstedt ('My Resistance is Low').
35. **Peter Duncan:** Bear Grylls took over in 2009.

HARD (3 Points)

36. **Peter Shelley:** Not to be confused with Pete Shelley who was the lead singer with the Buzzcocks.
37. **Peter Vaughan:** He also appeared in the first two series of *Citizen Smith* as Shirley's father.
38. **'Peter and the Wolf':** It teaches children about different instruments, each representing a different character.
39. **Peter Butterworth:** He was in 16 *Carry On* films after he met writer Talbot Rothwell in a German POW camp.
40. **Peter Green:** He left John Mayall & the Bluesbreakers in 1967 having previously replaced Eric Clapton.
41. **Peter Lawford:** He was married to Patricia Kennedy, sister of John F Kennedy, until their divorce in 1966.
42. **'Peter Gunn':** The song was written by Henry Mancini.
43. **Peter Baldwin:** Derek married Mavis Riley, played by Thelma Barlow, in 1988.
44. **Peter Fonda:** He is the son of Henry Fonda, brother of Jane Fonda and father of Bridget Fonda.
45. **Peter Tork:** His friend Stephen Stills was turned down for the Monkees but he then recommended Tork.
46. **Peter Wright:** Snakebite is his favourite drink.
47. **Peter Dinklage:** Has appeared in many films including *Elf* and *Three Billboards Outside Ebbing, Missouri*.
48. *Peter Grimes*: Benjamin Britten founded the Aldeburgh Festival in 1948, still held in the Suffolk town each year.
49. **Peter Cleall:** There was a spin-off series called *The Fenn Street Gang* which featured many of the same actors.
50. **Peter Hook:** Married to Caroline Aherne from 1994 to 1997, he played on the *Mrs Merton Show* in Hooky and the Boys.

1. **Music:** Which singer recorded the 2013 song 'Happy'?
2. **Sport & Games:** Which tennis player has won the most Grand Slam women's singles titles in the Open era?
3. **Music:** Which classical guitarist had a 1979 hit with 'Cavatina', the theme from the film *The Deer Hunter*?
4. **Films:** Who played the lead roles in *Good Morning, Vietnam*, *Dead Poets Society* and *Mrs Doubtfire*?
5. **Sport & Games:** Which snooker player won the World Championship in 2000, 2003 and 2018?
6. **Music:** Which singer had 1960s hits with 'Can't Get Used to Losing You' and 'Can't Take My Eyes Off You'?
7. **Religion:** Who was the Archbishop of Canterbury from 2002 to 2012, succeeded by Justin Welby?
8. **TV:** In 2018, who became a judge on *The X Factor* with his wife Ayda, with Louis Tomlinson and Simon Cowell?
9. **Music:** Whose only UK No. 1 was her 1977 hit 'Free'?

10. **Sport & Games:** Which Briton won the women's skeleton at the 2010 Winter Olympics in Vancouver?
11. **Films:** Which *Carry On* actor had as one of his catchphrases 'Stop messing about......!', spoken in his nasal tone of voice?
12. **Music:** Which US singer had her only UK Top 20 hit in 1992 with 'Save the Best for Last' which reached No. 3?
13. **Sport & Games:** Which then Swansea City defender captained Wales at Euro 2016 in France?
14. **Art & Literature:** Which playwright wrote *A Streetcar Named Desire* and *Cat on a Hot Tin Roof*?
15. **Music:** Which US country singer had a UK No. 13 hit in 1976 with 'I Recall a Gypsy Woman'?

16. **Sport & Games:** Which 1970s Welsh rugby union full back was known by his initials after J J Williams joined the team?

17. **TV:** Which actor played James Bellamy in the original 1970s TV series *Upstairs, Downstairs*?

18. **Politics:** The Social Democratic Party (SDP) was formed in 1981 by David Owen, Roy Jenkins, Bill Rodgers and who else?

19. **Music:** Which US country singer wrote and recorded 'Your Cheatin' Heart' and 'Hey, Good Lookin''?

20. **Sport & Games:** Who is the only tennis player to have won a medal at four Olympic Games?

21. **Entertainment:** What was the name of Britain's first well-known black stand-up comedian from Barnsley who appeared on the 1970s TV show *The Comedians*?

HARD (3 Points)

22. **Music:** Which English composer born in 1872 composed 'The Lark Ascending' in 1914?

23. **Sport & Games:** In 1980, Alan Jones was the first of seven drivers to win a Formula 1 World Drivers' Championship for a team in the name of which man?

24. **TV:** Who was Judi Dench's real-life husband who played her husband in the 1980s sitcom *A Fine Romance*?

25. **Music:** Who had a 1968 Top 10 hit with 'Classical Gas'?

26. **Sport & Games:** Which 7-time world billiards champion helped form the WPBSA and was chairman for 20 years?

27. **TV:** Who played Arya Stark in *Game of Thrones*?

28. **Music:** Who had a 1961 UK No. 1 with 'Moon River'?

29. **Sport & Games:** Which Ospreys wing retired from Welsh international rugby in 2012 having scored a record 58 tries?

30. **Films:** Which actress played Charity Hallett-Barnum in the 2017 film *The Greatest Showman*?

1. **Pharrell Williams:** It was in the film *Despicable Me 2*.
2. **Serena Williams:** Margaret Court won 24 Grand Slam singles titles but only 11 in the Open area.
3. **John Williams:** He was part of the group Sky who had a 1980 hit with 'Toccata', based on the J S Bach piece.
4. **Robin Williams:** He rose to fame after starring as the alien Mork in the TV sitcom *Mork & Mindy.*
5. **Mark Williams:** His first appearance in a World final was in 1999 when he lost to Stephen Hendry, his final win.
6. **Andy Williams:** The Osmonds used to make regular appearances on *The Andy Williams Show* in the 1960s.
7. **Rowan Williams:** He was preceded by George Carey.
8. **Robbie Williams:** His wife Ayda Field is a regular panellist on the TV show *Loose Women*.
9. **Deniece Williams:** Her last UK hit 'Let's Hear It for the Boy' reached No. 2 in 1984.

10. **Amy Williams:** She was the first individual British gold medal winner at the Winter Olympics since Robin Cousins in 1980.
11. **Kenneth Williams:** He was in more *Carry On* films than any other actor – 25, one more than Joan Sims.
12. **Vanessa Williams:** She was Miss America 1984 and was in the TV shows *Ugly Betty* and *Desperate Housewives*.
13. **Ashley Williams:** He joined Everton in August 2016.
14. **Tennessee Williams:** He rose to fame after he wrote the semi-autobiographical *The Glass Menagerie* in 1944.
15. **Don Williams:** He had another minor hit in 1976 with 'You're My Best Friend'.

16. **J P R Williams:** He was a good tennis player in his youth, beating David Lloyd in a British junior competition.
17. **Simon Williams:** His sister Polly married his co-star from the sitcom *Don't Wait Up*, Nigel Havers.
18. **Shirley Williams:** Named the 'Gang of Four' after four Communist Party officials during the Chinese Cultural Revolution.
19. **Hank Williams:** He died in 1953 of heart failure aged just 29.
20. **Venus Williams:** In 2001 she retained the Wimbledon and US Open titles that she had won in 2000.
21. **Charlie Williams:** He was also a pro footballer, playing centre-half for Doncaster Rovers from 1948 to 1959.

HARD (3 Points)

22. **Ralph Vaughan Williams:** His great-uncle was Charles Darwin and great-great-grandfather Josiah Wedgwood.
23. **Frank Williams:** K Rosberg (1982), N Piquet (1987), N Mansell (1992), A Prost (1993), D Hill (1996) and J Villeneuve (1997) won just one title for Williams but never won another title.
24. **Michael Williams:** A photo of daughter Finty is in the opening credits of the Dench sitcom *As Time Goes By*.
25. **Mason Williams:** He also co-wrote the 1968 UK No. 1 'Cinderella Rockefella' for Esther and Abi Ofarim.
26. **Rex Williams:** The oldest player to reach a ranking final at 53 and played 8 times at the Crucible but never won.
27. **Maisie Williams:** She was christened Margaret but nicknamed Maisie after the character in *The Perishers*.
28. **Danny Williams:** He was called 'Britain's Johnny Mathis'.
29. **Shane Williams:** Neil Jenkins holds the record for most points scored for Wales with 1,049.
30. **Michelle Williams:** She played Jen Lindley in *Dawson's Creek* and Alma in the 2005 film *Brokeback Mountain*.

QUIZ No. 91: **DOCTOR WHO**

1. **Music:** Which group had their first UK hit with 'Sylvia's Mother' which reached No. 2 in 1972?
2. **Films:** Which 1965 film starred Omar Sharif in the title role with Julie Christie and was set during the Russian Civil War?
3. **TV:** Which TV character from the planet Gallifrey appeared for the first time in 1963?
4. **Food & Drink:** Which carbonated soft drink was created in 1885 by pharmacist Charles Alderton in Waco, Texas?
5. **Art & Literature:** In the Sherlock Holmes books by Arthur Conan Doyle, what is the name of his assistant?
6. **Films:** In which 1967 film did Rex Harrison say he could 'talk to the animals'?
7. **Pot Luck:** Which children's charity opened its first home for poor orphans in 1867 in the East End of London?
8. **Art & Literature:** In Robert Louis Stevenson's 1886 novella, who turns into his evil alter ego Edward Hyde?
9. **TV:** Martin Clunes has played Dr Ellingham, a GP in the Cornish village of Portwenn, since 2004 in which series?

10. **Music:** Which song title was a 1984 UK No. 3 hit for the Thompson Twins and a different song for UFO in 1979?
11. **Films:** Which character, also played by Mike Myers, is his nemesis in the *Austin Powers* films?
12. **TV:** Which TV series based on books by Richard Gordon was the first to feature medical students at St Swithin's?
13. **Music:** Which group had a UK No. 1 hit in 1986 with a cover version of 'Spirit in the Sky'?
14. **Shopping & Fashion:** Which brand of leather boots were designed by a German Army doctor on leave?

15. **Pot Luck:** In bingo, what name is given to number 9?
16. **TV:** Suranne Jones plays which eponymous GP in a BBC drama series first shown in 2015?
17. **Sport & Games:** In Cluedo, who is the murder victim?
18. **Music:** What was the UK debut hit for the Miami Sound Machine, reaching No. 6 in 1984?
19. **Films:** Which Peter Sellers film had the alternative title *How I Learned to Stop Worrying and Love the Bomb*?
20. **People:** Who was the first suspect to be captured using wireless telegraphy, being caught in Canada in 1910?
21. **History:** In 1871, Henry Morton Stanley was sent to find which British explorer looking for the source of the Nile?

HARD (3 Points)

22. **Art & Literature:** In the H G Wells book, to whose island did shipwrecked Edward Prendick go when rescued?
23. **Music:** Which group's biggest UK hit was 'Milk and Alcohol' which got to No. 9 in 1979?
24. **Films:** Kirk Douglas played which gunfighting dentist in *Gunfight at the OK Corral* with Burt Lancaster as Wyatt Earp?
25. **TV:** Which Scottish doctor's 'Casebook' series was shown from 1962–71, set in the town of Tannochbrae?
26. **Music:** What was the title of the second UK No. 1 single for Aqua in 1998 after their 1997 debut hit 'Barbie Girl'?
27. **Art & Literature:** Which Chinese villain, who became famous for his long moustache, was created by author Sax Rohmer?
28. **TV:** Which medical drama series which ran from 1961 to 1966 starred Richard Chamberlain in the title role?
29. **Films:** Benedict Cumberbatch starred as which eponymous Marvel Comics superhero in a 2016 film?
30. **TV:** Jane Seymour starred as which 'Medicine Woman' in the TV series that ran from 1993 to 1998?

EASY (1 Point)

1. **Dr Hook:** The singer was Ray Sawyer who always wore an eye patch after losing his eye in a 1967 car accident.
2. *Doctor Zhivago*: The film was directed by David Lean and was based on the 1957 novel by Boris Pasternak.
3. *Doctor Who*: William Hartnell, Patrick Troughton and Jon Pertwee played the first three Doctors.
4. **Dr Pepper:** It contains a mixture of 23 different flavours.
5. **Dr (John) Watson:** He was played by Jude Law on film with Robert Downey Jr. as Holmes, and Martin Freeman on TV in *Sherlock*, Benedict Cumberbatch being Holmes.
6. *Doctor Dolittle*: It was adapted from a series of books written by Hugh Lofting.
7. **(Dr) Barnardo's:** Irish-born Thomas Barnardo did study medicine but he didn't qualify as a doctor.
8. **Dr (Henry) Jekyll:** He was played by Spencer Tracy in the 1941 film alongside Ingrid Bergman and Lana Turner.
9. *Doc Martin*: It is filmed in the fishing village of Port Isaac.

MEDIUM (2 Points)

10. **'Doctor Doctor':** There were actually three Thompson Twins – Tom Bailey, Alannah Currie and Joe Leeway.
11. **Dr Evil:** Real name Dougie Powers, he is a parody of Donald Pleasence's James Bond villain Blofeld.
12. *Doctor in the House*: Writers included John Cleese, Graham Chapman, Barry Cryer, Graeme Garden and Bill Oddie.
13. **Doctor and the Medics:** The original song also reached No. 1 in 1970 for Norman Greenbaum, his only UK hit.
14. **Dr Martens:** Their UK factory is at Wollaston and they used to sponsor local club Rushden & Diamonds.

15. **Doctor's Orders:** It is named after the number 9 pill given as a laxative to soldiers in World War II.
16. *Doctor Foster*: Jodie Comer plays Kate Parks in the series, but also starred as Villanelle in *Killing Eve*.
17. **Dr Black:** Known as Mr Boddy in the American version.
18. **'Dr Beat':** Their lead singer was Cuba-born Gloria Estefan.
19. *Dr Strangelove*: Sellers played three different parts and the film also stars George C Scott and Slim Pickens.
20. **Dr (Hawley) Crippen:** He was caught on board the SS *Montrose* when it arrived in Quebec and later hanged in Pentonville Prison for the murder of his wife Cora.
21. **Dr (David) Livingstone:** He found him after 8 months near Lake Tanganyika – in today's Tanzania.

HARD (3 Points)

22. **Dr Moreau:** The doctor was played on film by Marlon Brando (1996), Burt Lancaster (1977) and Charles Laughton (1932).
23. **Dr Feelgood:** The band was originally fronted by Wilko Johnson and Lee Brilleaux, who died in 1994 aged 41.
24. **Doc Holliday:** He was also played by Val Kilmer in *Tombstone* (1993) with Kurt Russell as Wyatt Earp.
25. **Dr Finlay:** The series was based on a novel by A J Cronin.
26. **'Doctor Jones':** The group were from Denmark and Norway.
27. **Dr Fu Manchu:** He was most famously played by Christopher Lee in five films from 1965 to 1969.
28. *Dr Kildare*: Richard Chamberlain played the lead roles in the 1980s TV miniseries *Shogun* and *The Thorn Birds*.
29. *Doctor Strange*: He reprised the role in the films *Avengers: Infinity War* and *Avengers: Endgame*.
30. **Dr Quinn:** Jane Seymour played Solitaire in the 1973 James Bond film *Live and Let Die*.

QUIZ No. 92: **SIMPLY RED**

EASY (1 Point)

1. **Sport & Games:** Which horse won the Grand National in 1973, 1974 and 1977?
2. **Places:** Which flower is the symbol of Lancashire?
3. **Music:** Which 1983 song was the first UK No. 1 for UB40?
4. **Pot Luck:** Which display team are officially known as the Royal Air Force Aerobatic Team?
5. **Food & Drink:** Which English cheese from the Midlands has an orange-coloured rind, despite its name?
6. **TV:** Which sci-fi comedy stars Craig Charles as Dave Lister, Chris Barrie as Arnold Rimmer and features a computer called Holly?
7. **Sport & Games:** What is the name of the American football team based in Washington who play in the NFL?
8. **Music:** Which song did Nena take to No. 1 in the UK in 1984?
9. **Pot Luck:** What traditionally leads to 'shepherds' delight'?

MEDIUM (2 Points)

10. **Films:** Which 1990 film was the first to feature the Tom Clancy character Jack Ryan?
11. **Politics:** Which song is the anthem of the Labour Party?
12. **People:** Which American oil well firefighter helped put out the Piper Alpha oil rig fire in the North Sea in 1988?
13. **Sport & Games:** What is the name of Boston's baseball team?
14. **Places:** The Kremlin and Saint Basil's Cathedral overlook which famous area of Moscow?
15. **Pot Luck:** Which red flag, with the Union flag in the top left corner, is the emblem of the British Merchant Navy?

16. **TV:** Which game show, hosted by Ant and Dec in 2011–12, was based on the spin of a roulette-type wheel?

17. **Films:** Which 2002 film was a prequel to *Silence of the Lambs* (1991) and *Hannibal* (2001)?

18. **Sport & Games:** For which F1 team did Sebastian Vettel win the world title four times from 2010 to 2013?

19. **Music:** Anthony Kiedis is the lead singer with which American rock group?

20. **Films:** Which 1984 film starred Gene Wilder and was Kelly LeBrock's first film role where she replicated a Marilyn Monroe scene from *The Seven Year Itch*?

21. **Pot Luck:** Which humanitarian organisation in Muslim countries is equivalent to the Red Cross?

HARD (3 Points)

22. **Art & Literature:** What is the name of the only painting sold by Vincent van Gogh during his lifetime?

23. **Music:** Which group had a UK No. 1 hit in 1994 with the song 'Cotton Eye Joe'?

24. **History:** The German World War I fighter pilot Manfred von Richthofen had which nickname?

25. **TV:** Which *Wacky Races* character, styled on the Red Baron, drove vehicle number 4, a car/plane hybrid?

26. **Music:** Daniel Merriweather had two UK Top 10 hits in 2009 – 'Change' and which other?

27. **Shopping & Fashion:** Which fashion brand was founded by Wayne Hemingway in London in 1982?

28. **Science & Medicine:** What is the familiar name for Jupiter's high-pressure region which creates an anticyclonic storm?

29. **Sport & Games:** Which horse won the 2001 Grand National when only four horses finished?

30. **Music:** Which group had two UK Top 10 hits in the mid-80s with 'Lean On Me (Ah-Li-Ayo)' and 'For America'?

EASY (1 Point)

1. **Red Rum:** Trainer Ginger McCain stabled him behind his car showroom and trained him on Southport beach.
2. **Red Rose:** The Wars of the Roses (1455–87) were fought between the Houses of Lancaster (red) and York (white).
3. **'Red Red Wine':** The song was written and originally recorded by Neil Diamond in 1967.
4. **Red Arrows:** They fly BAE Hawk T1 aircraft and have nine planes in a diamond formation.
5. **Red Leicester:** It is coloured orange by the condiment annatto, obtained from trees native to South America.
6. *Red Dwarf*: Kryten is played by Robert Llewellyn who also presented ten series of *Scrapheap Challenge*.
7. **Redskins:** They won the Super Bowl in 1982, 1987 and 1991.
8. **'99 Red Balloons':** Nena was the name of the band, named after the German singer.
9. **Red Sky at Night:** It appears in the Bible (Matthew 16).

MEDIUM (2 Points)

10. *The Hunt for Red October*: He was played by Alec Baldwin and later by Harrison Ford, Ben Affleck and Chris Pine.
11. **'The Red Flag':** The party was founded in 1900 and Ramsay MacDonald became the first Labour prime minister in 1924.
12. **Red Adair:** The 1968 John Wayne film *Hellfighters* is loosely based on the life of Red Adair.
13. **Red Sox:** In Boston, the Celtics play basketball, the Bruins play ice hockey and the New England Patriots play in the NFL.

14. **Red Square:** Lenin's Mausoleum, with his preserved body on display, has been there since his death in 1924.
15. **Red Ensign:** It is also known as the 'Red Duster'.
16. *Red or Black?*: The only other colour on a real roulette wheel is green, which contains the number zero.
17. *Red Dragon*: All the novels were written by Thomas Harris.
18. **Red Bull Racing:** Their team principal Christian Horner married Geri Halliwell in 2015.
19. **Red Hot Chili Peppers:** Their bassist Michael Balzary is known as Flea and has acted in over 20 films.
20. *The Woman in Red*: Stevie Wonder won the Oscar for Best Original Song for 'I Just Called to Say I Love You'.
21. **Red Crescent:** In 2005, a third, more generic red crystal symbol was introduced.

HARD (3 Points)

22. *The Red Vineyard*: In 1888, Paul Gauguin spent nine weeks painting at Van Gogh's Yellow House in Arles.
23. **Rednex:** The group came from Sweden.
24. **The Red Baron:** 'Snoopy vs the Red Baron' was a hit for the Royal Guardsmen in 1967 and the Hotshots in 1973.
25. **Red Max:** The vehicle was called the Crimson Haybailer.
26. **'Red':** He was born in Melbourne in 1982.
27. **Red Or Dead:** He and his wife Gerardine started by selling clothes on Camden Market.
28. **Great Red Spot:** Jupiter is the largest planet in the Solar System and consists of about 90% hydrogen and 10% helium.
29. **Red Marauder:** The horse was owned and trained by Norman Mason and in retirement lived with jockey Richard Guest.
30. **Red Box:** The group were founded by Simon Toulson-Clarke and Julian Close as a duo.

QUIZ No. 93: **IT'S ALL GREAT**

EASY (1 Point)

1. **Films:** Which classic 1963 war film set in a German POW camp starred Steve McQueen as 'the Cooler King'?
2. **Places:** Which series of Asian fortification constructions is over 13,000 miles long in total (over 21,000 km)?
3. **TV:** Which TV documentary series sees Michael Portillo travelling around on trains using his *Bradshaw's Guide*?
4. **History:** Which major London disaster started at a baker's in Pudding Lane in 1666?
5. **Animals & Nature:** The Peter Benchley novel and the 1975 film *Jaws* revolved around which type of creature?
6. **Food & Drink:** Which baking show, which first aired in 2010, was presented by Sue Perkins and Mel Giedroyc?
7. **Films:** The 1988 film *Buster*, starring Phil Collins as Buster Edwards, was about which 1963 major heist?
8. **Pot Luck:** Known informally as GOSH, what is the full name of the renowned children's hospital in London?
9. **Places:** Which is the world's largest coral reef system?

MEDIUM (2 Points)

10. **Music:** In 1987, Freddie Mercury had a UK No. 4 hit with which song, originally a hit for the Platters in 1956?
11. **TV:** Who was the oldest and wisest of the Wombles?
12. **Sport & Games:** Where is the most easterly racecourse in Great Britain?
13. **Places:** Which is the tallest pyramid in Egypt?
14. **Art & Literature:** Which 1925 novel by F Scott Fitzgerald is set in Long Island?
15. **Animals & Nature:** The Irish wolfhound is the tallest dog breed, on average, but what is the second tallest?
16. **History:** The brainchild of Prince Albert, what was held in the Crystal Palace in Hyde Park, London in 1851?

312

17. **Music:** Which song was Jerry Lee Lewis's only UK No. 1?
18. **Places:** Superior, Michigan, Huron, Erie and Ontario are collectively known as what?
19. **Art & Literature:** In which Charles Dickens novel are the characters Pip, Abel Magwitch and Miss Havisham?
20. **Films:** What was the main catchphrase of Emmett 'Doc' Brown in the *Back to the Future* films?
21. **History:** What was the severe economic downturn called in the years after the 1929 stock market crash?

HARD (3 Points)

---

22. **Places:** On which London street is the British Museum?
23. **Life & Lifestyle:** What was the full name of the largely mail order company who changed their name to GUS in 2001?
24. **TV:** Which TV series, first shown in 2014, featured husband and wife Timothy West and Prunella Scales on a narrowboat?
25. **Animals & Nature:** Which large flightless bird of the genus *Pinguinus* became extinct around 1850?
26. **Places:** Which natural feature runs for 62 miles from Inverness on the Moray Firth to Fort William on Loch Linnhe?
27. **Sport & Games:** What is the largest half marathon in the world, run between Newcastle upon Tyne and South Shields?
28. **TV:** Which BBC sewing show was first shown in 2013 and was hosted by Claudia Winkleman for the first four series?
29. **Transport & Travel:** Which railway, which ran from 1838 to 1948, was nicknamed the 'Holiday Line' as it took passengers from London to the SW of England?
30. **Places:** What is the name of the limestone headland in Llandudno which has a tram service to the top?

1. *The Great Escape*: It also starred James Garner, Richard Attenborough, Charles Bronson and Donald Pleasence.
2. **Great Wall of China:** It is a myth that it is the only man-made construction that you can see from space.
3. *Great British Railway Journeys*: It was first broadcast in 2010 and has included journeys in Europe, USA, Canada and India.
4. **Great Fire of London:** Despite destroying over 80% of London's homes, only six deaths were actually recorded.
5. **Great White Shark:** The film starred Roy Scheider, Richard Dreyfuss and Robert Shaw.
6. *The Great British Bake Off*: When the show moved to Channel 4, the presenters changed to Sandi Toksvig and Noel Fielding.
7. **Great Train Robbery:** Julie Walters played his wife, June.
8. **Great Ormond Street Hospital:** In 1929, J M Barrie donated the copyright of his *Peter Pan* works to the hospital.
9. **Great Barrier Reef:** It is located in the Coral Sea off Queensland, Australia.

10. **'The Great Pretender':** It was the first UK hit for the Platters and was released as a double A-side with 'Only You'.
11. **Great Uncle Bulgaria:** The Wombles were created by Elisabeth Beresford and the music written and performed by Mike Batt.
12. **Great Yarmouth:** Perth is the most northerly, Newton Abbot the most southerly and Ayr the most westerly.

13. **Great Pyramid of Giza:** It was the tallest man-made structure in the world until Lincoln Cathedral was finished in 1311.
14. ***The Great Gatsby:*** Robert Redford and Leonardo DiCaprio play Jay Gatsby in the 1974 and 2013 films.
15. **Great Dane:** The individual record for the tallest dog though is a Great Dane.
16. **Great Exhibition:** The Festival of Britain was held in 1951 to celebrate the centenary of the Great Exhibition.
17. **'Great Balls of Fire':** His career nosedived after he married his 13-year-old cousin Myra.
18. **Great Lakes:** Despite its name, the Caspian Sea is often considered to be the largest lake.
19. ***Great Expectations:*** Pip is an orphan, Magwitch is an escaped convict and Miss Havisham was a jilted bride.
20. **Great Scott!:** He was played by Christopher Lloyd.
21. **Great Depression:** It lasted from 1929 until about 1939.

HARD (3 Points)

22. **Great Russell Street:** The TUC's HQ is also there.
23. **Great Universal Stores:** The company acquired Argos in 1998 and Homebase in 2002.
24. ***Great Canal Journeys:*** They were married in 1963.
25. **Great Auk:** Native Americans used to bury great auk bones with the dead.
26. **Great Glen:** The glen contains four lakes, including Loch Ness, all joined up by the Caledonian Canal.
27. **Great North Run:** It was devised by former 10,000 metres runner and BBC commentator Brendan Foster.
28. ***The Great British Sewing Bee:*** Joe Lycett took over in 2019.
29. **Great Western Railway:** It was engineered by Isambard Kingdom Brunel.
30. **Great Orme:** It has Britain's only cable-hauled tramway.

QUIZ No. 94: **ALLITERATIVE NAMES – BB's**

All forenames and surnames begin with the same letter.

1. **Sport & Games:** Which rugby union lock captained England to their Grand Slam victory in 1980?
2. **Music:** Which singer was married to Whitney Houston from 1992 to 2007?
3. **Entertainment:** Which cartoon rabbit was being hunted by Elmer J Fudd?
4. **Art & Literature:** Which schoolboy created by Frank Richards went to Greyfriars School?
5. **People:** Which South Africa-born entrepreneur became synonymous with British holiday camps?
6. **Sport & Games:** Who won the Wimbledon Men's Singles title in 1985, 1986 and 1989?
7. **TV:** Which actor with a booming voice played PC 'Fancy' Smith in *Z Cars*?
8. **Sport & Games:** Which Leeds United midfielder was sent off with Kevin Keegan in the 1974 Charity Shield?
9. **TV:** Which English actress has played DCI Vera Stanhope in the crime drama series *Vera* since 2011?

10. **TV:** Which comedian starred with Dylan Moran and Tamsin Greig in the sitcom *Black Books*?
11. **Music:** Who had a hit in 1990 with 'Doin' the Do'?
12. **Films:** Which actor starred with his brother Jeff in the film *The Fabulous Baker Boys*?
13. **Sport & Games:** Who broke the world long-jump record at the Mexico Olympics in 1968?
14. **TV:** Who played Dr David Banner in *The Incredible Hulk?*

15. **Films:** Which actress shot to fame after the 1956 film *And God Created Woman*?
16. **People:** Who was the wife of the 41st US president?
17. **Music:** Whose first hit was 'Between the Wars' in 1985?
18. **Sport & Games:** Which ex-West Ham captain holds the record for most club appearances?
19. **Films:** Which US actress played the Bond girl Anya Amasova in the 1977 film *The Spy Who Loved Me*?
20. **People:** Who was the first female prime minister of Pakistan?
21. **Music:** Which acclaimed songwriter wrote many songs in collaboration with lyricist Hal David?

HARD (3 Points)

---

22. **History:** Which famous High King of Ireland died at the Battle of Clontarf in 1014?
23. **Films:** Which actress played the wife of Bruce Willis in the first two *Die Hard* films?
24. **Art & Literature:** Which novel was Herman Melville's last, the title character being a press-ganged seaman?
25. **TV:** Which *Carry On* actor played Private 'Popeye' Popplewell in *The Army Game*?
26. **Sport & Games:** Who was appointed head coach of the New England Patriots in 2000, the same year Tom Brady arrived?
27. **Films:** Which Australian actor starred alongside Tom Cruise in the 1988 film *Cocktail*?
28. **Music:** Which singer was a one-hit wonder with his 1970 song 'Montego Bay'?
29. **Art & Literature:** The 1954 play *The Quare Fellow* was the first written by which Irish poet and playwright?
30. **Sport & Games:** Which Welsh-born winger scored 478 tries in 487 matches for Wigan from 1953 to 1968 and was the first black player to play for the Lions?

1. **Bill Beaumont:** He was a captain on *A Question of Sport* for 14 years from 1982 to 1996.
2. **Bobby Brown:** He is a former member of New Edition, whose 'Candy Girl' was a hit in 1983.
3. **Bugs Bunny:** He was created in 1940 and famously voiced by Mel Blanc.
4. **Billy Bunter:** He was played in the 1950s TV series by Gerald Campion.
5. **Billy Butlin:** He opened his first holiday camp in Skegness in 1936.
6. **Boris Becker:** In 1985 he became the youngest and the first unseeded winner of Wimbledon.
7. **Brian Blessed:** He has climbed Mount Kilimanjaro and Mount Aconcagua and has sparred with the Dalai Lama.
8. **Billy Bremner:** He was portrayed by Stephen Graham in the 2009 film *The Damned United*.
9. **Brenda Blethyn:** She played Jane Horrocks's mother in the 1998 film *Little Voice*.

10. **Bill Bailey:** He is also a talented multi-instrumentalist and has perfect pitch.
11. **Betty Boo:** Born Alison Moira Clarkson, her first hit was with the Beatmasters.
12. **Beau Bridges:** His father was Lloyd Bridges; he was named after a boy in *Gone with the Wind*.
13. **Bob Beamon:** He beat the record by 55cm; it stood for 23 years until Mike Powell broke it.
14. **Bill Bixby:** He starred in *My Favorite Martian* and *The Magician* but died in 1993 aged 59.

15. **Brigitte Bardot:** She became an animal rights activist and turned down the Legion of Honour.
16. **Barbara Bush:** She developed the Barbara Bush Foundation for Family Literacy.
17. **Billy Bragg:** He famously wrote 'A New England' for the late Kirsty MacColl.
18. **Billy Bonds:** He led the team to two FA Cup final victories in 1975 and 1980.
19. **Barbara Bach:** She married Ringo Starr in 1981.
20. **Benazir Bhutto:** She was assassinated in Rawalpindi in 2007.
21. **Burt Bacharach:** He was married to Angie Dickinson from 1965 to 1980 and Carole Bayer-Sager from 1982 to 1991.

HARD (3 Points)

22. **Brian Boru:** The harp in Trinity College Dublin was once wrongly thought to be his harp.
23. **Bonnie Bedelia:** She is the aunt of Macauley Culkin, the son of her brother Kit.
24. *Billy Budd*: It was also a 1962 film starring Peter Ustinov and Terence Stamp.
25. **Bernard Bresslaw:** He had a Top 10 hit in 1958 with 'Mad Passionate Love' in the style of Popplewell.
26. **Bill Belichick:** They won the Super Bowl in the 2001, 2003, 2004, 2014, 2016 and 2018 seasons.
27. **Bryan Brown:** He met his wife Rachel Ward on the set of *The Thorn Birds* in 1983?
28. **Bobby Bloom:** He accidentally shot himself aged 28; the song was a hit for Amazulu in 1986.
29. **Brendan Behan:** He died in 1964 aged just 41.
30. **Billy Boston:** He was born in Tiger Bay, as was Shirley Bassey, and lived three doors from the boxer Joe Erskine.

QUIZ No. 95: **FROM A TO B**

All answers have the initials AB.

1. **Music:** Who won *The X Factor* in 2008 and released the single 'Hallelujah' written by Leonard Cohen?
2. **Films:** Which actor's first lead role was in the 1990 film *The Hunt for Red October* where he played Jack Ryan?
3. **Pot Luck:** In the traditional folk tale, who found a cave with treasure hidden by 40 thieves?
4. **History:** Who was the second wife of Henry VIII?
5. **TV:** Who is the leader of the dance troupe Diversity who won *Britain's Got Talent* in 2009?
6. **Music:** Who is the lead singer with the group Erasure?
7. **Art & Literature:** Which Yorkshire playwright wrote *Talking Heads*, *The Madness of King George* and *The History Boys*?
8. **Films:** Which Spanish actor played Zorro in *The Mask of Zorro* (1998) and *The Legend of Zorro* (2005)?
9. **Music:** Which English tenor has released albums called *Together* and *Together Again* with Michael Ball?

10. **TV:** Who starred as Dr Beth Glover in *Peak Practice* and Dr Sam Ryan in *Silent Witness*?
11. **Art & Literature:** Who wrote the novels *Agnes Grey* and *The Tenant of Wildfell Hall*?
12. **Politics:** Which Welsh Labour MP, as Minister of Health, was the chief architect of the National Health Service?
13. **Films:** Who won the Best Actor Oscar for Roman Polanski's 2002 film *The Pianist*?
14. **Music:** Which clarinettist and band leader had a UK No. 2 hit in 1961 with 'Stranger on the Shore'?

15. **TV:** Which *Coronation Street* character, played by Mark Eden from 1986–89, was killed by a tram in Blackpool?

16. **Sport & Games:** Which then Blackpool player was the youngest of England's 1966 World Cup final team?

17. **Politics:** Which former Labour MP became Mayor of Greater Manchester in 2017?

18. **TV:** Which actress played Alma Sedgewick (later Baldwin) in *Coronation Street* from 1981 to 1982 and 1988 to 2001?

19. **Films:** Who played the seductress, Mrs Robinson, in the 1967 film *The Graduate*?

20. **Music:** Which US singer's only UK Top 20 hit was 'Sweet Love' in 1986?

21. **TV:** Who starred as Sharron Macready in the only series of *The Champions* in the 1960s, a total of 30 episodes?

HARD (3 Points)

22. **Art & Literature:** Which author wrote the 1962 book *A Clockwork Orange*?

23. **People:** Which Surveyor of the Queen's Pictures was exposed as a Soviet spy in 1979, part of the Cambridge Five?

24. **Music:** Which Russian composed the opera *Prince Igor*?

25. **Sport & Games:** Who captained Australia to their first Cricket World Cup win in 1987?

26. **Politics:** Who was British prime minister from 1902–05?

27. **Music:** Whose 'Crazy World' had a UK No. 1 hit in 1968 with 'Fire'?

28. **Art & Literature:** Which author wrote the 'Jennings' books?

29. **Films:** Who was mistaken for Jesus Christ by Hayley Mills in the 1961 film *Whistle Down the Wind*?

30. **Music:** Which US singer's only UK hit was 'I Love the Nightlife (Disco Round)' in 1978?

1. **Alexandra Burke:** The single reached No. 1 in the UK as did her follow-up single 'Bad Boys' featuring Flo Rida.
2. **Alec Baldwin:** He married Kim Basinger in 1993 but they divorced in 2002.
3. **Ali Baba:** It was part of the collection of tales *One Thousand and One Nights*.
4. **Anne Boleyn:** He was excommunicated after their marriage in 1533 but she was beheaded in 1536.
5. **Ashley Banjo:** They beat Susan Boyle in the final and Banjo went on to present *Got to Dance* from 2009–14.
6. **Andy Bell:** The other member is Vince Clarke who was also in Depeche Mode, Yazoo and The Assembly.
7. **Alan Bennett:** His play *The Lady in the Van* was filmed at his old house – she had parked on his drive for 15 years.
8. **Antonio Banderas:** He was married to Melanie Griffith from 1996 to 2015 and voiced Puss in Boots in the *Shrek* series.
9. **Alfie Boe:** Alfie was born in Blackpool and played Jean Valjean in the 25th anniversary *Les Misérables* concert.

10. **Amanda Burton:** She had previously appeared in *Brookside* for four years as Heather Black.
11. **Anne Bronte:** Her novels were first published under the pen name Acton Bell but she died in 1849 aged just 29.
12. **Aneurin Bevan:** Often known as Nye Bevan, he oversaw the birth of the NHS in 1948.
13. **Adrien Brody:** He was the youngest ever winner of the award at the age of 29.

14. **Acker Bilk:** He always wore his trademark bowler hat and the song was the first US No. 1 by a British artist.
15. **Alan Bradley:** Sally Ann Matthews plays his daughter Jenny.
16. **Alan Ball:** He moved to Everton soon after but died in 2007 aged 61; Bobby Moore was the first to die in 1993.
17. **Andy Burnham:** He was Health Secretary in Gordon Brown's Cabinet and then Shadow Home Secretary.
18. **Amanda Barrie:** Born Shirley Broadbent, she played Cleopatra in the 1964 film *Carry On Cleo*.
19. **Anne Bancroft:** She married Mel Brooks in 1964.
20. **Anita Baker:** It won the Grammy for Best R&B Song.
21. **Alexandra Bastedo:** Stuart Damon as Craig Stirling and William Gaunt as Richard Barrett made up the team.

HARD (3 Points)

---

22. **Anthony Burgess:** It was adapted into a 1971 Stanley Kubrick film starring Malcolm McDowell.
23. **Anthony Blunt:** The other four members were Donald Maclean, Guy Burgess, Kim Philby and John Cairncross.
24. **Alexander Borodin:** Most of the music from the musical *Kismet*, including 'Stranger in Paradise', is by Borodin.
25. **Allan Border:** He is the only player to date to score over 150 in both innings of a Test match, at Lahore in 1980.
26. **Arthur Balfour:** He was also Foreign Secretary under David Lloyd George and issued the Balfour Declaration in 1917.
27. **Arthur Brown:** Carl Palmer, later of Emerson, Lake and Palmer, became the drummer after the 1968 hit.
28. **Anthony Buckeridge:** He also wrote the 'Rex Milligan' books.
29. **Alan Bates:** He starred in the 1969 film *Women in Love* with Oliver Reed and Glenda Jackson.
30. **Alicia Bridges:** The song was revived and remixed in 1994 for the film *Priscilla, Queen of the Desert*.

QUIZ No. 96: ALTERNATE A's

All answers contain alternate A's e.g. banana.

EASY (1 Point)

1.   **Places:** Which is the largest hot desert in the world?
2.   **Music:** Which group's chart debut was in 1982 with Fun Boy Three on 'It Ain't What You Do It's The Way That You Do It'?
3.   **Words:** What is the Spanish word for tomorrow?
4.   **Religion:** What is the ninth month of the Islamic calendar which is observed as a month of fasting, known as *Sawm*?
5.   **TV:** In the comedy drama series *Cold Feet*, which character does James Nesbitt play?
6.   **People:** What was the surname of Yasser, leader of the Palestine Liberation Organization from 1969 to 2004?
7.   **Places:** What is the capital of Cuba?
8.   **Films:** The 1969 film about the 1883 eruption of a volcano on the island of Krakatoa is called *Krakatoa, East of ...* where?
9.   **Music:** Which percussion instrument is shaken by a handle and is usually played as part of a pair?

MEDIUM (2 Points)

10. **Sport & Games:** What is the name of the football stadium in Rio de Janeiro, built for the 1950 World Cup?
11. **Places:** Which US state's capital is Montgomery, although its most populous city is Birmingham?
12. **Food & Drink:** Which Greek *meze* dish is largely made up of fish roe and is usually pink in colour?
13. **Shopping & Fashion:** Which type of brimmed straw hat is actually of Ecuadorian origin, despite its name?

14. **Sport & Games:** Which city in Senegal was the original destination of an annual car rally from Paris?
15. **Films:** Which 2009 film, directed by James Cameron, featured blue-skinned humanoids?
16. **Places:** Which city is the capital of Morocco?
17. **Science & Medicine:** Which English scientist's main discoveries related to the principles of electric motors, electrolysis and electromagnetism?
18. **Food & Drink:** Which oval fruit with orange flesh and black seeds is similar to the pawpaw fruit?
19. **Shopping & Fashion:** Which fashion and homeware retailer was founded by John Hargreaves in 1985?
20. **Places:** Nassau is the capital of which group of islands in the Atlantic Ocean?
21. **Sport & Games:** Which Dutch football club won the European Cup in 1971, 1972 and 1973?

HARD (3 Points)

---

22. **Art & Literature:** What is the name of the O'Hara family plantation in Margaret Mitchell's *Gone with the Wind*?
23. **Food & Drink:** Which Japanese restaurant chain opened its first restaurant in London in 1992?
24. **Sport & Games:** The 'Big Three' football clubs based in Istanbul are Beşiktaş, Fenerbahçe and which other?
25. **Places:** What is the capital of Venezuela?
26. **Words:** Which Sanskrit word for 'great ruler' or 'great king' has been used for rulers in Asia, especially India?
27. **Sport & Games:** Which 'Bryan', a South African RU wing, shares the record for most tries in World Cups?
28. **Entertainment:** In the comic strip, which superhero did Eric Wimp of 29 Acacia Road turn into?
29. **Art & Literature:** What nickname was given to the genre of books often about village or country life?
30. **Places:** Which desert is the driest non-polar place on earth?

EASY (1 Point)

1. **Sahara:** It means 'desert' in Arabic and is the third largest in the world after Antarctica and the Arctic.
2. **Bananarama:** They duetted with Fun Boy Three two months later on 'Really Saying Something'.
3. **Mañana:** The Spanish word for yesterday is 'ayer' and for today is 'hoy'.
4. **Ramadan:** It is one of the Five Pillars of Islam along with *Shahadah*, *Salat*, *Zakat* and *Hajj*.
5. **Adam:** The original characters were Adam Williams, Rachel Bradley, Pete and Jenny Gifford, David and Karen Marsden.
6. **Arafat:** In 1994 he received the Nobel Peace Prize along with Yitzhak Rabin and Shimon Peres.
7. **Havana:** Fidel Castro seized power in 1959 after the Cuban Revolution from the dictator Fulgencio Batista.
8. *Java:* Krakatoa is actually west of Java.
9. **Maracas:** Maracas are traditionally made from the fruit of the higuera tree in the Caribbean and Latin America.

MEDIUM (2 Points)

10. **Maracanã:** The 1950 World Cup final when Uruguay beat Brazil 2-1 had a record attendance of 199,854.
11. **Alabama:** The Montgomery bus boycott lasted over a year after Rosa Parks refused to give up her seat.
12. **Taramasalata:** In Greece, it is eaten on Clean Monday, the first day of Great Lent when no meat or dairy products are eaten.
13. **Panama:** They have been made since the 1600s.
14. **Dakar:** The race moved to South America from 2009 due to security concerns.

15. ***Avatar***: It broke box-office records set by Cameron's 1997 film *Titanic*, only surpassed in 2019 by *Avengers: Endgame*.

16. **Rabat**: Casablanca is by far the most populous city in Morocco, followed by Fez, Tangier and Marrakesh.

17. **Faraday**: The farad is the SI unit of capacitance named after Michael Faraday.

18. **Papaya**: It is native to Mexico and South America.

19. **Matalan**: It started in Preston as a membership only retailer but moved to Knowsley on Merseyside in 2015.

20. **Bahamas**: Often thought to be in the Caribbean, the Bahamas is between the southern Florida and Cuba.

21. **Ajax**: Johan Cruyff scored 190 goals in 240 games for the club who named their stadium after him when he died in 2016.

HARD (3 Points)

22. **Tara**: In the 1939 film, Vivien Leigh plays Scarlett O'Hara and Clark Gable plays Rhett Butler.

23. **Wagamama**: In 2018 it was bought by the Restaurant Group who own Frankie and Benny's and Garfunkel's.

24. **Galatasaray**: They won their only European trophy when they beat Arsenal to win the 2000 UEFA Cup.

25. **Caracas**: The island of Trinidad is only 6.8 miles off the northeast coast of Venezuela.

26. **Maharaja(h)**: The female equivalent is a maharani.

27. **Habana**: He scored 15 as did New Zealand's Jonah Lomu and both players scored eight in one tournament.

28. **Bananaman**: In the 1980s TV series, the voices were Tim Brooke-Taylor, Graeme Garden and Bill Oddie.

29. **Aga Saga**: It was named after the cast-iron AGA cookers found in many rural kitchens.

30. **Atacama**: The desert is west of the Andes and covers a large part of Chile.

All answers end with -oo e.g. cuckoo.

1. **Music:** What was the first UK hit for Alvin Stardust, reaching No. 2 in 1973?
2. **TV:** What is the name of the vacuum cleaner who acts as the housekeeper in the children's show *Teletubbies*?
3. **Animals & Nature:** A panda's daily diet consists of the leaves, stems and shoots of which plant?
4. **Art & Literature:** In A A Milne's *Winnie-the-Pooh*, what is the name of the young kangaroo?
5. **Music:** Which group had a 1983 No. 1 with 'Too Shy'?
6. **Food & Drink:** Which now spicy Indian curry from Goa originally meant 'meat in garlic wine' in Portuguese?
7. **Religion:** Which religion of African origin is a very important religion in Haiti?
8. **Entertainment:** Which glove puppet first appeared in 1964 as Sooty's girlfriend in *The Sooty Show*?
9. **Music:** Which song was the biggest UK hit for the group Black Lace, reaching No. 2 in 1984?

10. **TV:** Which diminutive character was played by Hervé Villechaize in *Fantasy Island* from 1977 to 1984?
11. **Pot Luck:** Which musical instrument creates a type of buzzing noise when a person hums or vocalises into it?
12. **Sport & Games:** Which children's toy involves placing various items on a mule's back without it bucking?
13. **History:** In which battle of 1815 was Napoleon defeated to mark the end of the Napoleonic Wars?
14. **Life & Lifestyle:** Which web services company was founded in 1994 by Jerry Yang and David Filo?

15. **Transport & Travel:** Which London Underground line is coloured brown on a map of the Underground?
16. **TV:** In the TV sitcom *Till Death Us Do Part*, what name did Alf Garnett often call his long-suffering wife Else?
17. **Animals & Nature:** Which dog is the cross-breed of a Cocker Spaniel and a poodle?
18. **Music:** Which female singer had UK Top 10 hits in 1990 with 'Doin' the Do' and 'Where Are You Baby?'?
19. **Theatre:** In the Gilbert and Sullivan comic opera *The Mikado*, who is the son of the mikado / emperor of Japan?
20. **Pot Luck:** Which long, cylindrical, wooden musical instrument was developed by indigenous Australians?
21. **TV:** What was the name of Yogi Bear's constant companion?

HARD (3 Points)

22. **Music:** Which group had a 1996 No. 1 with 'Spaceman'?
23. **Films:** Which 1987 film starred George Costigan as a married man having a fling with two young women?
24. **Places:** At which site near Woodbridge in Suffolk was a ship burial site discovered in 1939?
25. **Food & Drink:** Which cocktail consists of vodka, peach schnapps and cranberry juice?
26. **Music:** Which 1972 song was the highest charting release for Ringo Starr as a solo artist, reaching No. 2?
27. **Animals & Nature:** Which member of the parrot family, native to Australasia, is the loudest of the parrots?
28. **TV:** Which 2014 drama was about George Mottershead and his family opening Chester Zoo in 1931?
29. **Films:** Which 1975 film stars Warren Beatty as a Beverly Hills hairdresser with Julie Christie and Goldie Hawn?
30. **Music:** Which 1971 song was the debut UK hit for the US singer Lobo?

ANSWERS QUIZ No. 97: -OO ENDINGS

1. **'My Coo Ca Choo':** His real name was Bernard Jewry and he first recorded as Shane Fenton with the Fentones.
2. **Noo-Noo:** Tinky Winky is purple, Dipsy is green, Laa-Laa is yellow and Po is red.
3. **Bamboo:** The panda is native to south central China.
4. **Roo:** A young kangaroo is called a joey and the character is based on a stuffed toy that belonged to the author's son.
5. **Kajagoogoo:** Their lead singer was Limahl, the name being an anagram of his surname, real name Christopher Hamill.
6. **Vindaloo:** The dish was originally made with pork and Fat Les had a UK No. 2 hit in 1998 with a song called 'Vindaloo'.
7. **Voodoo:** Although inserting pins into dolls is often shown as part of voodoo, it does not usually form part of the religion.
8. **Soo:** She was originally voiced by the wife of the show's creator, Marjorie Corbett, until 1980.
9. **'Agadoo':** They first charted in 1979 with 'Mary Ann' which they sang in the 1979 Eurovision Song Contest.

MEDIUM (2 Points)

10. **Tattoo:** He also played Scaramanga's sidekick Nick Nack in the James Bond film *The Man with the Golden Gun*.
11. **Kazoo:** There is a 'swanee whistle and kazoo' round on the Radio 4 show *I'm Sorry I Haven't a Clue.*
12. **Buckaroo!:** Father Ted and Dougal used to play Buckaroo! in *Father Ted* as it was Ted's favourite game.

13. **Waterloo:** The two victorious armies were led by the Duke of Wellington (British) and Field Marshal Blücher (Prussian).
14. **Yahoo!:** They were both students at Stanford University.
15. **Bakerloo:** It got its name as it originally connected Baker Street to Waterloo Station.
16. **Silly (Old) Moo:** Alf Garnett was played by Warren Mitchell and his wife Else was played by Dandy Nichols.
17. **Cockapoo:** The dog could be a poodle bred with an American or an English Cocker Spaniel.
18. **Betty Boo:** Her real name is Alison Clarkson.
19. **Nanki-Poo:** He flees the royal court disguised as a minstrel to search for his love, Yum-Yum.
20. **Didgeridoo:** Most are around four feet long but can be up to ten feet in length.
21. **Boo-Boo (Bear):** Both Yogi Bear and Boo-Boo first appeared on *The Huckleberry Hound Show*.

> **HARD (3 Points)**

22. **Babylon Zoo:** The band were led by Jas Mann and the song featured in a 1995 advert for Levi's.
23. ***Rita, Sue and Bob Too*:** The two young women were played by Michelle Holmes and Siobhan Finneran.
24. **Sutton Hoo:** Most of the Anglo-Saxon artefacts, originally buried around 625, are in the British Museum.
25. **Woo Woo:** Add orange juice to make 'Sex on the Beach'.
26. **'Back Off Boogaloo':** He also had UK Top 10 hits with 'It Don't Come Easy', 'Photograph' and 'You're Sixteen'.
27. **Cockatoo:** They live on average for about 60 years.
28. ***Our Zoo*:** Lee Ingleby played George Mottershead and Liz White played his wife Lizzie.
29. ***Shampoo*:** The film was the film debut of Carrie Fisher.
30. **'Me and You and a Dog Named Boo':** He also had a 1974 hit with 'I'd Love You to Want Me'.

All answers start and end with the same letter e.g. America.

1. **Science & Medicine:** Which is the most abundant element in the earth's atmosphere, making up around 78% of it?
2. **TV:** Which private investigator did Tom Selleck play in the 1980s crime drama series set in Hawaii?
3. **Places:** What is the capital of Poland?
4. **Words:** What is the German word for Germany?
5. **Sport & Games:** Which game, first sold in 1967, includes a clear plastic tube, coloured rods and some marbles?
6. **Music:** Which alternative nine-letter word for the Devil is mentioned in the Queen song 'Bohemian Rhapsody'?
7. **Science & Medicine:** Which chemical element has the symbol Ne and the atomic number 10?
8. **TV:** Which black comedy series starring David Threlfall as Frank Gallagher is set on the Chatsworth estate?
9. **Sport & Games:** Which team won the 2005 Champions League after being 3-0 down to AC Milan at half-time?

10. **History:** What name was given to the system of forced labour camps during Joseph Stalin's time as leader?
11. **Art & Literature:** What is the surname of Prince Hal's chief companion in Shakespeare's *Henry IV Part 1* and *Part 2*?
12. **Mathematics:** What is the name of a straight line that touches a curve or a circle?
13. **Geography:** Which of the Great Lakes has the shortest name and is the shallowest and smallest by volume?
14. **People:** What is the first name of Will Smith's daughter?

15. **Food & Drink:** What is the alternative name for the herb wild marjoram?
16. **Science & Medicine:** What is the name of the closest large spiral galaxy to our galaxy, the Milky Way?
17. **TV:** In the Warner Bros. series of cartoons, which character was Wile E Coyote constantly chasing?
18. **History:** Boudicca, or Boadicea, was the queen of which tribe who revolted against the Romans *c.*AD 60?
19. **Pot Luck:** Which seat, usually with a canopy, is carried on the back of an elephant, or sometimes a camel?
20. **Art & Literature:** What is the nickname of the orphan, the main character and narrator, in *Great Expectations*?
21. **Sport & Games:** What is the name of the American football team based in Pittsburgh, Pennsylvania?

HARD (3 Points)

22. **Religion:** Which Jewish festival around December time is also known as the Festival of Lights?
23. **Music:** Which 1966 Beatles album includes the singles 'Eleanor Rigby' and 'Yellow Submarine'?
24. **Places:** What is the name of the famous Spanish palace and fortress complex in Granada, Andalusia?
25. **Politics:** When Margaret Thatcher became prime minister in 1979, who was her first Home Secretary?
26. **TV:** Which HBO US western series, starring Timothy Olyphant and Ian McShane, ran from 2004 to 2006?
27. **Science & Medicine:** With which autoimmune disease does the body attack its tissues when gluten is eaten?
28. **Sport & Games:** Which horse named after a country won the 2014 Epsom Derby?
29. **Art & Literature:** Which Shakespeare play is subtitled 'The Moor of Venice'?
30. **Places:** Which Aboriginal name is now used for what was Ayers Rock in Australia's Northern Territory?

EASY (1 Point)

1. **Nitrogen:** Oxygen is the most abundant in the earth's crust (47%) and hydrogen the most abundant in the universe (74%).
2. **Magnum:** John Hillerman played Higgins with Orson Welles doing voice 'appearances' as property owner Robin Masters.
3. **Warsaw:** It is situated on the River Vistula.
4. **Deutschland:** 'Deutschlandlied' (Song of Germany) is the national anthem composed in 1797 by Joseph Haydn.
5. **Kerplunk:** Introduced by Ideal Toys who first marketed the Rubik's Cube in 1980 for its Hungarian inventor.
6. **Beelzebub:** It reached No. 1 in 1975 and in 1991 after Freddie Mercury's death, the first to be No. 1 twice.
7. **Neon:** It is one of the six noble gases along with helium (2), argon (18), krypton (36), xenon (54) and radon (86).
8. *Shameless*: It also originally featured James McAvoy, was written by Paul Abbott and ran from 2004 to 2013.
9. **Liverpool:** They have now won the competition six times: 1977, 1978, 1981, 1984, 2005 and 2019.

MEDIUM (2 Points)

10. **Gulag:** The first camp was set up in 1919 and they started to be closed down after Stalin's death in 1953.
11. **Falstaff:** He also appears in *The Merry Wives of Windsor* and Giuseppe Verdi wrote an opera called *Falstaff*.
12. **Tangent:** Tangent is also a method of calculating an angle in a right-angled triangle using opposite and adjacent sides.
13. **Erie:** The other Great Lakes are Lake Superior, Lake Huron, Lake Michigan and Lake Ontario.

14. **Willow:** Her brother is Jaden and Smith's other son is Willard 'Trey' Smith – Willard is Smith's full name too.
15. **Oregano:** It is a staple herb of Italian cuisine and soldiers introduced it to the USA after World War II.
16. **Andromeda:** On a clear night you can see Andromeda in the sky, even though it is 2.5 million light years away.
17. **Road Runner:** 'Roadrunner' was also a UK No. 11 hit in 1977 for Jonathan Richman and the Modern Lovers.
18. **Iceni:** Julius Caesar first landed in 55 BC, but the Roman Conquest started in AD 43 under Claudius until AD 410.
19. **Howdah:** The word is of Arabic origin.
20. **Pip:** His full name is Philip Pirrip, his brother-in-law is Joe Gargery and he is in love with Estella.
21. **Steelers:** They won the Super Bowl in 1974, 1975, 1978, 1979, 2005 and 2008.

HARD (3 Points)

22. **Hanukkah:** Candles are lit in special candelabra with nine branches, although menorahs usually have seven.
23. *Revolver*: The singles were released as a double A-side at the same time as the album.
24. **Alhambra:** It was built as a fortress in 889 and converted by the Moors into a royal palace in 1333.
25. **(William) Whitelaw:** The first Secretary of State for Northern Ireland in 1972 and always her deputy leader.
26. *Deadwood*: Olyphant (Seth Bullock) and McShane (Al Swearengen) reprised the roles for the 2019 film.
27. **Coeliac (disease):** Gluten can be found in wheat, barley and rye, and often in oats due to cross-contamination.
28. **Australia:** His sire Galileo won the 2001 Derby and his dam Ouija Board won the 2004 Oaks.
29. **Othello:** Othello is a general in the Venetian army, married to Desdemona; Iago is his treacherous ensign.
30. **Uluru:** It is about 450 km south-west of Alice Springs.

All answers have repeated words e.g. Hear hear.

EASY (1 Point)

1. **Music:** Which group's only two UK No. 1 hits were 'Is There Something I Should Know' in 1983 and 'The Reflex' in 1984?
2. **Sport & Games:** What football phrase means that each player has an equal chance of winning the ball?
3. **Food & Drink:** Which N African dish by origin consists of tiny steamed balls of durum wheat semolina?
4. **Music:** What was the first UK hit for B A Robertson in 1979 and a similar title was a hit for Cher in 1966?
5. **Places:** What is the name of the maximum security prison about 30 miles north of New York City?
6. **Entertainment:** Which lively, high-kicking dance originated in the French music halls in the 1840s?
7. **Music:** Which song was Status Quo's only UK No. 1 hit?
8. **Politics:** Which phrase came to be used in 2010 about former Italian prime minister Silvio Berlusconi's parties?
9. **TV:** Which Teletubby is yellow and has a curly antenna?

MEDIUM (2 Points)

10. **Music:** Whose 2008 No. 1 was 'That's Not My Name'?
11. **History:** What was the name of the militant movement who fought the British in Kenya in the 1950s?
12. **Food & Drink:** Which chilli pepper is used to make a spicy sauce which is very popular in Portuguese cuisine?
13. **Music:** In the Barry Manilow song 'Copacabana', which dance completes the lyrics 'She would merengue and do the ... ...'?
14. **Science & Medicine:** Which disease is caused by a lack of vitamin B-1, also known as thiamine deficiency?

15. **TV:** In which 1990s TV series did Robson Green and Jerome Flynn play Dave Tucker and Paddy Garvey?
16. **Music:** Which band had UK Top 20 hits in 1986 with 'Life's What You Make It' and in 1990 with 'It's My Life'?
17. **History:** What nickname was given to William Joyce who broadcast Nazi propaganda during World War II?
18. **Words:** What is a type of drum or a make of satnav?
19. **Music:** Which US band had a UK No. 4 hit in 1985 with 'Broken Wings' and a No. 11 hit in 1986 with 'Kyrie'?
20. **Food & Drink:** Which fruit is sometimes confused with the papaya as both are from the same species, *Carica*?
21. **Science & Medicine:** A bite from which fly, common in tropical Africa, causes sleeping sickness?

HARD (3 Points)

---

22. **Music:** The only UK chart hit for Denise LaSalle was in 1985 and was called 'My ....'?
23. **Films:** In the 1967 film *Barbarella*, Jane Fonda starred as a space traveller looking for which scientist?
24. **Pot Luck:** What is the common name of the expanding bullets, named after the arsenal where they were made near Calcutta?
25. **Music:** What was the title of Sophia George's only UK hit which reached No. 7 in 1985?
26. **Art & Literature:** Which character in Joseph Heller's novel *Catch-22* had the same forename and surname?
27. **Animals & Nature:** What is the name of the lemur with big eyes and ears and a long, thin middle finger?
28. **Music:** What was the only UK chart hit for The Assembly, reaching No. 4 in 1983?
29. **Films:** In the 1967 film *Doctor Dolittle*, what was the name of his chimpanzee?
30. **Places:** Which spa town in SW Germany is on the edge of the Black Forest and near the border with France?

EASY (1 Point)

1. **Duran Duran:** The group was Simon Le Bon, Nick Rhodes and Andy, John and Roger Taylor (but none were related).
2. **Fifty-fifty:** There was a BBC children's game show called *50/50* that ran from 1997 to 2005.
3. **Couscous:** There are 3 types of couscous: Moroccan, the smallest, then Israeli (pearl) and Lebanese, the largest.
4. **'Bang Bang':** Dirty Pretty Things also had their biggest hit in 2006 with 'Bang Bang You're Dead'.
5. **Sing Sing:** It got its name from the Sintsink tribe from whom the land was bought, on the bank of the Hudson.
6. **Can-can:** It is often danced to Jacques Offenbach's 'Galop Infernal' from *Orpheus in the Underworld*.
7. **'Down Down':** They had three No. 2 hits: 'What You're Proposin'', 'In the Army Now' and 'Anniversary Waltz - Part 1'.
8. **Bunga Bunga:** He was prime minister briefly in 1994/95 but then from 2001 to 2006 and from 2008 to 2011.
9. **Laa-Laa:** The character is female, as is Po (red), but Tinky Winky (purple) and Dipsy (green) are male.

MEDIUM (2 Points)

10. **Ting Tings:** They are Katie White and Jules De Martino.
11. **Mau Mau:** Jomo Kenyatta was appointed the first prime minister of an independent Kenya in 1963.
12. **Piri Piri:** It is also popular in some of the former Portuguese colonies like Goa, Angola and Mozambique.
13. **Cha Cha:** It is thought to have been invented by Cuban composer and violinist Enrique Jorrin in the 1950s.
14. **Beriberi:** Scurvy is caused by a lack of vitamin C; rickets, a lack of vitamin D; and pellagra, a lack of vitamin B-3.

15. *Soldier Soldier*: Ex-TV presenter Chris Kelly (*Wish You Were Here...?*, *Clapperboard*) wrote some episodes.
16. **Talk Talk:** Their lead singer was Mark Hollis and their 1982 debut hit was also called 'Talk Talk'.
17. **(Lord) Haw-Haw:** He was captured at the end of the war, tried and hanged for treason in 1946.
18. **Tom Tom:** Tom Tom Club were formed by husband and wife Tina Weymouth and Chris Frantz of Talking Heads.
19. **Mr Mister:** They were mentioned in the lyrics of the 2009 song by Train, rhyming with 'Hey, Soul Sister'.
20. **Pawpaw:** They are different as a papaya is oval with orange flesh and a pawpaw is round with yellow flesh.
21. **Tsetse:** The name 'tsetse' means fly in a Bantu language of southern Africa.

HARD (3 Points)

22. **Toot Toot:** The US singer's real name was Denise Allen.
23. **Durand Durand:** Director Roger Vadim was married to Jane Fonda and had been married to Brigitte Bardot.
24. **Dum-Dum:** They were banned by the Hague Convention of 1899.
25. **'Girlie Girlie':** The song was used in Adam Sandler's first film *Going Overboard* in 1989.
26. **Major Major:** Other characters include Captain Yossarian, Colonel Cathcart and Milo Minderbinder.
27. **Aye-Aye:** There are 88 species of lemurs, all native to Madagascar, but the island has no other primates.
28. **'Never Never':** The Assembly were Vince Clarke, Feargal Sharkey and record producer Eric Radcliffe.
29. **Chee Chee:** He had a dog named Jip, a parrot called Polynesia and a Pushmi-pullyu, like a llama with two heads.
30. **Baden-Baden:** Baden means to bathe in German and it is in Baden-Württemberg, whose capital is Stuttgart.

All answers have rhyming words e.g. Humpty Dumpty.

EASY (1 Point)

1. **Music:** Which 1964 Petula Clark song starts, 'When you're alone and life is making you lonely, you can always go....'?
2. **Food & Drink:** Which brand of McVitie's biscuit is a digestive-type biscuit but made with rolled oats?
3. **Entertainment:** Which novelty dance involves putting your arms and legs 'in, out and shaking them all about'?
4. **Music:** Which single was the last UK No. 1 for ABBA?
5. **Life & Lifestyle:** Which facility allows people to connect to the Internet wirelessly in a particular area?
6. **Films:** Which slang term has been given to romantic films that relate primarily to a young female audience?
7. **Music:** In Brian Hyland's 1960 song, which type of yellow polka dot bikini did he sing about?
8. **TV:** In the children's TV show, whose two friends are called Teddy and Looby Loo?
9. **Pot Luck:** What other name is given to a two-way radio?

MEDIUM (2 Points)

10. **Music:** Which magical term gave the Steve Miller Band a UK No. 2 hit in 1982?
11. **Entertainment:** Which fairground amusement features a spiral slide winding around a tall tower?
12. **Sport & Games:** In which popular casino card game do players try to get cards totalling up to 21 but no more?
13. **Music:** Which 1986 Madonna album included three UK No. 1 hits: 'Papa Don't Preach', 'La Isla Bonita' and the title track?
14. **TV:** Which Teletubby is the largest and the oldest?

15. **Food & Drink:** Which culinary term means food that includes elements of Mexican and southern USA food?
16. **Music:** The Dutch prog rock band Focus had two UK chart hits in 1973: 'Sylvia' and which other?
17. **Entertainment:** Which term was used for equipment to play CDs and records in high fidelity sound?
18. **TV:** Alison King starred as Lynda Block in which Sky One drama series about Harchester United Football Club?
19. **Music:** Which 1967 Donovan song starts, 'I'm just mad about Saffron, Saffron's mad about me...?
20. **Sport & Games:** In Monopoly, the pink properties are Whitehall, Northumberland Avenue and which other?
21. **Films:** Which actor's films include *Shallow Hal* (2001), *School of Rock* (2003) and *The Holiday* (2006)?

HARD (3 Points)

---

22. **Music:** John Miles is best known for his 1976 hit 'Music', but what was his first chart entry in 1975?
23. **TV:** Paul Kaye played which 1990s spoof celebrity interviewer with dyed red hair and thick glasses?
24. **Transport & Travel:** What was the nickname of the Hughes H-4 Hercules aircraft, intended for use in WWII?
25. **Music:** Which type of 'Bugle Boy' of Company B did the Andrews Sisters sing about during the war?
26. **Food & Drink:** Which cocktail usually consists of dark rum, white rum, an orange liqueur and lime juice?
27. **Animals & Nature:** What is the common name for the plant *Impatiens walleriana*?
28. **Music:** Which stringed instrument produces a sound when its hand-turned wheel rubs against its strings?
29. **Pot Luck:** Which phrase of Greek origin has come to be a derogatory term for the masses or common people?
30. **TV:** Which 1987 drama series starred Robbie Coltrane and Emma Thompson in a Scottish rock 'n' roll band?

1. **'Downtown':** The song reached No. 2 but she did have two UK No. 1 hits with 'Sailor' in 1961 and 'This is My Song' in 1967.
2. **Hobnob:** The 'marines' of biscuits according to Peter Kay as they don't crumble when dipped in your brew!
3. **Hokey-cokey:** It gave the Snowmen a Top 20 hit in 1981.
4. **'Super Trouper':** It was from the album of the same name, but it wasn't their last album – that was *The Visitors* in 1981.
5. **Wi-Fi:** The name was derived from 'wireless' and 'hi-fi' rather than being short for 'Wireless Fidelity' as some people think.
6. **Chick flick:** The term, though, is thought by some feminists to be derogatory, along with the 'chick lit' term for literature.
7. **Itsy Bitsy Teeny Weeny:** His biggest hit was 'Sealed with a Kiss' which reached the UK Top 10 in 1962 and 1975.
8. **Andy Pandy:** The show started in 1950, then new colour episodes in 1970 followed by a full relaunch in 2002.
9. **Walkie-talkie:** Multiple walkie-talkies can use one radio channel but only one person can transmit at a time.

10. **'Abracadabra':** They had a 1990 No. 1 with 'The Joker'.
11. **Helter-skelter:** The Beatles recorded 'Helter Skelter' on their 1968 album *The Beatles*, often known as 'The White Album'.
12. **Blackjack:** Similar card games are Twenty-One and Pontoon.
13. ***True Blue:*** It included two other singles: 'Live to Tell' which got to No. 2 and 'Open Your Heart' got to No. 4.

14. **Tinky Winky:** He is purple with a triangular antenna and carries a red bag.
15. **Tex-Mex:** The border between Mexico and Texas is formed by the Rio Grande River.
16. **'Hocus Pocus':** The band's 'House of the King' was the theme tune to the 1970s TV science show *Don't Ask Me*.
17. **Hi-fi:** The Kids from Fame had a UK No. 5 hit in 1982 with a song called 'Hi-Fidelity'.
18. ***Dream Team:*** There were ten series from 1997 to 2007.
19. **'Mellow Yellow':** His full name is Donovan Leitch and his first UK chart entry was 'Catch the Wind' in 1965.
20. **Pall Mall:** The US version was the original version based on the streets of Atlantic City, New Jersey.
21. **Jack Black:** He also plays in a comedic rock group called Tenacious D with Kyle Gass.

HARD (3 Points)

22. **'High Fly':** He had a Top 10 hit in 1977 with 'Slow Down'.
23. **Dennis Pennis:** He originally featured in 1995 on BBC2's *The Sunday Show*.
24. **Spruce Goose:** It was made of wood, mainly birch, due to a shortage of materials like aluminium in the war.
25. **Boogie-woogie:** Boogie-woogie became popular in the 1920s in African-American communities and started with the piano.
26. **Mai Tai:** The orange liqueur could be triple sec, Cointreau but originally Curaçao, from the Dutch island in the Caribbean.
27. **Busy Lizzie:** They come in a variety of colours but are most commonly pink.
28. **Hurdy-gurdy:** The name is sometimes wrongly used for a barrel organ, which has a handle but has preset tunes.
29. **Hoi polloi:** In Greek it simply means 'the many'.
30. ***Tutti Frutti:*** Richard Wilson played the band's manager.